MATH TRAILBLAZERS™

A Mathematical Journey Using Science and Language Arts

Student Guide
Grade 1

**A TIMS® Curriculum from the
University of Illinois at Chicago**

KENDALL/HUNT PUBLISHING COMPANY
4050 Westmark Drive   Dubuque, Iowa 52002

MATH TRAILBLAZERS™

Dedication

This book is dedicated to the children and teachers who let us see the magic in their classrooms and to our families who wholeheartedly supported us while we searched for ways to make it happen.

The TIMS Project

 UIC The University of Illinois at Chicago

This material is based on work supported by the National Science Foundation under grant No. MDR 9050226 and the University of Illinois at Chicago. Any opinions, findings, and conclusions or recommendations expressed in this publication are those of the author(s) and do not necessarily reflect the views of the granting agencies.

Printed in the United States of America
10   9   8   7   6

Acknowledgments

TIMS Elementary Mathematics Curriculum Project

Director and Co-Principal Investigator
Philip Wagreich

Co-Principal Investigator
Howard Goldberg

Associate Director
Joan L. Bieler

TIMS Senior Curriculum Developers

Janet Simpson Beissinger
Howard Goldberg
Catherine Randall Kelso

Astrida Cirulis
Carol Inzerillo
Leona Peters

Marty Gartzman
Andy Isaacs
Philip Wagreich

TIMS Curriculum Developers

Janice C. Banasiak
Kathryn Chval
Sandy Niemiera

Lynne Beauprez
Diane R. Czerwinski
Polly Tangora

Lindy M. Chambers
Janice Ozima
Paul Trafton

Research Consultant
Andy Isaacs

Mathematics Education Consultant
Paul Trafton

Editors
Jay Becker
Lynelle Morgenthaler

Designer/Production Coordinator
Sarah Nelson

Production Staff

Glenda Genio
Mini Joseph
Sarah Nelson
Biruté Petrauskas

Illustrator
Kris Dresen

National Advisory Committee

- Carl Berger, Director, Instructional Technology, University of Michigan, Ann Arbor, Michigan
- Tom Berger, Professor of Mathematics Education, Colby College, Waterville, Maine
- Hugh Burkhardt, Project Director, Balanced Assessment for the Mathematics Curriculum, University of California, Berkeley and Shell Centre for Mathematical Education, University of Nottingham, England
- Donald Chambers, Director of Dissemination, National Center for Research in Mathematical Sciences Education, University of Wisconsin at Madison, Madison, Wisconsin
- Naomi Fisher, Co-Director, Mathematicians and Education Reform Network, University of Illinois at Chicago, Chicago, Illinois
- Glenda Lappan, Professor of Mathematics, Michigan State University, East Lansing, Michigan
- Mary Lindquist, Callaway Professor of Mathematics Education, Columbus College, Columbus, Georgia
- Eugene Maier, President, Math Learning Center, Portland, Oregon
- Lourdes Monteagudo, Director, Teachers' Academy for Mathematics and Science, Chicago, Illinois
- Elizabeth Phillips, Specialist in the Department of Mathematics, Michigan State University, East Lansing, Michigan
- Thomas Post, Professor of Mathematics Education, University of Minnesota, Minneapolis, Minnesota

Acknowledgments

Research and Outreach Staff

Birch Burghardt
Marty Gartzman

Andy Carter
Michelle Perry

Barbara Crum
Maria Varelas

Teacher Contributors

Jean Clement
Donna Holt

Ann Watson Cohn
Jenny Knight
Beth Savage

Catherine Hamilton
Mary Pat Larocca

Institute for Mathematics and Science Education Support Staff

David Browdy
Shanila Dada
Helen Gary
Judy Kim
Alex Mak
Enrique Puente
Leah Rosenstein
Patty Stevenson
Marie Walz

Jocelyn Buchanan
Robert Denton
Byron S. Gudiel
Frannie Los Banes
Christie Manisto
Laura Ratcliffe
Ellen Rydell
Ami Thaker
Mikka Whiteaker

Philomina Cox
Nadine Dombrowski
Miriam Gutierrez
Cassandra Lucas
Kim Meyer
Monica Rodriguez
Dorothy Sholeen-Modrzyk
Greg Waddoups

Copyeditor
Anne Roby

Video and Photographic Documentation

Joan L. Bieler

Henrique Cirne-Lima

Paul A. Wussow

Contributing Writers and Artists

Steven Bloom
Karen Harrington
Heather Miller

Pam Conrad
Vida Ivancevic
Betty Romanek

Julie Hall
Songgu Kwon
Cora Lee Wentzel

Field Test Schools and Teachers

Abraham Lincoln School, Oak Park, Illinois
Principal: Carol Dudzik

Sandra Adams
Peggy Callahan
Catherine Hamilton
Donna Holt
Susan McNish
Karl Radnitzer
Shirley Warner

Marilyn Blenz
Susan Casagrande
James Harrington
Paula Hughes
Miraflor Metropoulos
Jane Samuelson
Kathleen Wiedow

Nell Bloyd
Cheryl Cohen
Karen Heffner
Frank LoCoco
Joyce Moore
Jarvia Thomas
Lynne Zillman

Anderson Elementary School, Chicago, Illinois
Principal: Marie Iska
Alicia Acevedo

Acknowledgments

Daniel Boone School, Chicago, Illinois
Principal: Paul Zavitkovsky

Sybil Bennin	Ruta Buntinas	Myung Chi
Deanna Gramatis	Susan Dietz	Norma Duarte
Paula Hyman	Sandra Kantz	Juliet Kasha
Mila Kell	Julia Kline	Barbara Mandel
Janice Ozima	Vlada Polin	Lizette Rhone
Dixie Rouleau	Mariah Seton	Cecilia Somma
Jennifer Soro	Cheryl Strong	Margaret Therriault-Jenkins
Lauretta Williams	Constance Winschel-Cook	Elina Yelishevich
	Argentina Yousif	

Drexel School, Cicero, Illinois
Principal: Cliff Pluister

Deborah Fantozzi	Jeanette Ibarra	Kristin Wilderman

Edith Wolford Elementary School, Colorado Springs, Colorado
Principal: Gary Langenhuizen

Sherrie Antes	Karen Combs	Jeremy Cramer
Carol Eames	Kelly Garnhart	

Edward H. White School, Chicago, Illinois
Principal: Yvonne Womack

Judy Hobson	Harrison Jackson	Kathleen Pidrak

Elmwood School, Elmwood Park, Illinois
Principal: Doug Lia

Joanne Hoffmann	Mary Anne Kirsch	Linda Norris	Marlene Ryan

Emma Stark Hampton Elementary School, Detroit, Michigan
Principal: Chrystal Tibbs

Margaret Erle	Janet Flessa	Therese Sadlier
Clare Whitaker	Michelle Williams	

Gavin Central School, Ingleside, Illinois
Principal: Theresa Dunkin

Nannette Borzewski	Judith Dahl	Betty Denk
Carrie Frebault	Jennifer McCracken	Jodi Minsky
Peggy Owczarski	Pat Scully	Barbara Smejkal
	Dawn Smith	

Hammerschmidt Elementary School, Lombard, Illinois
Principal: James Adams

Shelly Humphreys

James McCosh School, Chicago, Illinois
Principal: Barbara Eason-Watkins

Louise Dearman	Leah Fulton	Shelley Hefner
Inez Jacobson	Dorothy Turner	Jacquelyne White

Acknowledgments

James Shields School, Chicago, Illinois
Principal: Rita Gardner

Julie Cartwright	Iris Delgado	Bob Kaszynski
Wilhelmina McGee	Terry McInerney	Maranielly Vazquez

John C. Burroughs School, Chicago, Illinois
Principal: Richard Morris
Paul Durkin
Michelle Sanborn

John Mills School, Elmwood Park, Illinois
Principal: Patricia Duggan

Deanna Crum	Lisa Loffredo	Cathy McGovern	Bonnie Mize

Mt. Hope Elementary School, Lansing, Michigan
Principal: Betty Nichols

Corin Bennett	Deidre Bennett	Sue Fillingham
Della Gregory	Geneva Martin	Deborah Muth
Sue Usiak	Terri Weinlander	Dawn Vanzee

Piedmont Elementary School, Charleston, West Virginia
Principal: Steve Knighton

Beth Brown	Brigid Haney	Catherine Hastings
Eva Jones	Louise Tabor	

Pilsen Community Academy, Chicago, Illinois
Principal: Ana Espinoza

Jennifer Chadwick	Judy Rappin	Juliet Rempa

Spring Hill School, Roselle, Illinois
Principal: Sally Pryor
David R. Vilmin

St. Ambrose School, Chicago, Illinois
Principal: Sr. Dolores Lytle
Dorothy Rivers

Westwood Primary School, Phoenix, Arizona
Principal: Martha Braly

Denise Ahart	Denise Arnold	Shelley Carson
Merrillyn Curtis	Antoinette DiCarlo	Ginny Fields
Alphine Glenn	Nancy Herbert	Jane Hoyle
Nancy Hunt	Cecilia Kelly	Cindy Lauersdorf
Candace Manger	Diane Nonack	Kathie Pabst
Lori Perry	Denise Pizzi	Maureen Riordan
Anita Rothman	JoAnn Salem	Timothy Salem
Kathy Schaeffer	Ken Schofield	Sheri Starke
Susie Sweeney	Jamie Tinkelman	Jackie Williams
	Nan Williams	

William H. Ray School, Chicago, Illinois
Principal: Cydney Fields
Bill Salvato
Marie Schilling

Table of Contents

Additional student pages may be found in the *Discovery Assignment Book,*
Adventure Book, or the *Unit Resource Guide.*

Table of Contents

Additional student pages may be found in the *Discovery Assignment Book,*
Adventure Book, or the *Unit Resource Guide.*

Dear Parents,

MATH TRAILBLAZERS™ is based on the belief that all children deserve a challenging mathematics curriculum and that mathematics is best learned through solving many different kinds of problems. The program provides a careful balance of concepts and skills. Traditional arithmetic skills and procedures are covered through their repeated use in problems and through distributed practice.

MATH TRAILBLAZERS™, however, offers much more. Students using this program will become proficient problem solvers, will know how to approach problems in many different ways, will know when and how to apply the mathematics they have learned, and will be able to clearly communicate their mathematical knowledge. They will learn more mathematics than in a traditional program—computation, measurement, geometry, data collection and analysis, estimation, graphing, patterns and relationships, mental arithmetic, and simple algebraic ideas are all an integral part of the curriculum. They will see connections between the mathematics learned in school and the mathematics used in everyday life. And, they will enjoy and value the work they do in mathematics.

This curriculum was built around national recommendations for improving mathematics instruction in American schools and the research that supported those recommendations. It has been extensively tested with thousands of children in dozens of classrooms over five years of development. **MATH TRAILBLAZERS™** reflects our view of a complete and well-balanced mathematics program that will prepare children for a world in the 21st century where proficiency in mathematics will be a necessity. We hope that you enjoy this exciting approach to learning mathematics as you watch your child's mathematical abilities grow throughout the year.

Philip Wagreich

Philip Wagreich
Teaching Integrated Mathematics and Science Project
University of Illinois at Chicago
Chicago, Illinois

UNIT

1

Counting at the Toy Store

How Many Are There?

Count objects on the Counting at the Toy Store Activity Page.

Object	Number Counted
clock	
horse	
teddy bear	
supercycle	
wheel	
doll	
teacup	
tennis ball	

UNIT **2**

Shirt and Pants Pockets

Record the number of shirt pockets, pants pockets, and total pockets you are wearing today. Then, write a number sentence.

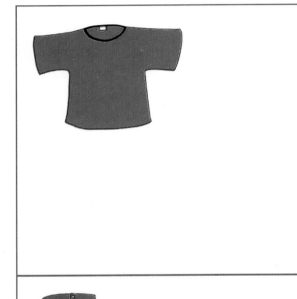

☐ + ☐ = ☐

Pocket Parts 1

Find the total number of pockets. Then, write a number sentence for each.

1 + 4 = 5

_____

_____

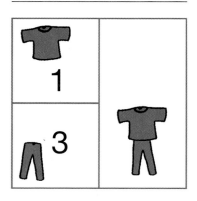

_____

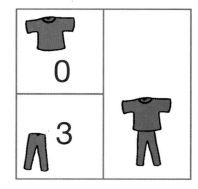

_____

Pocket Parts 2

Find the total number of pockets for each. Then, write a number sentence for each.

$4 + 4 =$ _____

_____

_____

_____

_____

_____

Pocket Parts

Missing Parts

Find the number of pants pockets for each. Then, write a number sentence for each.

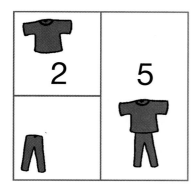

$$2 + 3 = 5$$

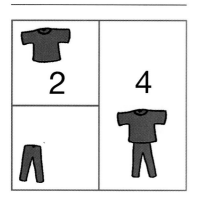

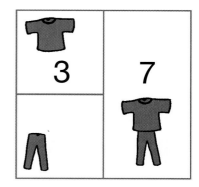

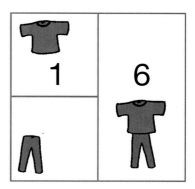

How Many Pockets?

Find the total number of pockets for each. Then, write a number sentence to show the three parts and the whole.

2

2

4

_____

1

4

2

_____

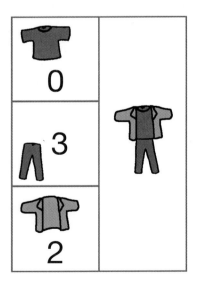

0

3

2

_____

3

5

4

_____

Pockets

Find the missing number or the total number of pockets for each. Then, write a number sentence for each.

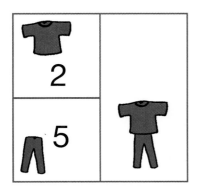

_____

_____

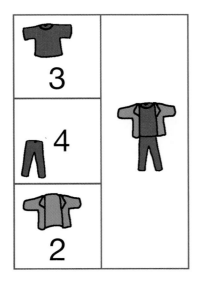

_____

_____

Two Pockets Work Mat

Place your pennies on the pockets. Find and record the different ways you can arrange them.

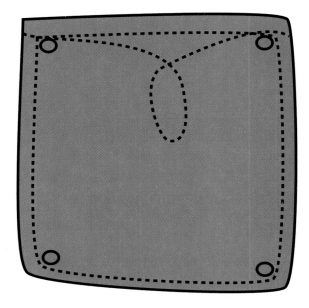

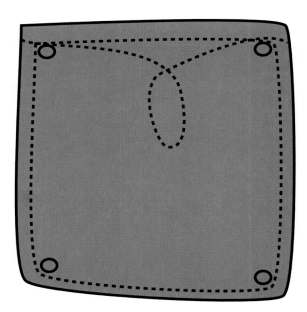

What's in that Pocket?

Two Pockets Data Table

How many ways can you arrange ten pennies in two pockets? Record as many ways as you can. Then, write a number sentence for each one.

		Total Pennies	Number Sentence

Three Pockets Work Mat

Place your pennies on the pockets. Find and record the different ways you can arrange them.

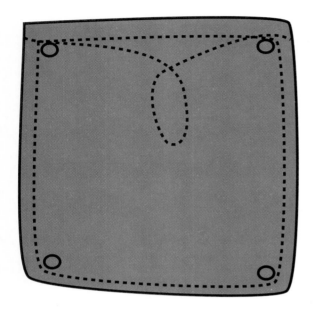

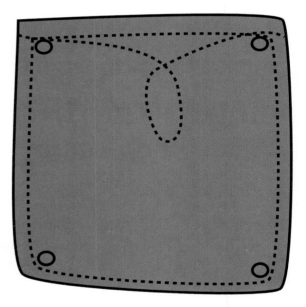

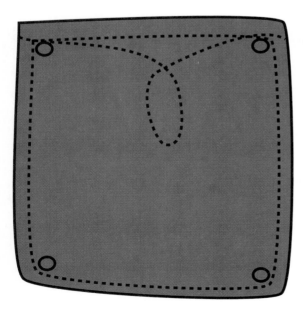

Three Pockets Data Table

How many ways can you arrange ten pennies in three pockets? Record as many ways as you can. Then, write a number sentence for each one.

			Total Pennies	Number Sentence
1	2	7	10	1 + 2 + 7 = 10

Eight Pennies Data Table

Homework

Dear Family Member:

Your child will need eight pennies for this assignment. He or she should divide the pennies in different combinations among two pockets. The total should equal eight for each problem. Please help your child complete the data table.

Thank you for your cooperation.

How many ways can you arrange eight pennies in two pockets? Record as many ways as you can. Then, write a number sentence for each one.

		Total Pennies	Number Sentence
0	8	8	0 + 8 = 8

Nine Pennies Data Table

How many ways can you arrange nine pennies in two pockets? Record as many ways as you can. Then, write a number sentence for each one.

		Total Pennies	Number Sentence

UNIT 3

Weather 1 Data Table

Collect

Record the data from your Weather Calendar in the table below.

T Type of _____	*N* Number of _____	
	Tallies	**Total**

Name _____   Date _____

Weather 1 Graph

Graph

Make a graph of your data.

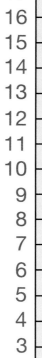

N
Number of _____

19
18
17
16
15
14
13
12
11
10
9
8
7
6
5
4
3
2
1
0

T

Type of _____

Thinking about the Weather

Explore

Use your data table and graph to answer the following questions.

1. Which type of sky did you see *most* often?

_____

2. Which type of sky did you see *least* often?

_____

3. How many sunny *and* partly sunny skies were there in all?

_____

4. A. Were there more cloudy skies or more sunny skies?

_____

B. How many more?

_____

Shapes in Nature

Nature is filled with shapes. Circle the shapes you see in the picture.

Alike and Different 1

One way these shapes are alike:

_____

One way these shapes are different:

_____

One way these shapes are alike:

_____

One way these shapes are different:

_____

Alike and Different 2

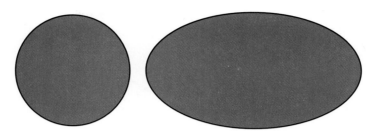

One way these shapes are alike:

_____

One way these shapes are different:

_____

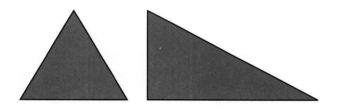

One way these shapes are alike:

_____

One way these shapes are different:

_____

The Snake

Fill in the snake with pattern blocks.

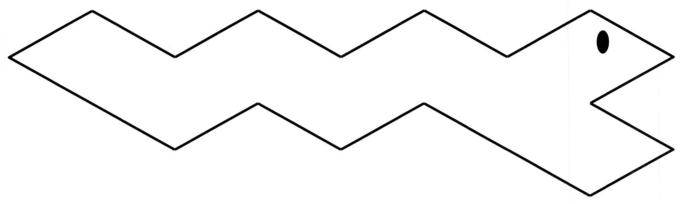

Write how many of each pattern block you used.

Shape	First Way	Second Way	Third Way
⬡			
⬢			
▲			
▪			
▱			
▱			
Total			

Name _____   Date _____

The Turtle

Fill in the turtle with pattern blocks.

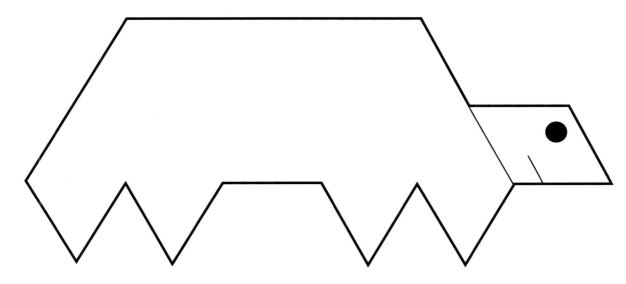

Write how many of each pattern block you used.

Shape	First Way	Second Way	Third Way
⬡			
▽			
▲			
▮			
▰			
▱			
Total			

The Rocket

Fill in the rocket with pattern blocks. Then, write how many of each pattern block you used.

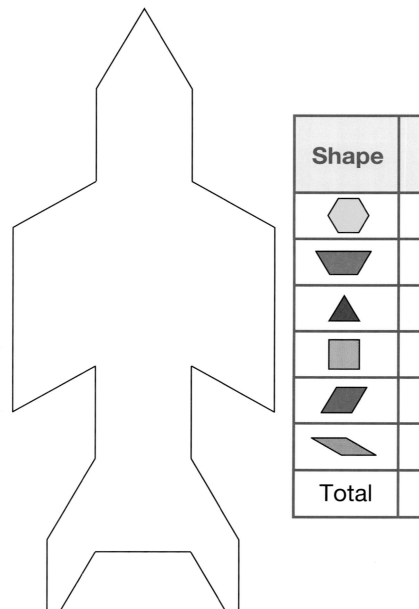

Shape	First Way	Second Way
⬡		
▽		
△		
◻		
▱		
▱		
Total		

My Own Design

Make a design with pattern blocks in the frame below.

I made a picture of _____

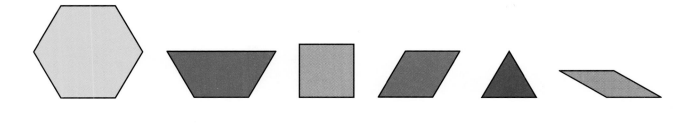

_____   _____   _____   _____   _____   _____

UNIT 4

Animals in the Pet Shop

Pets at Home

Solve the following problems.

1. Sylvia's block has three kittens and five puppies. How many pets are on Sylvia's block? Press the keystrokes below to find out.

3	+	5	=

2. For each problem, fill in the missing keystroke boxes. Then, find the answer.

   A. Marcus's block has 5 dogs and 11 cats. How many dogs and cats do they have?

5	+		=

   B. Tom's family has 2 pets. There are 16 other pets in Tom's building. How many pets are in the building?

	+		=

   C. Marsha counted 12 dogs and 13 cats on her block. How many pets are there in all?

   D. Samantha has two turtles, five frogs, and six lizards as pets. How many pets does Samantha have?

It's in the Mail

Homework

Dear Family Member:

The number sentence 7 + 2 = 9 describes the following: I mailed a letter on October 7. It arrived 2 days later. My letter was received on October 9. By counting on, "7, 8, 9," students can solve the problem. Help your child complete this page by counting on the calendar.

Thank you for your cooperation.

Sunday	Monday	Tuesday	Wednesday	Thursday	Friday	Saturday
						1
2	3	4	5	6	7	8
9	10	11	12	13	14	15
16	17	18	19	20	21	22
23	24	25	26	27	28	29
30	31					

Date Sent	Arrived	Number Sentence	Date Received
10 mailed	2 days later	_____	
13 mailed	3 days later	_____	
24 mailed	4 days later	_____	
30 mailed	1 day later	_____	
5 mailed	5 days later	_____	

Counting On to Add

Happy Helpers Club

Homework

Dear Family Member:

In class, your child uses the counting-on strategy to help him or her solve problems. To do 11 + 3, for example, start by saying "11" and then count on, "12, 13, 14." Encourage your child to use counting on to solve the problems below.

How much money will each student have after receiving 3 more cents?

13¢ + 3¢ = _____   18¢ + 3¢ = _____   20¢ + 3¢ = _____

24¢ + 3¢ = _____   29¢ + 3¢ = _____   32¢ + 3¢ = _____

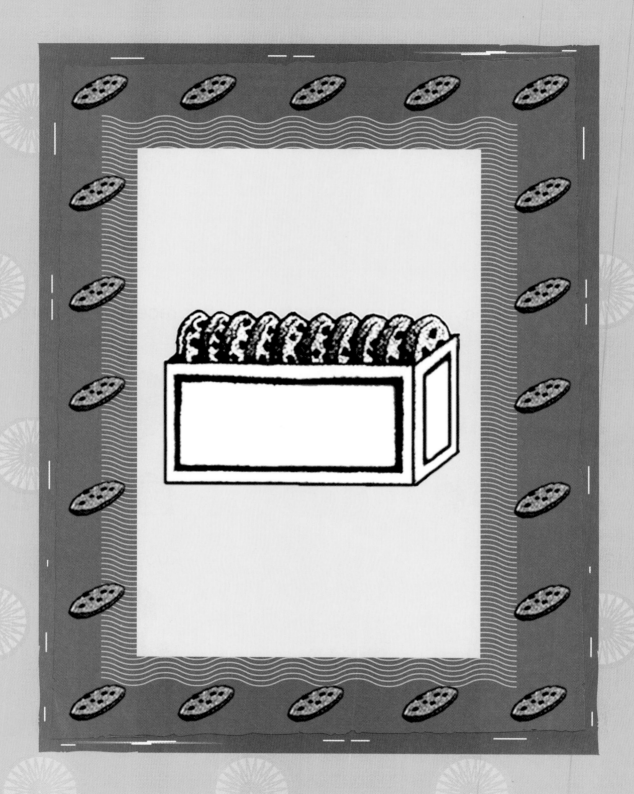

UNIT 5

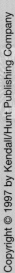

Name _____   Date _____

Counting by Twos

Homework

Dear Family Member:

Your child is learning to skip count by twos. Discuss things that come in twos such as shoes and twin sisters. Encourage your child to skip count by twos to complete this page.

A. Count the eyes by twos.

2, _____, _____   There are _____ eyes.

B. Count the bicycle wheels by twos.

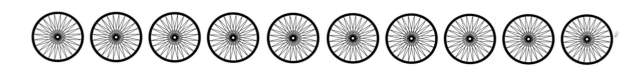

2, _____, _____, _____, _____   There are _____ wheels.

C. Count the mittens by twos.

2, _____, _____, _____, _____, _____, _____

There are _____ mittens.

Things in Twos

Homework

Dear Family Member:

Your child is learning how to skip count by twos. Discuss things
that come in groups of two such as wheels on a bicycle and ears.
Have your child choose an object that comes in twos, draw several
of them, and then count, in twos, the number he or she drew. Help
him or her complete the bottom of the page.

Find things that come in twos. Then, draw and count them.

I counted twos like this:

2, _____, _____, _____, _____, _____, _____, _____, _____, _____, _____

What did you draw? _____

How many did you draw? _____

Fair Shares

Share cookies as shown in the table below.

The total number of cookies = _____

People	Fair Shares	Leftovers	Words
👤 👤			Two groups of _____ and _____ left over
👤 👤 👤			Three groups of _____ and _____ left over
👤 👤 👤 👤			Four groups of _____ and _____ left over
👤 👤 👤 👤 👤			Five groups of _____ and _____ left over
👤 👤 👤 👤 👤 👤			Six groups of _____ and _____ left over

Sharing Cookies

Name _____   Date _____

Packing Grandma's Cookies

Help Grandma pack her cookies. Group your counters in groups of ten. Draw one box for every group of ten. Then, draw the leftovers.

Work Slip 1	Number of Cookies	Boxes	Leftover Cookies

Work Slip 2	Number of Cookies	Boxes	Leftover Cookies

Colors Picture

Draw a picture of the experiment.

Colors Data Table

Collect

Colors

C Color	P Number of Pieces

Colors Graph

Colors

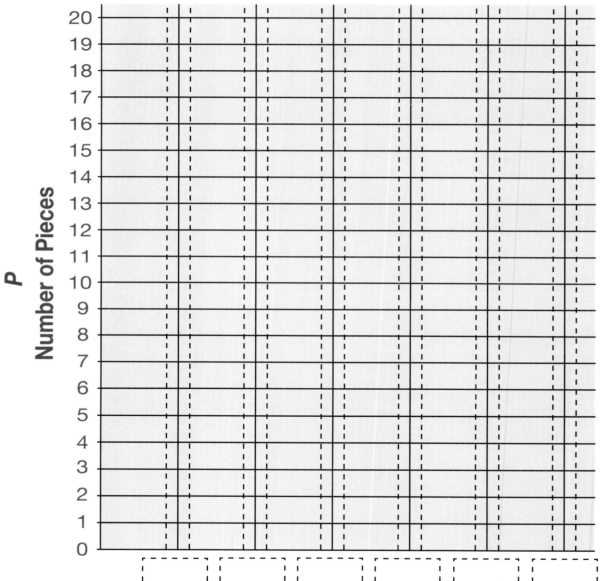

P
Number of Pieces

C
Color

Colors

Reading a Colors Graph

Mary's Class Graph

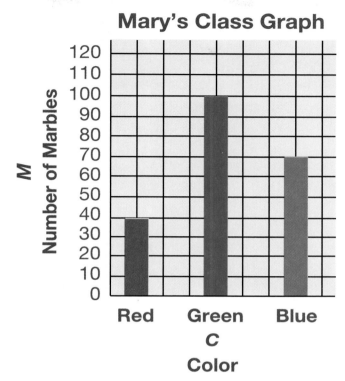

1. How many reds did Mary's class pull out altogether?

_____

2. What color was most common? _____

3. If the principal took a handful of marbles, which color do you think she would find the most common?

_____

4. If you combine the blues and the reds Mary's class pulled out, would they be more than the greens?

_____

UNIT 6

Measuring Our World

Here are some things in Maria's classroom. Are they bigger or smaller in your classroom? Measure to find out.

Maria's desk is 18 links tall.

My desk is _____ links tall.

tall

long

Maria's desk is 24 links long.

My desk is _____ links long.

Maria measured the distance around her book. The distance around an object is called a **perimeter**.

The perimeter of Maria's book is 39 links.

The perimeter of my book

is _____ links.

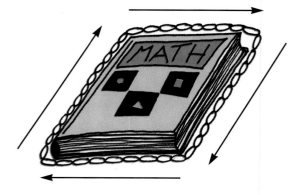

Linking Up

Measuring Ourselves

Julio's arm is 12 links long.

My arm is _____ links long.

Julio's foot is 5 links long.

My foot is _____ links long.

Use the links to measure another part of your body. Draw a picture to show what you measure.

My _____ is _____ links long.

Rolling Along with Links

Draw a picture of the experiment setup. Include the parts of the experiment that must remain the same.

Collect

Record the distance each type of car rolled in the data table below.

Rolling Along with Links

T Type of Car	D Distance Rolled (in links)

Graph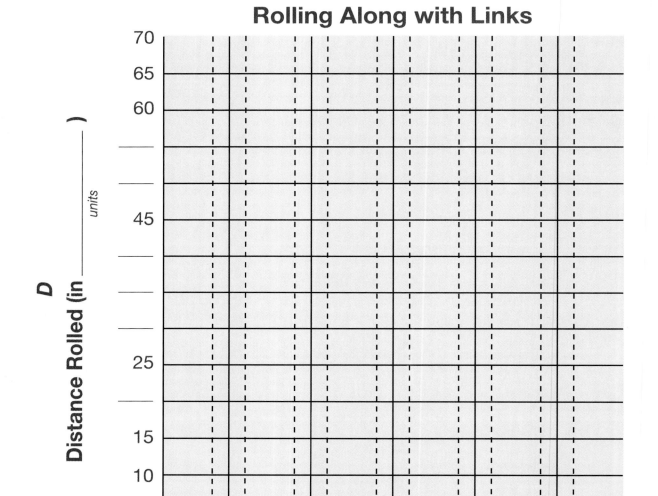

Make a bar graph of your data. Remember to fill in the proper units.

Rolling Along with Links

D
Distance Rolled (in _____ units)

70
65
60

45

25

15
10
5
0

T
Type of Car

Discuss

Use your data table and graph to answer the questions below.

1. Which car was the best roller? _____

2. How far did the best roller go? _____

3. Which car was the worst roller? _____

4. How far did the worst roller go? _____

5. How much farther did the best roller go than the worst roller? Discuss how you got your answer.

_____

6. Susan's car rolled 20 links. David's car rolled 12 links farther than Susan's. How far did David's car roll?

_____

7. Write a number sentence for your answer to Question 6.

_____

Watch Your Step

Use your footprint to measure distances in your classroom. Record your measurements in this table.

From	To	Number of 👣

Unusual Units

Estimate how many of each unit you need to measure the bathtub.

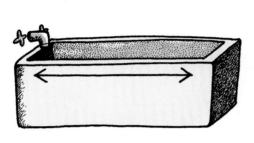

Unit	Length of Tub
soap 🟦	_____
toothbrush	10
wash cloth	_____
(fish tank)	
towel	_____

It takes 3 soda pop bottles to measure the width of the refrigerator. Match the rest of the numbers with their units of measure.

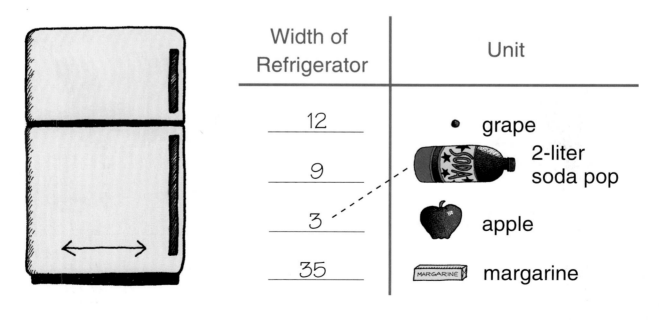

Width of Refrigerator	Unit
12	• grape
9	2-liter soda pop
3	apple
35	margarine

Delightful Dachshunds

1. Which dog is longer? Make a prediction. Then, compare the lengths of the chains. Write the answer in the box.

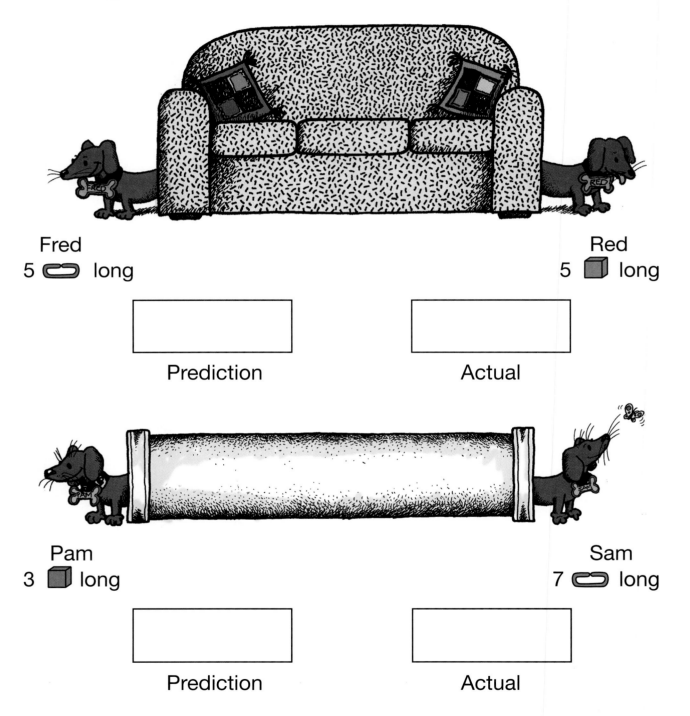

Fred
5 ⬭ long

Red
5 🔲 long

Prediction	Actual

Pam
3 🔲 long

Sam
7 ⬭ long

Prediction	Actual

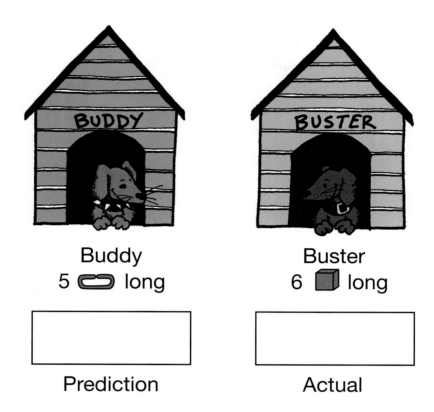

Buddy
5 ⊂⊃ long

Buster
6 ◻ long

Prediction

Actual

2. Which length is longer? Make a prediction. Then, compare the lengths of the chains. Circle the longer one.

Prediction		**Actual**	
18 ⊂⊃ long	25 ◻ long	18 ⊂⊃ long	25 ◻ long
9 ⊂⊃ long	8 ◻ long	9 ⊂⊃ long	8 ◻ long
3 ⊂⊃ long	7 ◻ long	3 ⊂⊃ long	7 ◻ long
8 ⊂⊃ long	12 ◻ long	8 ⊂⊃ long	12 ◻ long

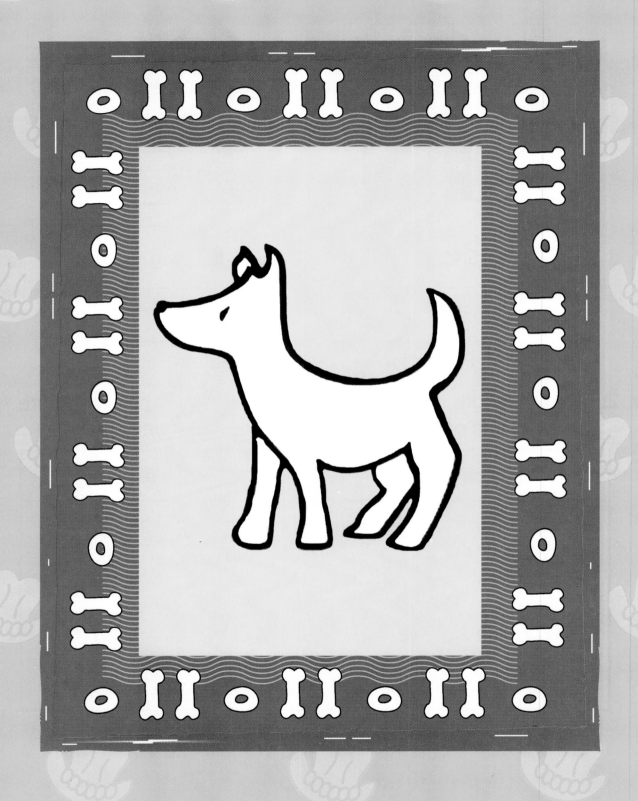

UNIT 7

Translating and Recording Patterns

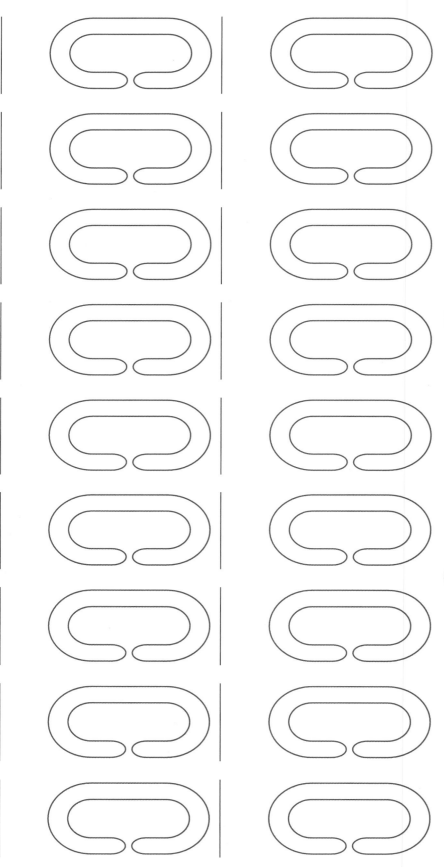

Colors and Shapes

What patterns do you see?

Colors:

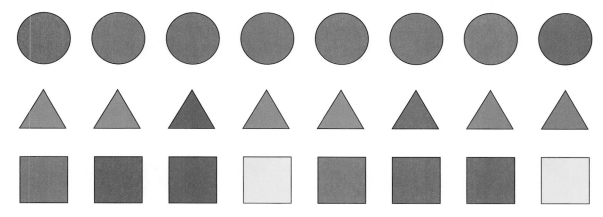

Shapes:

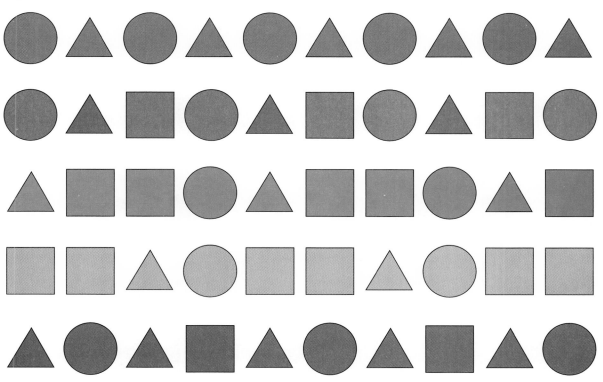

Dinosaurs, Diamonds, and Dog Biscuits

What patterns do you see?

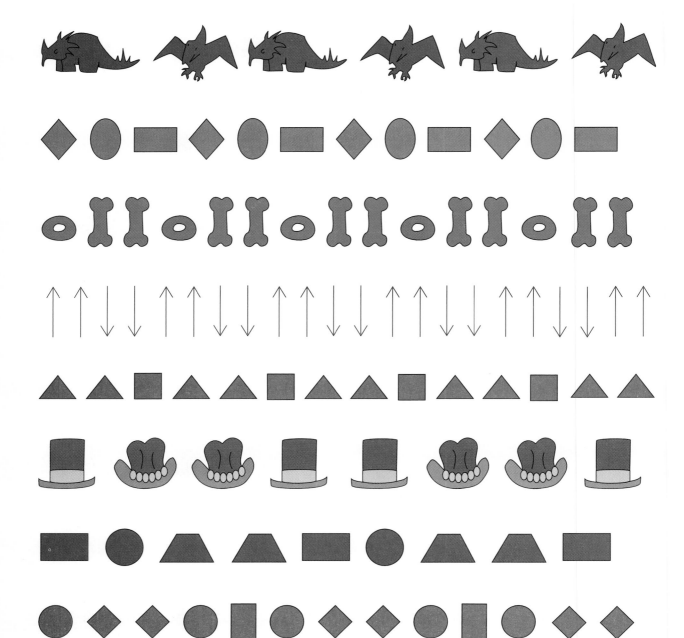

Pick Apart a Pattern

Super Sleuth

H✿mework

Dear Family Member:

In this assignment, your child should find the part of the pattern that repeats itself and represent the pattern using the letters A, B, C, etc. For example, a boy-girl-boy-girl-boy-girl pattern could be translated as ABABAB with letters.

Record the pattern shown on the lines below.

1.

_____

2.

_____

3.

_____

4.

_____

Trapezoid Man

1. Cover this side.   **2.** Make this side balance.

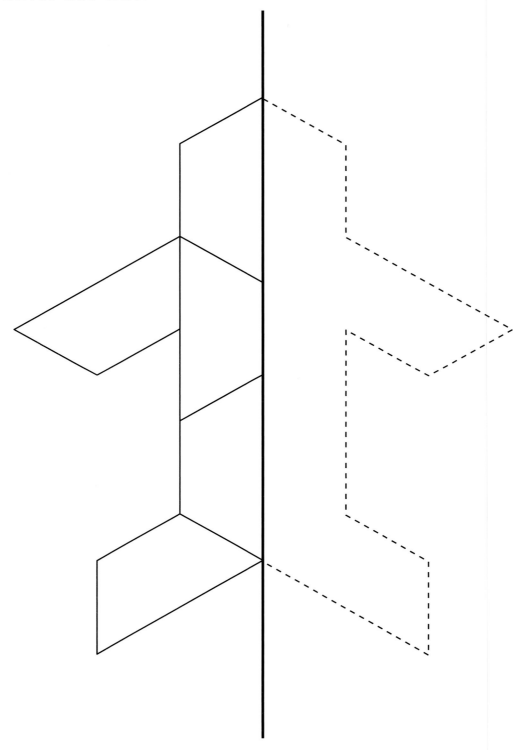

Pattern Block Symmetry

Butterfly

1. Cover this side.

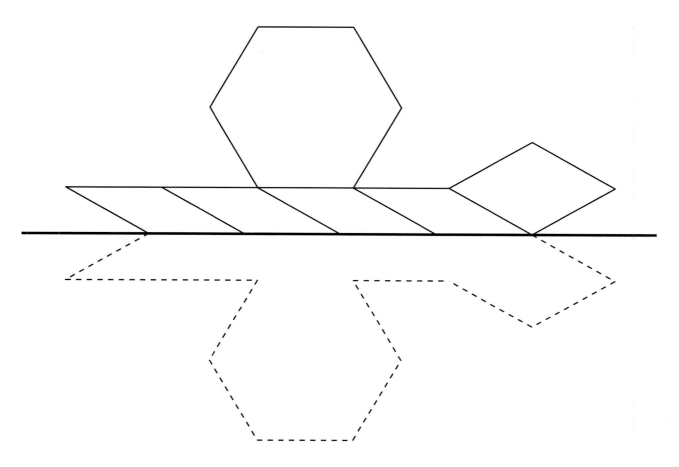

2. Make this side balance.

UNIT 8

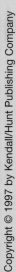

Recording Subtraction Sentences

_____ − _____ = _____
whole   part   part

_____ − _____ = _____
whole   part   part

_____ − _____ = _____
whole   part   part

_____ − _____ = _____
whole   part   part

_____ − _____ = _____
whole   part   part

_____ − _____ = _____
whole   part   part

_____ − _____ = _____
whole   part   part

_____ − _____ = _____
whole   part   part

Our Own Stories

How Many in the Bag?

_____ − _____ = _____
in the bag · · · · · taken out · · · · · left in the bag

_____ − _____ = _____
in the bag · · · · · taken out · · · · · left in the bag

_____ − _____ = _____
in the bag · · · · · taken out · · · · · left in the bag

_____ − _____ = _____
in the bag · · · · · taken out · · · · · left in the bag

_____ − _____ = _____
in the bag · · · · · taken out · · · · · left in the bag

_____ − _____ = _____
in the bag · · · · · taken out · · · · · left in the bag

_____ − _____ = _____
in the bag · · · · · taken out · · · · · left in the bag

_____ − _____ = _____
in the bag · · · · · taken out · · · · · left in the bag

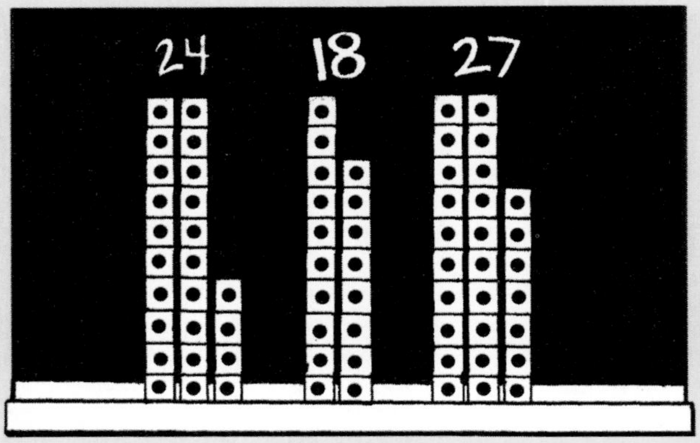
24
18
27

UNIT 9

Group and Count

Homework

Dear Family Member:

In class, we are counting by grouping objects in tens and leftover ones. You can help provide additional practice for your child by gathering a collection of objects and setting it out for your child to group and count. Change the total number of objects at least two times. Some ideas for objects to use are cereal pieces, nuts, pasta, raisins, pennies, buttons, and marbles. There should be 40–70 objects each time your child groups and counts.

Thank you for your cooperation.

Ask an adult or an older sister or brother to help you find objects to count.

Object	Number of Groups of 10	Number of Leftovers	Number

Return this paper on _____ .

Spin for Beans 50

Materials

Spin for Beans 50 Playing Mat

50 baby lima beans for each player

clear plastic spinner or a pencil and paper clip

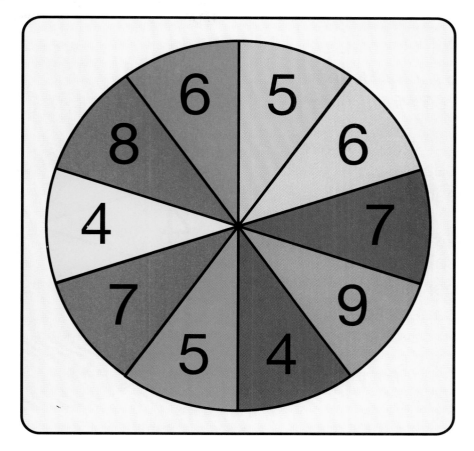

Directions

1. Place a plastic spinner over the spinner above. If you do not have a clear spinner, use a pencil and a paper clip.
2. Spin to find out how many beans to take.
3. Place the beans on the ten frame, one in each square.
4. Write the number of tens you have on your playing mat. Write the number of leftovers you have, too.
5. Write the total number of beans you have.
6. Each time you spin, add the beans to your collection on the ten frame until someone collects 50 beans.

Spin for Beans 100

Materials

Spin for Beans 100 Playing Mat

100 baby lima beans for each player

clear plastic spinner or a pencil and paper clip

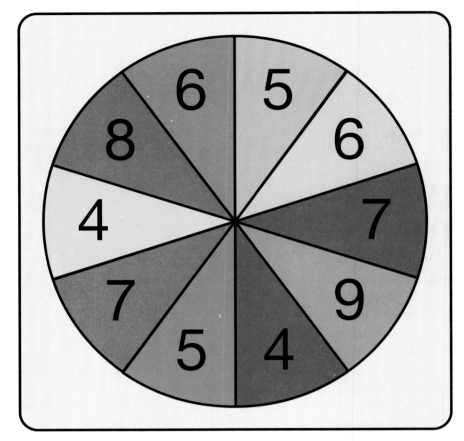

Directions

Follow the directions for *Spin for Beans 50*, except:

1. Play until someone collects **100** beans.

2. Say the number of tens, leftovers, and total number of beans after every turn. You do not need to write the numbers down.

You may use a pencil and a paper clip as a spinner. This is shown in the picture.

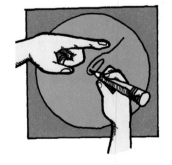

100 Chart

1	2	3	4	5	6	7	8	9	10
11	12	13	14	15	16	17	18	19	20
21	22	23	24	25	26	27	28	29	30
31	32	33	34	35	36	37	38	39	40
41	42	43	44	45	46	47	48	49	50
51	52	53	54	55	56	57	58	59	60
61	62	63	64	65	66	67	68	69	70
71	72	73	74	75	76	77	78	79	80
81	82	83	84	85	86	87	88	89	90
91	92	93	94	95	96	97	98	99	100

Counting by Tens

Homework

Count by tens and fill in the missing numbers. Use the 100 chart to help you. Color each column on the 100 chart using the colors below.

yellow	green	orange	blue	red	purple
8	10	2			
18					
28			25		
38					36
				51	

Find Numbers in the News

Homework

Dear Family Member:

Help your child find a newspaper headline with a number on it. Glue the headline in the space provided on the back of this paper. If he or she cannot find one in the paper, your child can use one of the numbers shown below.

To get your child started, write one sentence that compares the number to other numbers. For example, 34 is 10 more than 24. More examples are listed for the number 34 below.

Encourage your child to think of his or her own sentences. He or she should record them on the lines provided on the back of this paper.

Thank you for your cooperation.

13-Hour Sale

32 TOTAL BODY EXERCISES

Dist. 87 gets tougher on bad checks

75 years later, medals honor veterans of World War I

34 Kids Think in Math Marathon

34 is

- large compared to 5;
- about the same size as 30;
- a lot less than 100;
- between 30 and 40;
- 10 more than 24;
- 10 less than 44;
- 1 more than 33;
- 1 less than 35.

Paste your headline below.

_____

_____

_____

_____

_____

_____

_____

_____

Full of Beans

Draw a picture of the lab setup.

Collect

Write the kind of bean and the number of beans you counted in this table.

Group Data Table

Kind of Bean	Number of Beans

Class Data Table

Kind of Bean	Number of Beans

Graph

Full of Beans Class Data

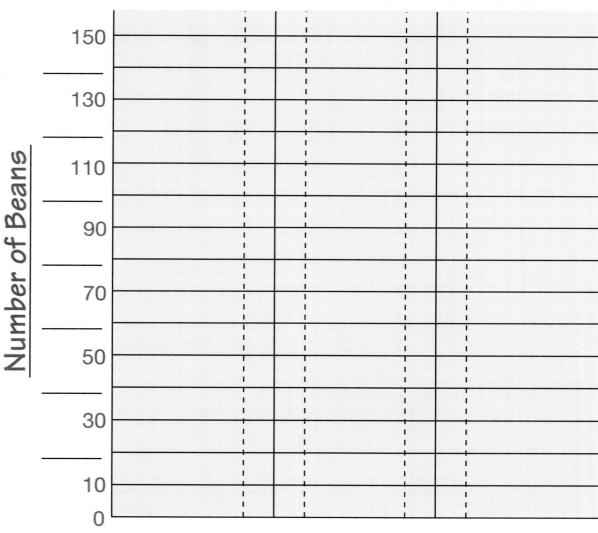

Number of Beans

150
130
110
90
70
50
30
10
0

_____   _____

Kind of Bean

Explore

1. Which kind of bean did your cup hold more of?

   _____

2. Which kind of bean was bigger?

   _____

3. Will a cup always hold more small beans than big beans?
   Explain your answer.

   _____

   _____

   _____

4. Work with your partner to answer this question. Then, tell
   the rest of the class how you found an answer.

   If we had a big cup that holds 200 of the small beans, about
   how many large beans would the cup hold?

   _____

Maria and José

Homework

Maria and José did the *Full of Beans* experiment with lima beans and kidney beans. Here is a bar graph of their data.

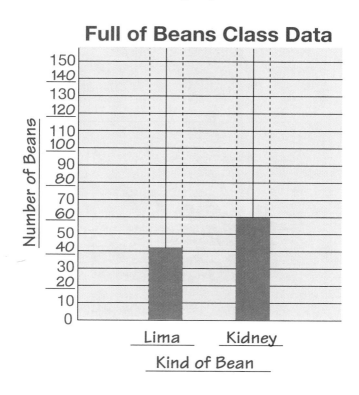

Full of Beans Class Data

1. About how many lima beans were in the cup? _____

2. Which beans were bigger, the lima or the kidney beans?

   _____

3. About how many more kidney beans were there than lima beans?

   _____

Maria's Marble Mart

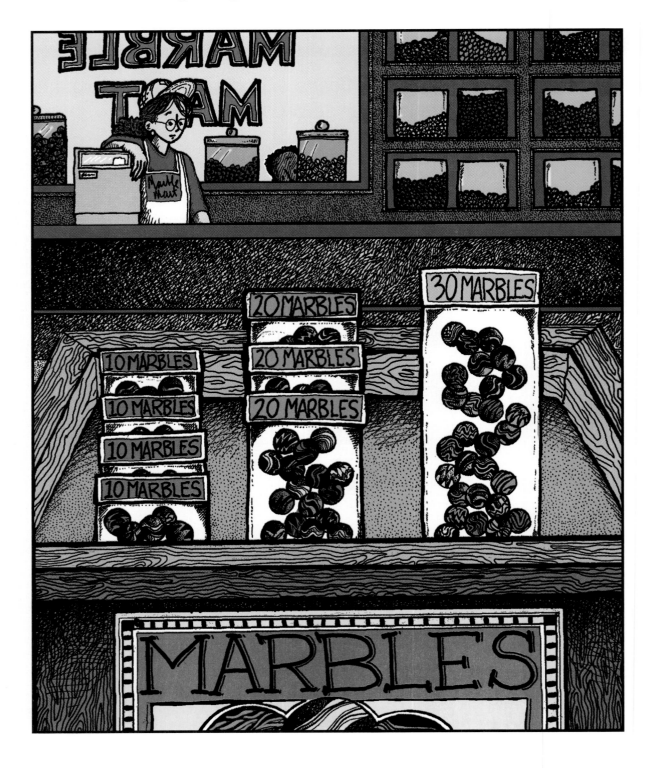

Marble Orders

This order is for _____ marbles.

_____   _____   _____
tallies   *tallies*   *tallies*

_____
number sentence

This order is for _____ marbles.

_____   _____   _____
tallies   *tallies*   *tallies*

_____
number sentence

This order is for _____ marbles.

_____   _____   _____
tallies   *tallies*   *tallies*

_____
number sentence

This order is for _____ marbles.

_____   _____   _____
tallies   *tallies*   *tallies*

_____
number sentence

UNIT 10

Partly Cloudy

More Clouds

Cloud A

How many pennies? _____

Cloud B

How many pennies? _____

Name _____ Date _____

Goldilocks and the Three Rectangles

Name _____ Date _____

The Three Rectangles

Randy
Rectangle

Ruthie Rectangle

Rebecca Rectangle

Rectangle Table

Record Randy's, Rebecca's, and Ruthie's measurements in the table below.

Name	Tall (in inches)	Wide (in inches)
Randy		
Rebecca		
Ruthie		

Goldilocks and the Three Rectangles

Name _____ Date _____

Tiles 1

Find and record the area of each figure below. Use square-inch tiles and halves of square-inch tiles to help you.

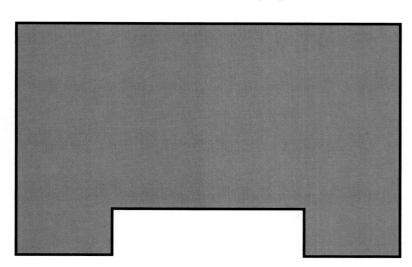

1. _____ square inches   **2.** _____ square inches

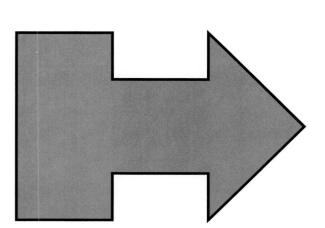
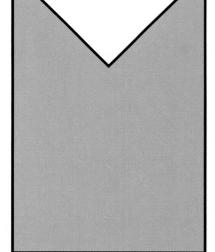

3. _____ square inches   **4.** _____ square inches

Tiles 2

Find and record the area of each figure below. Use square-inch tiles and halves of square-inch tiles to help you.

1. _____
square
inches

2. _____
square
inches

3. _____
square
inches

4. _____
square
inches

Name _____ Date _____

Tiles 3

What is the area of each shape?
Use square-inch tiles and halves
of square-inch tiles to help you.

1. _____ square inches

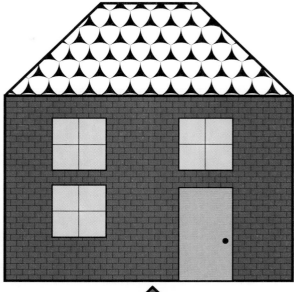

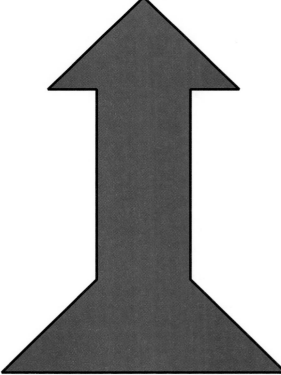

2. _____ square inches

3. _____ square inches

Which Two?

Find which two shapes have the same area. There is one shape on the next page.

1.

Area _____

2.

Area _____

Unit Designs

3.

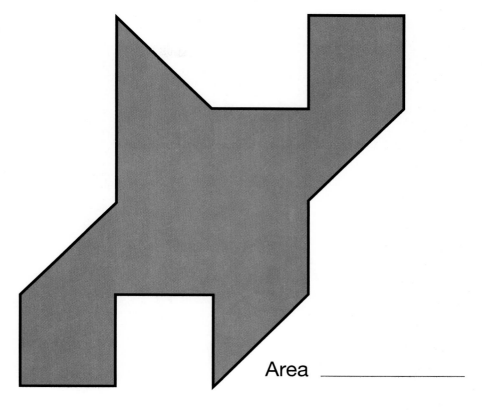

Area _____

4. Which two shapes have the same area?

_____

5. Does the other shape have a larger or smaller area than the two shapes with the same area?

_____

UNIT 11

100-Link Chain

Two Parts

Break your chain into two parts. Count the number of links in each part. Then, write a number sentence.

_____ + _____ = _____

Three Parts

Break your chain into three parts. Count the number of links in each part. Then, write a number sentence.

_____ + _____ + _____ = _____

Connect the three parts to form your 100-link chain again. Then, find three more ways to break the chain into three parts. Write a number sentence for each.

_____ + _____ + _____ = _____

_____ + _____ + _____ = _____

_____ + _____ + _____ = _____

Pennies

Arrange 10 pennies into two piles in as many ways as you can. Write a number sentence for each. Write some subtraction number sentences, too. Then, arrange your pennies into three piles and write a number sentence.

Pennies
_____ + _____ = 10
_____ + _____ = 10
_____ + _____ = 10
_____ + _____ = 10
_____ + _____ = 10
10 − _____ = _____
10 − _____ = _____
10 − _____ = _____
_____ + _____ + _____ = 10

Dimes

Arrange 10 dimes into two piles in as many ways as you can. Write an addition number sentence for each. Write some subtraction number sentences, too.

Dimes
_____ + _____ = 100
_____ + _____ = 100
_____ + _____ = 100
_____ + _____ = 100
_____ + _____ = 100
100 − _____ = _____
100 − _____ = _____
100 − _____ = _____
100 − _____ = _____
100 − _____ = _____

Pennies and Dimes

Three Piles

Divide your group of dimes into three piles. How many different piles can you think of?

_____ + _____ + _____ = 100

_____ + _____ + _____ = 100

_____ + _____ + _____ = 100

_____ + _____ + _____ = 100

_____ + _____ + _____ = 100

_____ + _____ + _____ = 100

_____ + _____ + _____ = 100

_____ + _____ + _____ = 100

Twins' Day at the County Fair

Draw the coins, and record the amount of money from each twin.

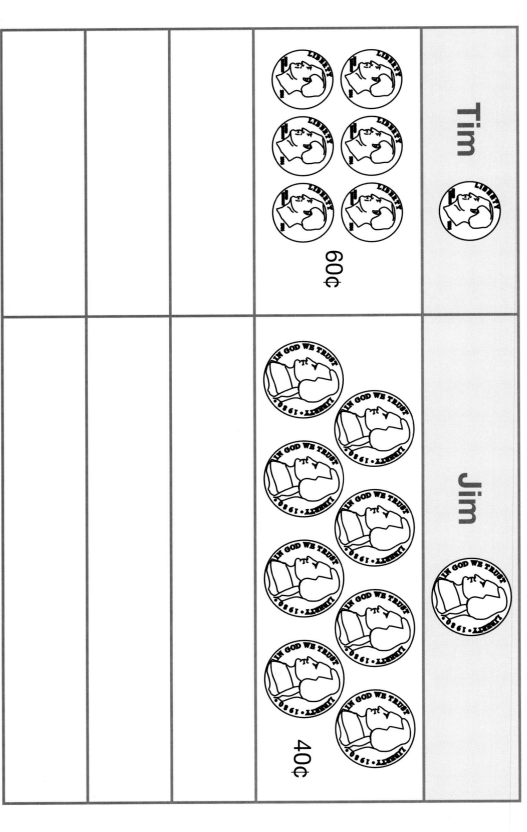

Tim	Jim
🪙🪙🪙🪙🪙🪙 60¢	🪙🪙🪙🪙🪙🪙🪙🪙 40¢

Shuttle Bus #100

Shuttle bus #100 carries exactly 100 people each trip. It stops at three different parking lots, where it picks up people in groups of ten. The bus driver needs to record the number of people that are picked up at each stop. Sometimes, he forgets to record all of the numbers. Help the driver fill in the missing numbers on his chart. You can use beans on the number strip to find the missing number.

10	10	10	10	10	10	10	10	10	10

Parking Lot 1		Parking Lot 2		Parking Lot 3	
20	+	50	+	_____	= 100
40	+	40	+	_____	= 100
10	+	60	+	_____	= 100
_____	+	20	+	60	= 100
60	+	_____	+	40	= 100
30	+	_____	+	40	= 100
50	+	40	+	_____	= 100
80	+	10	+	_____	= 100

Shuttle Bus #50

Homework

Shuttle bus #50 carries exactly 50 people each trip. The bus stops at three different parking lots, where it picks up people in groups of five. Help the driver fill in the missing numbers on his chart. You can use beans on the number strip to find the missing numbers.

5	5	5	5	5	5	5	5	5	5

Parking Lot 1		**Parking Lot 2**		**Parking Lot 3**	
25	+	5	+	_____	= 50
10	+	30	+	_____	= 50
15	+	_____	+	20	= 50
5	+	_____	+	35	= 50
_____	+	20	+	10	= 50
25	+	_____	+	20	= 50
40	+	_____	+	5	= 50
25	+	15	+	_____	= 50

Dimes, Nickels, and Quarters

Arrow Dynamics Game Board

Materials

100 chart

clear spinner
(or paper clip
and pencil)

game markers

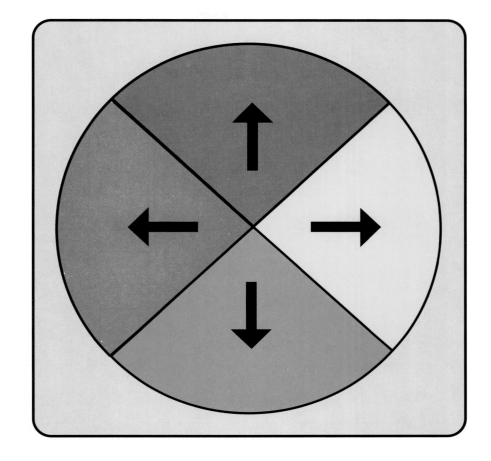

Rules

1. Each player places a game marker on the number 45 on the 100 chart to start. Take turns, using the rules below.

2. Spin to find out what direction to move your marker.

3. Say a number sentence that describes your move. Then, write it on your record sheet. Example: Starting at 45 and moving up one space would be 45 − 10 = 35.

4. The player who reaches the largest number after 7 spins is the winner.

100 Chart

1	2	3	4	5	6	7	8	9	10
11	12	13	14	15	16	17	18	19	20
21	22	23	24	25	26	27	28	29	30
31	32	33	34	35	36	37	38	39	40
41	42	43	44	45	46	47	48	49	50
51	52	53	54	55	56	57	58	59	60
61	62	63	64	65	66	67	68	69	70
71	72	73	74	75	76	77	78	79	80
81	82	83	84	85	86	87	88	89	90
91	92	93	94	95	96	97	98	99	100

Who Is Winning?

Read the directions for playing *Arrow Dynamics* before answering these questions. Use your 100 chart to find the answers to the moves three players made during a game.

Player 1 Starts on 45 and moves:

Lands on _____

Player 2 Starts on 45 and moves:

Lands on _____

Player 3 Starts on 45 and moves:

Lands on _____

The goal for the game is to have the largest number.

Which player is winning? _____

Arrow Dynamics Record Sheet

Write a number sentence to describe each move.

Player 1	Player 2

Here is another record sheet for playing a second game of *Arrow Dynamics.*

Player 1	Player 2

Follow the Arrows

Write a number sentence to describe each of the moves made during a game of *Arrow Dynamics*. Use your 100 chart.

1. Start on 45. Move . Land on _____

Number Sentence: _____

2. Start on 55. Move . Land on _____

Number Sentence: _____

3. Start on 58. Move . Land on _____

Number Sentence: _____

4. Start on 92. Move  . Land on _____

Number Sentence: _____

5. Start on 12. Move ↑ ← . Land on _____

Number Sentence: _____

Arrow Dynamics

100 Seconds

Draw one X in each box. How many X's do you think you can draw in 100 seconds? Try it for 10 seconds and then make a prediction.

How many X's did you draw in 10 seconds?

_____

How many X's do you think you could draw in 100 seconds?

_____

Try it. How many X's did you draw in 100 seconds?

_____

Look at your prediction. Were you close? Why or why not?

_____

_____

_____

_____

Weather 2 Picture

Draw a picture of your experiment.

Weather 2 Data Table

Collect

Record your data in the table below.

Weather 2

T Type of _____	N Number of _____	
	Tallies	**Total**

Weather 2 Graph

Graph

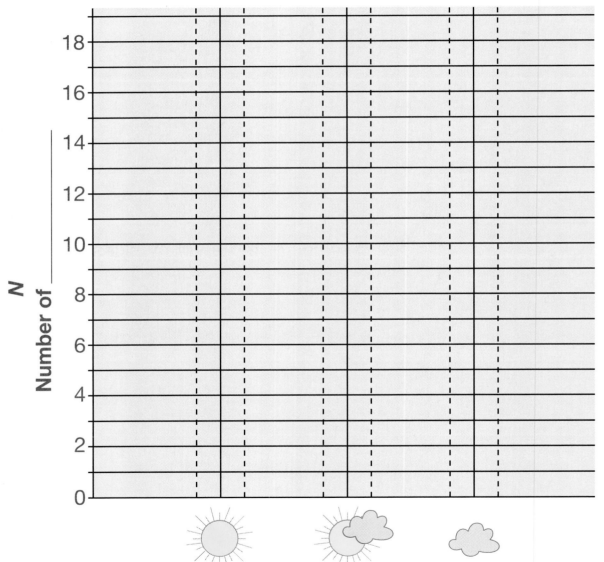

Type of _____

Weather 2: Winter Skies

Thinking about Winter Skies

 **Explore**

1. Which type of sky did you see *most* often?

   _____

2. Which type of sky did you see *least* often?

   _____

3. How many sunny *and* partly sunny skies were there in all?

   _____

4. Were there more cloudy skies or more sunny skies?

   _____

5. How many days are there in half of the winter month
   we studied?

   _____

6. **A.** Was any type of sky seen on more than half the

   days in the month? _____

   B. Which type of sky was it? _____

Comparing Fall and Winter Skies

Explore

Record your data for each month's weather in the data table.

T Type of Sky _____	N Number of Days	
	_____ month	_____ month
☀		
☁		
⛅		

1. **A.** Which month had a greater number of sunny days?

   _____

   B. How many more? _____

   C. Is this a big difference or a small difference?

   _____

2. A. Which month had a greater number of partly

sunny days? _____

B. How many more? _____

C. Is this a big difference or a small difference?

_____

3. A. Which month had a greater number of cloudy days?

_____

B. How many more? _____

C. Is this a big difference or a small difference?

_____

4. In which month would you expect a greater number of cloudy days—a month in autumn or a month in winter?

_____

Tell how you can use the data to answer this question:

_____

_____

_____

Weather Data

September's Weather

T Type of Day	N Number of Days
☀	16
☁	9
⛅	5

October's Weather

T Type of Day	N Number of Days
☀	13
☁	4
⛅	14

November's Weather

T Type of Day	N Number of Days
☀	7
☁	15
⛅	8

December's Weather

T Type of Day	N Number of Days
☀	3
☁	17
⛅	11

Weather 2: Winter Skies

Name _____ Date _____

Weather Problems

For their science project, Michael and Bianca are comparing the data they collected for four months. They recorded their data on the *Weather Data* Activity Page. Use this data to answer the questions below.

1. How many sunny days did they record for the months of December and November?

   _____

   Write a number sentence to show how you found the answer.

   _____

2. How many more cloudy days were there in September than there were in October? _____

   Write a number sentence to show how you found the answer.

   _____

3. How many days were cloudy in September and October?

   _____

   Write a number sentence to show how you found the answer.

   _____

4. Michael and Bianca found out there were 39 sunny days in the four months. Is their total correct? _____

How did you decide?

_____

_____

_____

What is another way to find the total number of sunny days?

_____

_____

_____

Think of some other problems you can ask about these data tables. Write the problems in your journal.

U.S.A. Map

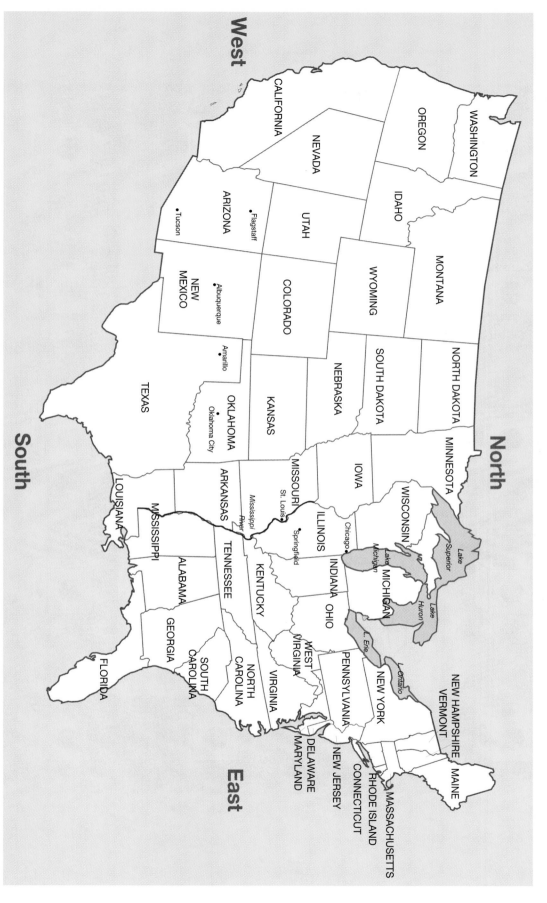

North

West

South

East

CALIFORNIA
OREGON
WASHINGTON
NEVADA
IDAHO
ARIZONA
•Flagstaff
•Tucson
UTAH
MONTANA
WYOMING
NEW MEXICO
•Albuquerque
COLORADO
SOUTH DAKOTA
NORTH DAKOTA
•Amarillo
TEXAS
OKLAHOMA
•Oklahoma City
KANSAS
NEBRASKA
MINNESOTA
IOWA
WISCONSIN
MISSOURI
St. Louis•
Mississippi River
ARKANSAS
LOUISIANA
MISSISSIPPI
ALABAMA
TENNESSEE
KENTUCKY
ILLINOIS
Springfield•
Chicago•
INDIANA
OHIO
MICHIGAN
Lake Michigan
Lake Superior
Lake Huron
L. Erie
L. Ontario
GEORGIA
SOUTH CAROLINA
NORTH CAROLINA
VIRGINIA
WEST VIRGINIA
FLORIDA
PENNSYLVANIA
NEW YORK
NEW HAMPSHIRE
VERMONT
MAINE
MASSACHUSETTS
RHODE ISLAND
CONNECTICUT
NEW JERSEY
DELAWARE
MARYLAND

UNIT 12

My 8-Cube Building

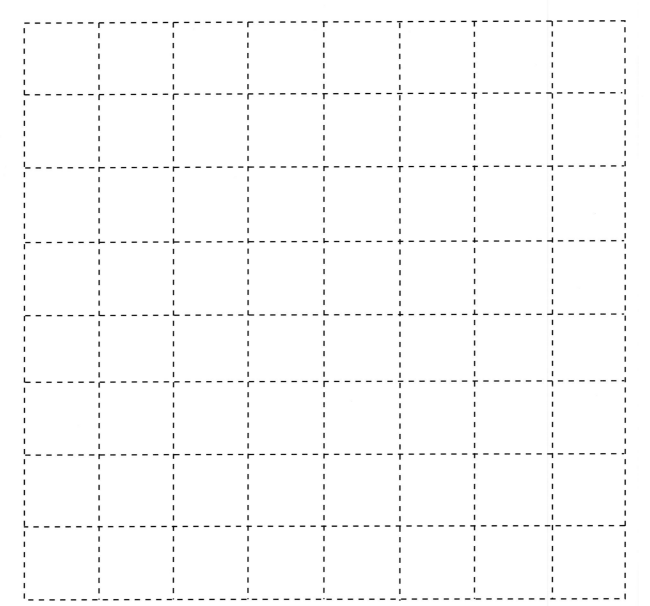

1. The **area** of the floor plan in square units is _____ .

2. The **volume** in cubic units is _____ .

3. The **height** in number of floors is _____ .

Cube Models

1. Select an object. Then, draw a picture of it.

2. Make a **life-size** cube model of the object.

3. Count the cubes to find the volume of the model. The

   volume of my cube model is _____ .

4. Decide whether the volume of the cube model is **just the same as, less than,** or **greater than** the volume of the real object. The **volume** of my cube model is

   _____ that of the real object.

TIMS Towers 1

Your group can use cubes to make buildings just like these. Think of different ways to find the volume of each building. Record the volume on the TIMS Towers Data Table.

Twin Towers

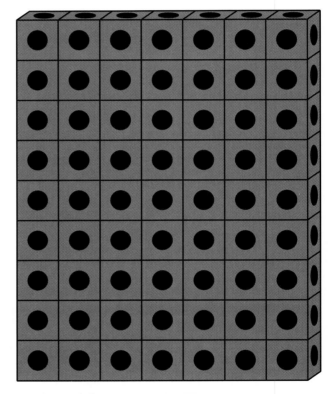

Sky-High Towers

TIMS Towers

Name _____ Date _____

TIMS Towers 2

Record the volume on the TIMS Towers Data Table.

Triple Double Towers

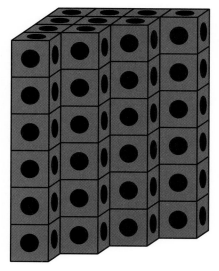

Saw-Tooth Towers

TIMS Towers Data Table

TIMS Towers

Building	Number of Cubes
Twin Towers	
Sky-High Towers	
Triple Double Towers	
Saw-Tooth Towers	

TIMS Radio Tower

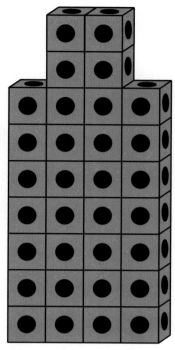

TIMS Radio Tower

Height = _____

Volume = _____

How did you find your answer?

Ruffy and the Snake

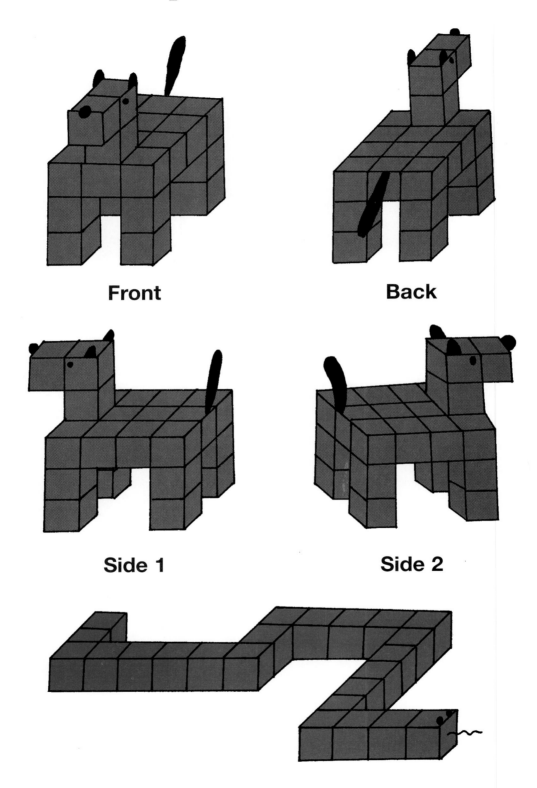

Front

Back

Side 1

Side 2

A World of Cubic Animals

Comparing Ruffy and the Snake

Look at the different views of Ruffy and the snake on the *Ruffy and the Snake* Activity Page. Use these pictures for help in answering the questions below.

That's pretty amazing!

1. Who looks bigger, Ruffy or the snake? Explain your answer.

_____

_____

_____

_____

2. Work with a partner to find the volume of Ruffy and the volume of the snake. You may build them with cubes.

Ruffy has a volume of _____ .

The snake has a volume of _____ .

UNIT
13

Make Ten at Home

Homework

Dear Family Member:

Your child played the game *Make Ten* in school and is ready to teach it to someone at home. You may use the digit cards your child has brought home or use a deck of playing cards by removing the kings, queens, and jacks. The aces can represent the number 1. Have beans, toothpicks, or other small objects handy for your child to use in solving problems that arise during the game. Also, please help your child keep a record of the number of people he or she teaches to play the game.

Thank you for your cooperation.

Make a tally mark for each person you teach to play the game.

Tallies _____

Make a tally mark for every five minutes you play the game.

Tallies _____   Total minutes _____

Parent's signature

_____

Child's signature _____

Return this sheet to school by _____ .

Make Ten

Doubles Problems

Think of two doubles. Draw a picture of the doubles in each of the spaces provided. Write a number sentence that fits each picture. Then, tell a story about each picture.

1.

_____ + _____ = _____

_____

_____

_____

2. Draw your second picture here. Write your number sentence and story in the spaces below.

_____ + _____ = _____

_____

_____

_____

_____

_____

Seeing Doubles

Doubles Railroad

Materials

*Doubles Railroad
Game Board*

1 baby lima bean
for each player

clear plastic spinner
or a pencil and
paper clip

50 connecting cubes

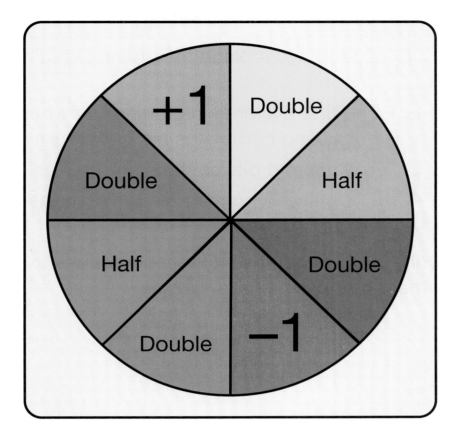

Double means to double the circled number where your bean is
placed on the game board. After you find the answer, move to this
number on the game board.

Half means to find half of the circled number on the game board.
After you find the answer, move to this number on the game board.

+1 means to move forward to the next largest number.

–1 means to move backward to the next smallest number.

Directions

This is a game for two players.

1. Both players place their beans on circle number 1 on the game board.

2. The first player spins to find out where to move on the game board and completes his or her turn.

3. The second player spins and makes a move.

4. The player who reaches 50 first wins the game.

Hint: Players can use connecting cubes to help them figure out where to move.

Doubles and Halves

Problem Set 1-8

Use ten frames, counters, or mental math to solve the problems.

1. Ruth had 7 stickers. Mrs. Rhoton gave her 3 more. How many did Ruth have in all?

2. Mo is 6 years old. Her sister Ann is 14 years old. How much older is Ann?

3. Beau has $2. How much more money does he need for an action figure that costs $6?

4. Frank has 14 action figures. Three are bad guys. The rest are good guys. How many good guys does he have?

5. Marie had some dolls. For her birthday she got 3 more. Then, she had 9 dolls. How many dolls did she have before her birthday?

6. Jessica had some toy cars. She gave 3 toy cars to Jim. Then, she had 5. How many toy cars did she have before she gave 3 away?

7. In November, Ellen lost 3 teeth. She then had 12. How many teeth did she have to start with?

8. Jack had 12 raffle tickets. He sold some to his friends. He then had 8 tickets. How many raffle tickets did he sell?

Milly and Billy's Data

Colors

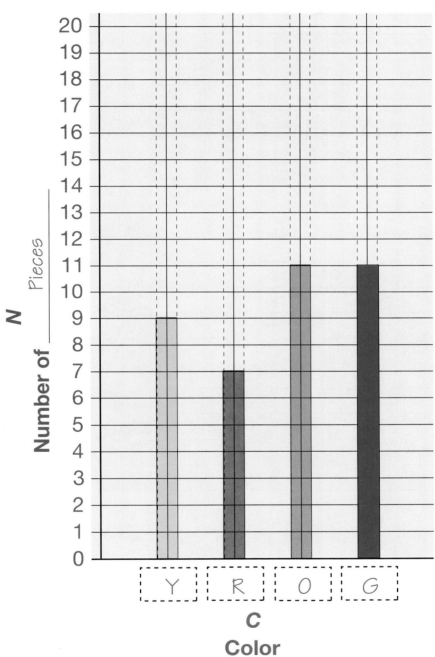

Y = yellow
R = red
O = orange
G = green

C
Color

Name ______________________ Date ______________

Weather 1

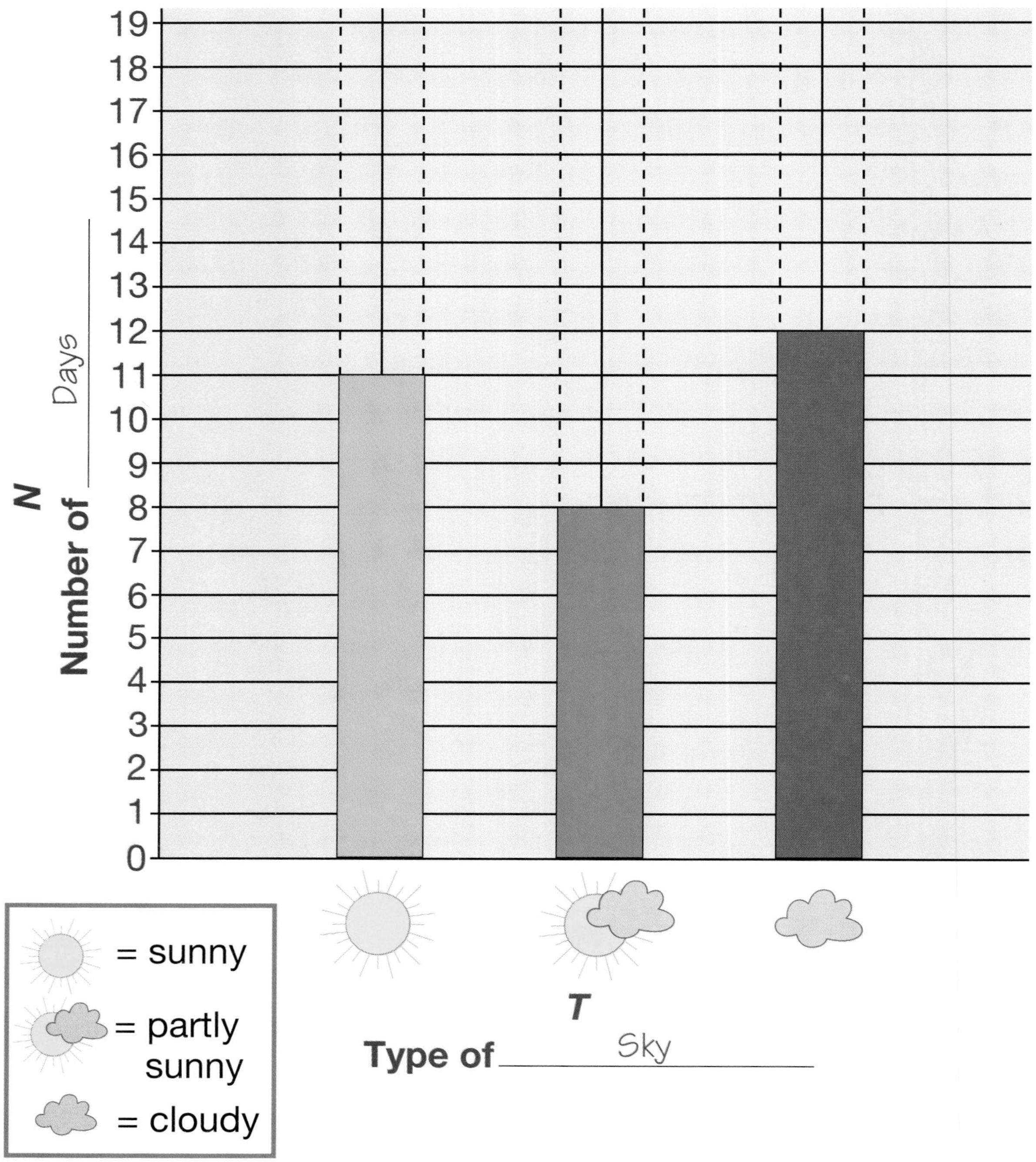

19
18
17
16
15
14
13
12
11
10
9
8
7
6
5
4
3
2
1
0
N
Number of Days
T
Type of Sky
= sunny
= partly sunny
= cloudy

Rolling Along with Links

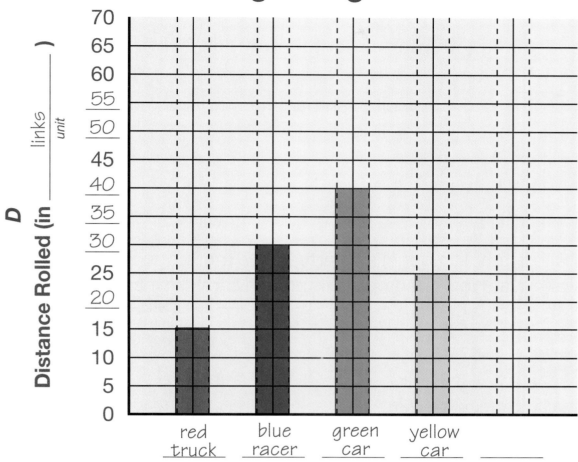

More Problems

Homework

Use ten frames, counters, mental math, or drawings to solve the problems.

1. Stephen has 9 pencils. Ishmael has 5 pencils. How many more pencils does Stephen have?

2. LaTonya has 5 pencils. Marty has 7 more pencils than LaTonya. How many pencils does Marty have?

3. Lauren has 12 books. There are 8 hardcover books. The rest of the books are paperbacks. How many paperbacks does she have?

4. Blanca had $8. She spent $3 on a book. How much money did she have left?

5. Maria has 4 goldfish and 6 angelfish. How many fish does she have?

6. Nick has 9 erasers. He has 5 more erasers than Jennifer. How many erasers does Jennifer have?

7. There were 12 birds on a wire. Then 3 flew away, looking for a tree. How many birds were left on the wire?

8. Eight fat frogs croaked really loud. More frogs came to make a crowd. Now, there are 12 frogs. How many came?

UNIT 14

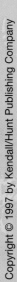

Squid Squares

Homework

Draw arms and eyes on the two squid squares below so that they look just like the example squid square.

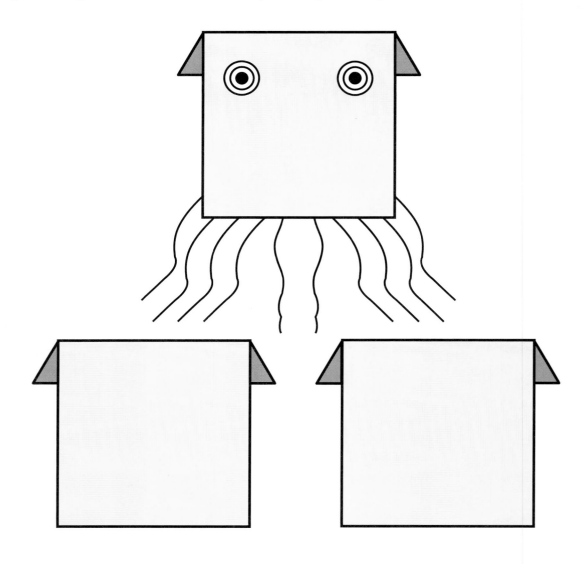

Math Mice

1. How many circles did you have to draw to make eyes for one squid? Draw a picture that shows how you know.

2. How many circles did you have to draw to make eyes for **two** squid? Show how you know this.

3. How many legs did you draw for **two** squid? What number could you count by to help you?

4. If you saw **ten** eyes glowing under the sea, how many squid would there be? Show a way you might figure this out.

Counting Pets

Homework

Dear Parent or Guardian:

In class, we are looking at the types of pets students own. We are using the information to create number problems. In this homework assignment, we ask your child to count the number he or she has of each type of pet as well as those in another household. Then, he or she will write number problems. If there are no pets in your household, please help your child get this information from two other households that have at least one pet.

Here is a sample chart.

Family Name	Dog	Cat	Fish	Turtle	Bird	Other
Smith		1	5			

Please help your child fill in the chart below.

Thank you for your cooperation.

Family Name	Dog	Cat	Fish	Turtle	Bird	Other

Write five number problems for the data you collected. Show how you solved each problem.

1. _____

_____

2. _____

_____

3. _____

_____

4. _____

_____

5. _____

_____

Room 222's Pets Graph

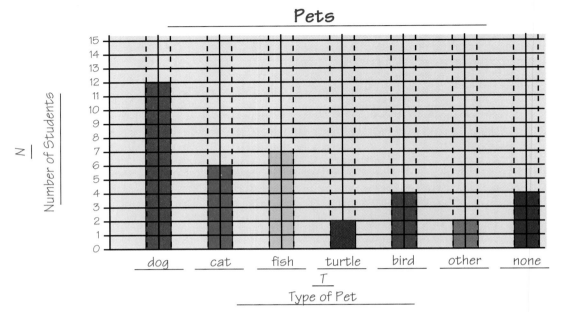

Pets

Number of Students

15
14
13
12
11
10
9
8
7
6
5
4
3
2
1
0

dog   cat   fish   turtle   bird   other   none

T

Type of Pet

1. What is the most common pet? _____

2. What is the least common pet? _____

3. Which pet is owned by double the number of students

with cats? _____

4. A. How many students have turtles, birds, and fish?

_____

B. Are there more students with dogs than turtles, birds,

and fish? _____

5. Tell a story you see in the graph. _____

_____

More Pet Problems

Answer the questions. Show your work with a picture.

1. Imagine that you keep six birds in one cage. How many wings are there in the cage? Show how you found your answer.

2. Imagine you have 15 small turtles and 3 large rocks in your turtle tank. How many turtles need to share each rock? Show how you solved this problem.

Animal Boots

A farmer wants to buy boots for his animals. The farmer has horses and chickens. How many boots will he need to buy?

Animals	Number of Boots
	20
	18

Is there another answer to the last one? Draw a picture to show your idea.

Problems that Will Knock Your Socks Off!

Animal Shelter

Answer the questions. Show your work.

Maria, Jose, Juan, Celina, and Angela are brothers and sisters. Their mother has promised them that they can adopt a puppy from an animal shelter if they can save $45. The children decide that, to be fair, they must each save the same amount of money.

1. How much money does each child need to save?

2. The children adopted a cute puppy they named Rex. On the way home, they bought Rex a collar that cost $10. If each child pays the same amount, how much money did each child spend on the collar?

Name _____ Date _____

The Old Woman and Her Cats

Answer the questions. Show your work in words or pictures on another piece of paper.

There was an old woman who wore pretty hats.
Within her house, she kept a number of cats.
Of love, they had plenty, but food they did need.
With each bowl of food, three cats she could feed.

She had nine large bowls, all ready to use.
But the bowls and the cats she began to confuse.
"Do I have enough bowls? Can I feed every cat?
Can somebody please help me figure out that?"

1. How many cats can the woman feed using nine bowls?

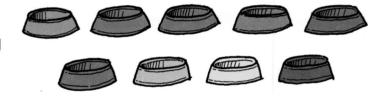

2. A. If she had 25 cats, how many bowls would she need?

B. Would she have room for any more cats?

Problems that Will Knock Your Socks Off!

Basil the Basset Hound

Answer the questions. Show your work in words or pictures.

1. Basil the basset hound had 23 beautiful bones buried in his yard. One weekend, he dug up 12 of them. How many bones are still buried? Show how you found your answer.

2. Basil and his three buddies found 16 bones in back of the grocery store. They agreed to share them equally. How many bones will each dog get? Draw a picture to help you find the answer.

3. It was Basil's lucky day! His owner made a roast which had two bones in it. Basil wished his owner would make the same kind of roast every day for a week. How many bones would Basil have if his owner granted his wish? Show how you know.

UNIT 15

The Boy Who Traveled to Find a Hard Problem

Once, there was a man who had a daughter and a son. The children were clever and hard-working.

The son could never understand when people said, "I can't figure that out; it's a hard problem." He always knew the answer right away.

Daily Practice and Problems

Name _____ Date _____

Dinner Guests

One evening, the family had some dinner guests. The father wanted to set the table. He said, "There are four of us in the family, and we have three guests. How many plates do we need?"

Show your work here.

The family needs _____ plates.

Name _____   Date _____

Shepherd

The boy set out from home in search of a hard problem. Soon, he came to a shepherd who was sitting with 18 sheep by the roadside. The poor shepherd was crying. The boy asked what the matter was.

The shepherd said, "I have a really hard problem. I am watching 18 sheep for Farmer Bigshoe and Farmer Digdeep. I know that Bigshoe gave me 12 sheep, but I'll never figure out how many Digdeep gave me: It's too hard!"

Show your work here.

Digdeep gave the shepherd _____ sheep.

Ducks

Soon, he came upon two women arguing over ducks. The boy asked what was wrong. One woman said, "I had 5 ducks and some of her ducks flew over here. Now, there are 13 ducks here, and we don't know how many are hers. What a hard problem!"

Show your work here.

_____ ducks flew over here.

Describe That Shape

Test what each shape can do. Record your findings in the table below. The bottom row of the table is for any other words you think are important to describe these shapes.

	Cylinders (Tubes)	Prisms (Boxes)	Cubes	Spheres (Balls)
This shape can roll.				
This shape can stack.				
This shape can slide.				

Homework

Dear Family Member:

In class, your child has explored various three-dimensional shapes. I have asked your child to find everyday objects that have a cylindrical shape and to record them in the data table on the back of this page. (Your child should write in the column headings on the blank table as shown below.) Objects like soup cans are good examples of cylinders because they have circular ends and straight sides. Some objects like most paper cups are almost cylinders, but their sides are not quite straight.

After your child has completed the data table, he or she should bring five to ten of the cylinders to school. Students will use these objects in a class activity. Please help your child find and select non-breakable examples that have circular ends and straight sides to bring to school for this activity.

Thank you for your cooperation.

Cylinder Search

Search for objects that have a cylinder shape, like the toilet paper core. Then, record the names of the cylinder shapes you see at your home. Make the headings in your data table look like the ones below.

Cylinder Shape	Almost Cylinder Shape

Choose five to ten items from your data table to bring to school.

Tubes, Boxes, Spheres, and Cubes

Sorting Cylinders

Your team will work together to sort your cylinders into three different groups. Each of these groups is listed on the Cylinders Data Table.

Directions

1. Your teacher will give you and your partner a copy of the *Categories for Sorting Cylinders*. Cut out the names of the three categories:

   A. **Height Longer** than the Circumference

   B. **Circumference Longer** than the Height

   C. **Same** Circumference and Height

2. Which group does your team predict will have the greatest number of cylinders?

   _____

3. Use string to compare the height and circumference of each cylinder.

4. Sort the cylinders into the three groups. Place each cylinder in the corrrect category.

5. Record the results on the Cylinders Data Table.

Cylinders Data Table

Groups of Cylinders	Number of Cylinders
Height Longer than the Circumference	
Circumference Longer than the Height	
Same Circumference and Height	

Total number of cylinders measured: _____

3-D Shapes

Cut out the pictures and paste them under their names. Then, describe each shape.

1. Cylinder

_____

_____

_____

_____

_____

2. Cube

_____

_____

_____

_____

_____

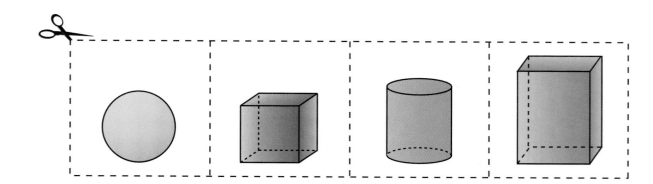

3. **Prism**

_____

_____

_____

_____

_____

_____

4. **Sphere**

_____

_____

_____

_____

_____

_____

Find the Shapes

Two construction workers are having lunch. The picture below contains many different shapes. Color all the shapes you can find with the colors listed below:

- Blue crayon for cylinders.
- Red crayon for rectangular prisms.
- Orange crayon for cubes.
- Green crayon for spheres.

UNIT 16

Gold Pieces

The boy who traveled to find a hard problem went to town. He found the king sitting in his counting house scratching his head. The king said, "Who are you? Can you help me? I have 39 gold pieces, but I need to pay the army 57 gold pieces. I can't figure out how many more gold pieces I need."

Show your work here.

The king needs _____ more gold pieces.

Daily Practice and Problems

Royal Rabbits

Next, the king and the boy went to the royal rabbit hutch. The king said, "I had some rabbits before, but 15 new ones have been born. Now, there are 55 rabbits. My problem is that I don't know how many I started with. If you can solve this problem for me, I will reward you with a bird that lays golden eggs."

Show your work here.

The king started with _____ rabbits.

Home Again

The boy thanked the king for the bird and set out for home. When he got there, everybody was happy to have him back. They were also happy to have the golden bird.

The family was rich now, and everyone was very content, especially the boy. He could think of lots of hard problems about the bird and the golden eggs. Can you? Write one below.

_____

_____

_____

Food Group Sort 1

You will need your *Favorite Foods* homework. Sort your favorite foods into these six food groups. Write the names of your favorite foods in the boxes below.

Bread, Cereal, Rice, and Pasta Group	Milk, Yogurt, and Cheese Group
Vegetable Group	**Meat, Poultry, Fish, Dry Beans, Eggs, and Nuts Group**
Fruit Group	**Fats, Oils, and Sweets**

Food Group Sort 2

Sort these foods into the six food groups by writing the number(s) of the group(s) after each food.

Food Groups

1. **Bread, Cereal, Rice, and Pasta Group**
2. **Vegetable Group**
3. **Fruit Group**
4. **Milk, Yogurt, and Cheese Group**

5. **Meat, Poultry, Fish, Dry Beans, Eggs, and Nuts Group**
6. **Fats, Oils, and Sweets**

french fries _____

corn on the cob _____

pineapple _____

ice cream _____

orange juice _____

grapes _____

hamburger _____

rice and beans _____

corn flakes _____

boiled egg _____

chicken taco _____

yogurt _____

hot cocoa _____

shrimp fried rice _____

pizza _____

carrots _____

chili _____

peanut butter sandwich _____

I Ate That!

Homework

Dear Family Member:

Your child has learned to categorize food into food groups in class. Now, your child is ready to gather data about everything he or she eats during the course of one day. On the reverse are guidelines about the amount of food that constitutes one serving. You and your child can use it to record his or her daily servings in each food group. It is not important that measurements be precise. If a combination food needs to be recorded, such as a hamburger with toppings, you can simply record a tally mark in the box for each of the major food groups that can be seen easily.

Please complete this full-day data collection beginning the morning of _____ .

Thank you for your cooperation.

Use a tally mark to record one serving of each type of food eaten.

Food Group	Breakfast	Lunch	Dinner	Snacks	Total
Bread					
Vegetable					
Fruit					
Milk					
Meat					
Fats					

What counts as one serving according to the U.S. Department of Agriculture?

Food Group	Serving Size for Selected Food Items
Bread, Cereal, Rice, and Pasta	• 1 slice of bread, 1 tortilla, or $\frac{1}{2}$ pita • $\frac{1}{2}$ hamburger bun, English muffin, bagel • a small roll, biscuit, or muffin • 4 small or 2 large crackers • $\frac{1}{2}$ cup cooked cereal, rice, or pasta • $\frac{1}{2}$ cup ready-to-eat breakfast cereal
Vegetable	• $\frac{1}{2}$ cup cooked vegetables • $\frac{1}{2}$ cup chopped raw vegetables • 1 cup leafy raw vegetables, such as lettuce, greens, or spinach
Fruit	• a whole fruit, such as medium apple, banana, or orange • $\frac{1}{2}$ grapefruit • a melon wedge • $\frac{1}{2}$ cup of juice • $\frac{1}{2}$ cup of berries • $\frac{1}{2}$ cup cooked or canned fruit • $\frac{1}{4}$ cup dried fruit
Milk, Yogurt, and Cheese	• 1 cup milk • 1 cup yogurt • $1\frac{1}{2}$ ounces natural cheese • 2 ounces processed cheese
Meat, Poultry, Fish, Dry Beans, Eggs, and Nuts	• 1 piece of lean meat, poultry, or fish • 1 or 2 slices of lunch meat • 1 egg, $\frac{1}{2}$ cup tofu • 4 tablespoons peanut butter • $\frac{1}{2}$ cup cooked beans
Fats, Oils, and Sweets	• a small amount of salad dressing • ketchup • yogurt • butter or margarine • jelly • $\frac{1}{2}$ candy bar • $\frac{1}{2}$ cup ice cream • $\frac{1}{2}$ cup frozen yogurt

Healthy Kids

Draw a picture of the experiment.

Record what you eat for one day on the *I Ate That!* Homework Page.

Name _____   Date _____

Healthy Kids Graph

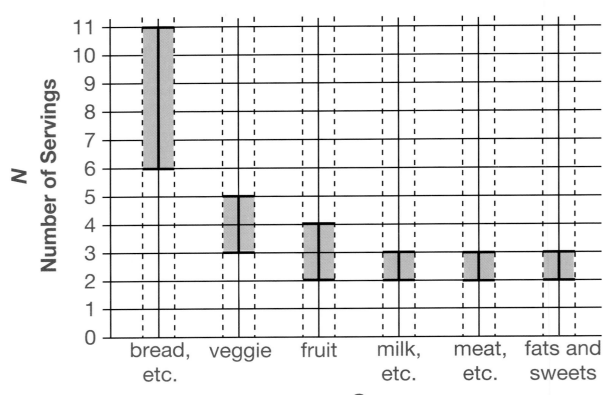

1. Use your graph to tell the story of the food you ate in one day. How does what you ate compare to what you should be eating? Are there things you should change? Are there things you should keep the same?

2. If you try to eat better and collect data six months from now, show how you would like the graph to look.

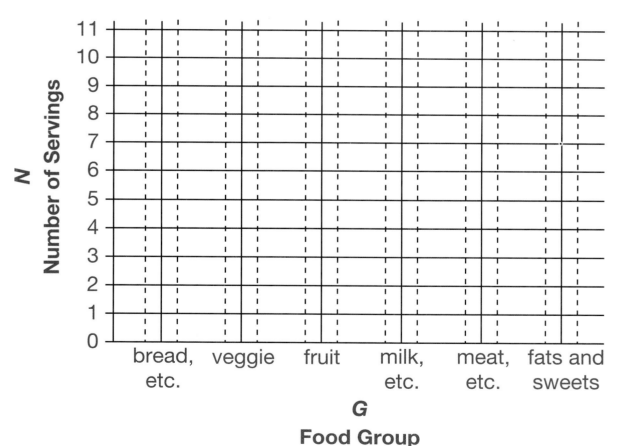

Healthier Kids

N
Number of Servings

11
10
9
8
7
6
5
4
3
2
1
0

bread, etc. | veggie | fruit | milk, etc. | meat, etc. | fats and sweets

G
Food Group

UNIT 17

At School in Tensland

In another class, students are also collecting buttons.
J.D. has circled his buttons to help count them.

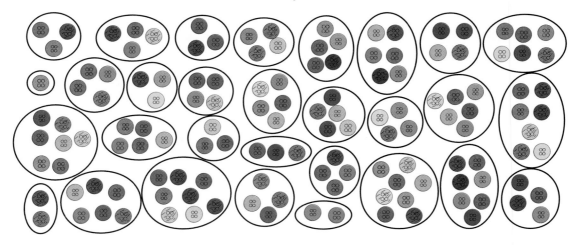

Jonay has organized her buttons, too.

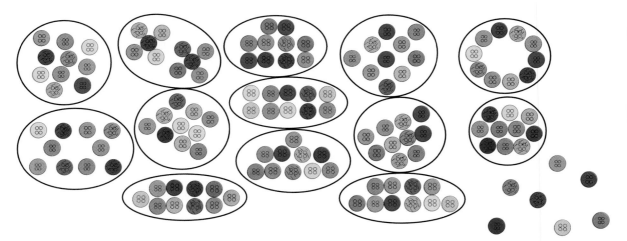

Whose buttons would you rather count:
J.D.'s buttons or Jonay's buttons? _____

Explain why you picked that group to count.

_____

How many buttons are in the group you counted? _____

Pumpkin Patch

Silvia and Douglas went pumpkin picking in the pumpkin patch. Silvia wondered how many pumpkins there were in all. Count the number of pumpkins. Draw a picture showing how you counted the number of pumpkins. Then, tell your strategies.

_____

_____

_____

_____

_____

Counting One Hundred Seventy-two

Adding Numbers

Set 1

$7 + 2 =$ _____ $70 + 20 =$ _____ $700 + 200 =$ _____

Set 2

$$\begin{array}{r} 6 \\ +\ 3 \\ \hline \end{array}$$ $$\begin{array}{r} 60 \\ +\ 30 \\ \hline \end{array}$$ $$\begin{array}{r} 600 \\ +\ 300 \\ \hline \end{array}$$

Set 3

$$\begin{array}{r} 3 \\ +\ 3 \\ \hline \end{array}$$ $$\begin{array}{r} 30 \\ +\ 30 \\ \hline \end{array}$$ $$\begin{array}{r} 300 \\ +\ 300 \\ \hline \end{array}$$

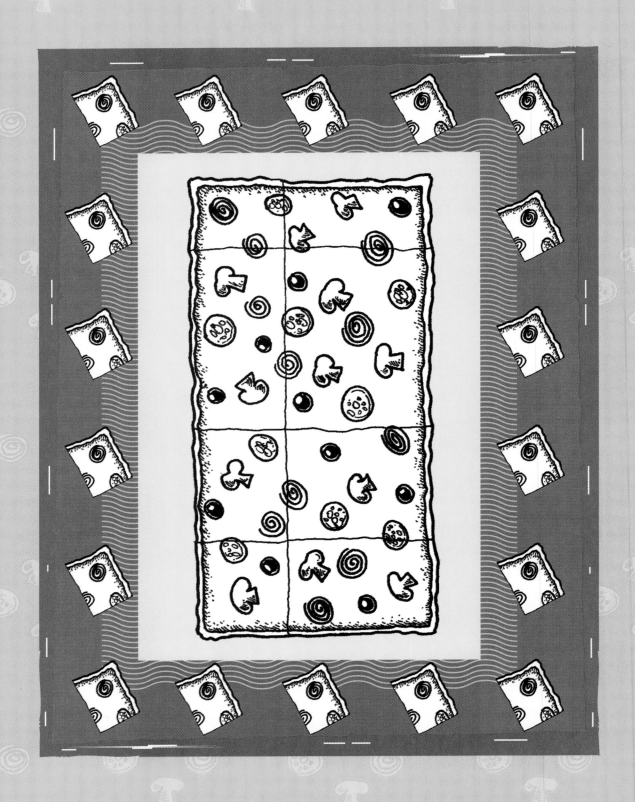

UNIT 18

Folding and Showing Halves

Cut out the shapes on the *Fold and Color 1* Activity Page. Fold each shape in half and then color one-half of each shape. Paste the cutouts on the shapes below. Then, complete the sentence for each shape.

Daniel cut out a hexagon.
He folded it in half.
He colored one-half.

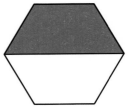

I colored $\frac{1}{2}$ of

this _____hexagon_____ .

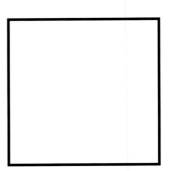

1. I colored _____ of

this _____ .

2. I colored _____ of

this _____ .

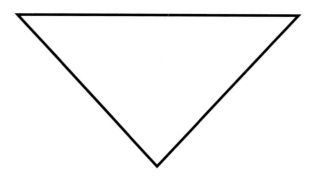

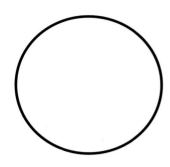

3. I colored _____ of

this _____ .

4. I colored _____ of

this _____ .

Folding and Showing Fourths

Cut out the shapes on the *Fold and Color 2* Activity Page. Fold each shape and then color one-fourth of each shape. Paste the cutouts on the shapes and complete the sentence for each shape.

Daniel cut out a hexagon.
He folded it in fourths.
He colored one-fourth.

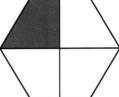

I colored _____$\frac{1}{4}$_____ of

this _____hexagon_____ .

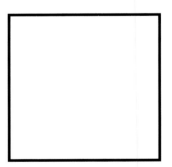

1. I colored _____ of

this _____ .

2. I colored _____ of

this _____ .

Fold and Color

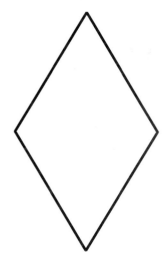

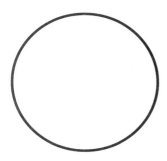

3. I colored _____ of

this _____ .

4. I colored _____ of

this _____ .

Halves and Fourths

Use a green crayon to color all the drawings that show halves.
Use a yellow crayon to color all the drawings that show
fourths. Use a red crayon to trace the lines of symmetry you
see. You might not color all of the shapes.

1.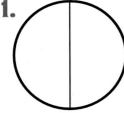

2.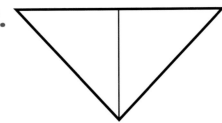

3.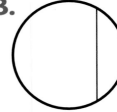

4.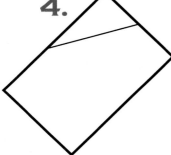

5.

6.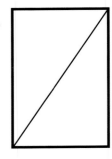

8.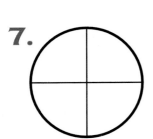

7.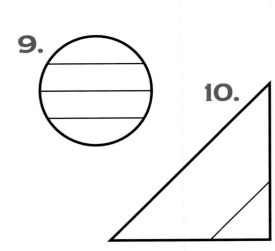

9. **10.**

Fold and Color

Circles and Ovals

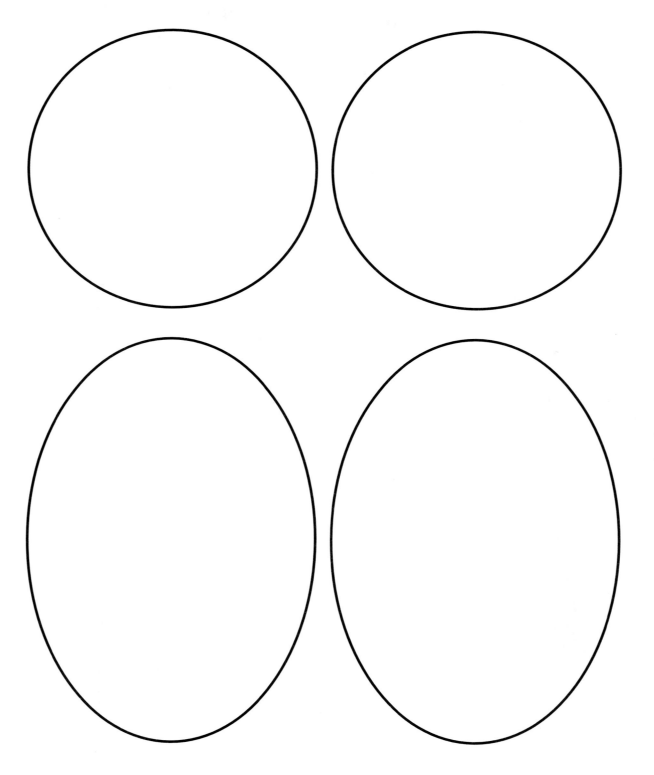

Rectangles and Squares

Fraction Puzzles

Find the Missing Half or Fourth
Homework

Draw a line from the half or fourth to its whole.

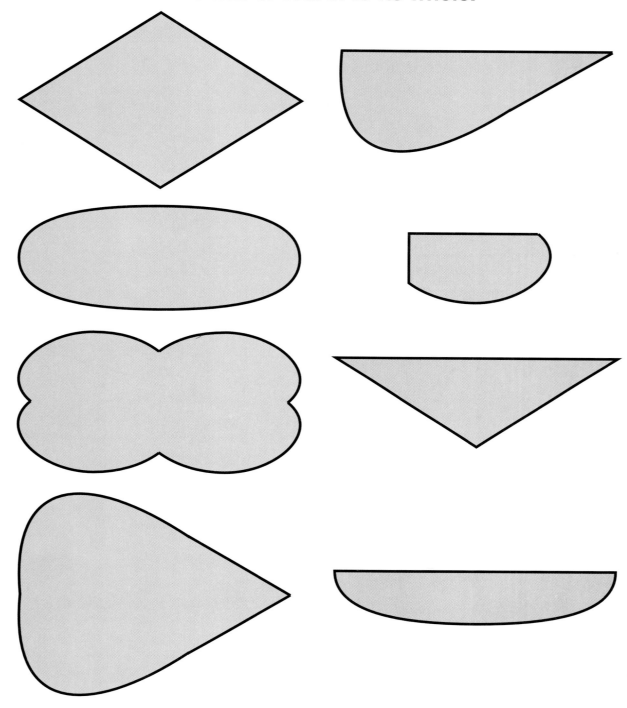

Which Shape Is It?

 Is it $\frac{1}{2}$ or $\frac{1}{4}$ of shape A, B, C, or D? Complete each sentence below by writing the correct fraction and letter of the shape.

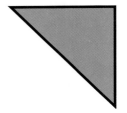

1. This is _____ of

shape _____ .

3. This is _____ of

shape _____ .

2. This is _____ of

shape _____ .

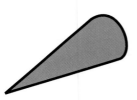

4. This is _____ of

shape _____ .

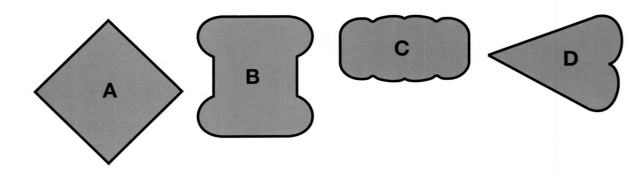

Fraction Puzzles

Drawing Fractions

1. Add to the picture to show that **one-third** of the children in the class are wearing red shirts.

2. Add to the picture to show that **three-eighths** of the dogs have bones.

3. Add to the picture to show that **two-sixths** of the
children are wearing boots.

4. What **fraction** of the kittens below have bowls?

_____

A Class Full of Fractions

Pieces of Eighths

Jerome wanted to share a pizza with seven friends. He said, "I will cut the pizza into eighths. I will make eight pieces." This picture shows how Jerome's pizza looked when he finished.

1. On the lines below, tell what you think about the way Jerome cut the pizza. Did he cut the pizza into eighths?

_____

_____

_____

2. Show how you would divide the pizza fairly among eight children.

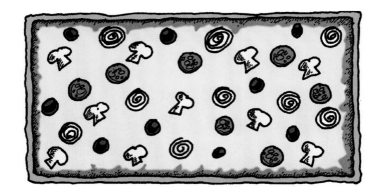

UNIT 19

Mr. O's Map and Data Table

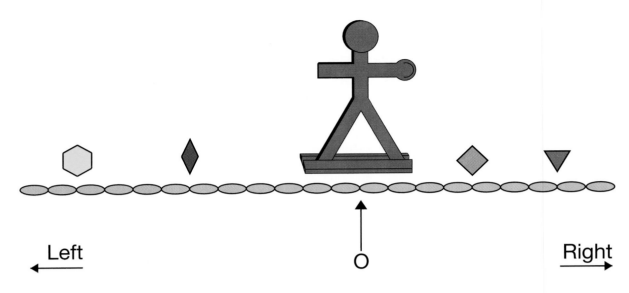

Left ←

O ↑

Right →

Mr. O's Data Table

Object	Distance (in ___links___) unit	Direction
triangle ▼	7	Right
square ◆		
rhombus ◆	6	
hexagon ⬡		

Mr. O Left/Right

Collect

Work with your group to find the distance and direction of each shape from Mr. O. Put your data in the table below. Remember to label which setup your group used. Make a map before you answer the questions.

Mr. O Left/Right Data Table

Setup _____

Object	Distance (in _____) unit	Direction
triangle		
square		
rhombus		
hexagon		

Explore

To answer Questions 1–4 use your setup or your map.

1. What object is farthest from Mr. O? _____

2. How far is it from Mr. O? _____

3. What direction is it from Mr. O? _____

4. **Use your setup.** How far is the rhombus from the triangle?

   _____

5. **Now use your map.** Measure the distance between the rhombus and the triangle with links. Record your answer.

   _____

6. **Use your map.** How far is the square from the hexagon?

   _____

7. **Use your setup.** Measure the distance between the square and the hexagon with links. Record your answer.

   _____

Thinking about Mr. O

Homework

Jan has a Mr. O on her desk. She uses links to measure distances.

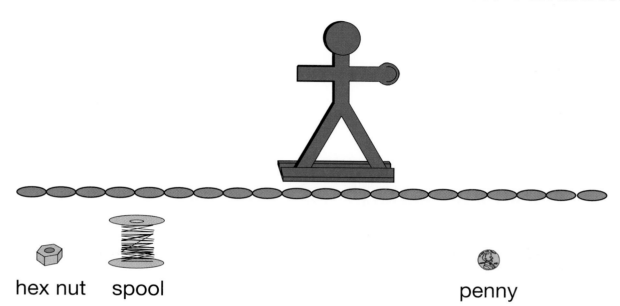

hex nut   spool   penny

1. Mark the location of each object with a dot on the line below. Put **HN** by the dot for hex nut, **S** by the dot for spool, and **P** by the dot for penny.

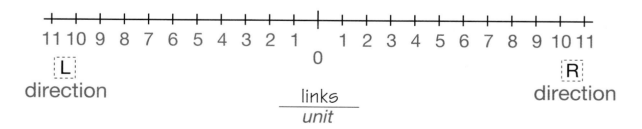

$$\overset{\text{links}}{\underline{}}$$
unit

L
direction

R
direction

2. How far is the center of the hex nut from the center of

the spool? _____

Here is Juan's map.

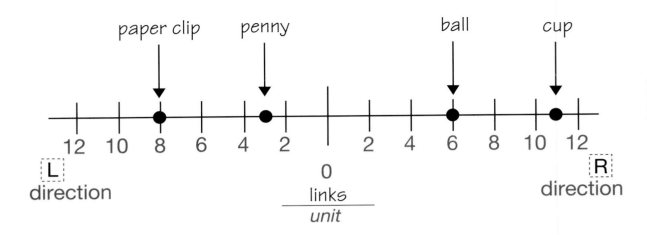

3. How far is the penny from the ball? _____

4. Fill in the data table using Juan's map.

Object	Distance (in _____ unit)	Direction
paper clip		
penny		
ball		
cup		

Vanessa Finds Her Money

Vanessa does a Mr. O activity. This is her map.

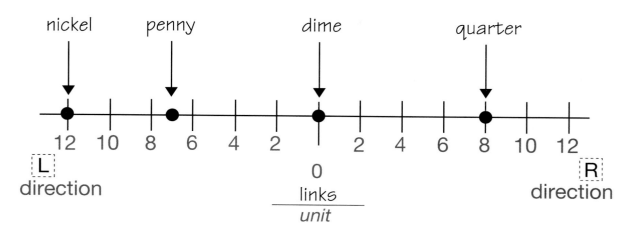

Fill in the data table.

Vanessa's Data Table

Object	Distance (in _____) *unit*	Direction

1. How far is the nickel from the quarter? _____

2. How far is the penny from the nickel? _____

UNIT 20

Lesson 1   **Problem Solving**

Lesson 2   **End-of-Year Test**

Problem-Solving Problems 1-24

Problem 1

Complete each of the following part-part-whole problems.
Write a number sentence for each one.

Part	Part
5	3
Whole	

_____

Part	Part
50	
Whole	
80	

_____

Part	Part
	300
Whole	
800	

_____

Problem 2

Pretend you have measured the following objects in your
classroom. Write the names of the objects in the proper
column of the table below.

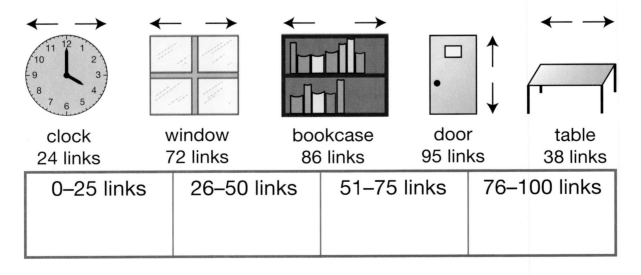

| clock
24 links | window
72 links | bookcase
86 links | door
95 links | table
38 links |

0–25 links	26–50 links	51–75 links	76–100 links

Problem Solving

Problem 3

Write the number that each drawing of beans represents.

_____

_____

_____

Problem 4

Draw a picture for this story:

Alex had 15 marbles. Seven of them rolled under the stairs. How many marbles did he still have?

Problem 5

Make a triangle that is one toothpick long on each side. To make each side twice as long, how many toothpicks would you need? Show your work.

Problem 6

Look at the following design:

If you wanted to make the design longer by repeating the whole pattern 5 more times, how many would you need? Show your work.

Problem Solving

Problem 7

How many ☐ can you make from 23 toothpicks? Show your work.

Problem 8

You need 2 inches of string for every worm you make. How many worms can you make from 17 inches of string? Show your work.

Problem 9

Let's look at the rainfall for the month of October.

Sunday	Monday	Tuesday	Wednesday	Thursday	Friday	Saturday
	1 $\frac{1}{2}$ inch	**2**	**3**	**4**	**5** $\frac{1}{2}$ inch	**6**
7	**8**	**9**	**10**	**11**	**12** $1\frac{1}{2}$ inches	**13**
14	**15**	**16**	**17** $\frac{1}{2}$ inch	**18**	**19**	**20**
21	**22**	**23**	**24**	**25**	**26** $\frac{1}{2}$ inch	**27**
28	**29**	**30**	**31** 3 inches			

A. How much rain did we have in October? _____

B. How much rain did we have on Fridays? _____

Problem 10

$2 + 2 = $ _____ $5 + 3 = $ _____

$2 + 9 = $ _____ $6 + 3 = $ _____

Problem 11

One inch of rain would make 10 inches of snow. If 7 inches of rain had been snow instead, how many inches of snow would there be? Show your work.

Problem 12

Shawna's little brother takes a nap every day from 3:00 until 4:30. How many hours does he nap in one week?

Sunday   Monday   Tuesday   Wednesday

Thursday   Friday   Saturday

Problem 13

Juan uses $5\frac{1}{2}$ square centimeters of paper to cover a shape.
Marta uses $7\frac{1}{2}$ square centimeters of paper to cover another
shape. How many more square centimeters of paper does
Marta use than Juan?

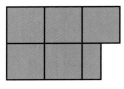

Problem 14

$4 + 4 =$ _____

$7 + 5 =$ _____

$8 + 4 =$ _____

$4 + 6 =$ _____

Problem 15

Draw the missing shape.

Draw the next shape in the pattern.

Problem 16

It takes 6 square inches of paper to cover a shape. How many square inches of paper would it take to cover an area double the size? Show your work.

Problem 17

Georgina made a building that was 12 cubes on the first floor, 8 cubes on the second floor, 2 cubes on the third floor, and 1 on top. How many cubes did she use altogether? Show your work.

Problem 18

You find a pile of 53 cubes. How many 8-cube buildings can you make? Show your work.

Problem Solving

Problem 19

$8 + 6 =$ _____

$6 + 6 =$ _____

$5 + 9 =$ _____

$9 + 8 =$ _____

Problem 20

Carlos begins with a 7-cube building. He wants to make a 26-cube building. How many cubes does he have to add? Show your work.

Problem 21

Twenty-seven children from the Springs School are going on a field trip. Each bus holds twelve children. How many buses will the Springs School need to order for the field trip? Show your work.

Problem 22

If you are in school 6 hours each day, how much time do you spend in school a week? Show your work.

Problem 23

A square is 4 inches long on each side. How many inches would the perimeter measure? Show your work.

Problem 24

$10 + 9 =$ _____

$6 + 10 =$ _____

$3 + 10 =$ _____

$9 + 3 =$ _____

The Fish Lake Site

AMERICAN BOTTOM ARCHAEOLOGY
FAI-270 Site Reports
Volume 8

Series Editors:

Charles J. Bareis (Principal Investigator and Program Coordinator)
and
James W. Porter (Project Director)

Technical Editor:

Carolyn L. Handell-McElrath

Investigations conducted under the auspices of
the Illinois Archaeological Survey in
cooperation with:

The United States Department of Transportation
Federal Highway Administration

The United States Department of the Interior
National Park Service

The State of Illinois
Department of Transportation

J. Paul Biggers (Chief of Environment)
Earl H. Bowman (Chief of Environment, retired)

John A. Walthall, Ph.D. (Chief Archaeologist)

The Fish Lake Site

(11-Mo-608)

Andrew C. Fortier, Richard B. Lacampagne, and Fred A. Finney

with contributions by
Lucretia Kelly and Sissel Johannessen

Published for the Illinois Department of Transportation
by the University of Illinois Press
Urbana and Chicago
1984

Library of Congress Cataloging in Publication Data

Fortier, Andrew C., 1947-
    The Fish Lake site (11-Mo-608)

    (American Bottom archaeology : FAI-270 site reports ;
v. 8)
    Bibliography: p.
    1. Fish Lake Site (Ill.)   2. American Bottom (Ill.) —
Antiquities.   I. Lacampagne, Richard B., 1954-
II. Finney, Fred A., 1954-   . III. Illinois. Dept.
of Transportation. IV. Title. V. Series: American
Bottom archaeology ; v. 8.
E78.I3A58   1984, vol. 8   970s [977.3'91]   84-4607
ISBN 0-252-01069-8 (vol. 8)
ISBN 0-252-01061-2 (set)

CONTENTS

PREFACE

In June of 1977, the University of Illinois at Urbana-Champaign signed an agreement with the Illinois Department of Transportation for the mitigation of archaeological resources within the right-of-way of Federal Aid Interstate 270 (redesignated 255) in the American Bottom in Monroe, St. Clair, and Madison Counties, Illinois. As part of this agreement, the University, in cooperation with the State and the Illinois Archaeological Survey, has the right to publish the results of these archaeological investigations. This volume by Andrew C. Fortier, Richard B. Lacampagne, and Fred A. Finney is a revised version of Report 61 originally submitted by the FAI-270 Archaeological Mitigation Project to the Illinois Department of Transportation in partial fulfillment of contractual obligations of the agreement. This volume also represents one of a series of major site reports that have been selected by the Project for publication by the University of Illinois Press. Each of the descriptive site reports will present a detailed summary of the archaeography of particular sites investigated by the Project. These volumes will not attempt to make regional comparisons or interpretations, since such syntheses are presented in a summary volume of the FAI-270 Archaeological Mitigation Project, entitled "American Bottom Archaeology," edited by Charles J. Bareis and James W. Porter, and published by the University of Illinois Press (March, 1984).

For the Department of Anthropology, University of Illinois at Urbana-Champaign, I would like to acknowledge the support and cooperation of the United States Department of Transportation, Federal Highway Administration; the State of Illinois, Illinois Department of Transportation; the Illinois Archaeological Survey; and the University of Illinois Press.

Charles J. Bareis
Principal Investigator and
Program Coordinator

ACKNOWLEDGMENTS

The authors would like to thank those individuals who contributed to the completion of the Fish Lake site investigations. A progression of crews and supervisors, dating from 1976 to 1982, has been responsible for the survey, testing, and mitigation phases carried out at the site. In particular, we acknowledge the efforts of the 1981 testing crew under the overall direction of Warren Wittry. The notes and feature records left by this crew were more than adequate to ensure continuity between the testing and mitigation phases. The authors gratefully acknowledge the help given to the 1981-1982 crews by landowners Woodrow W. Jackson and Kenneth Stumpf, and by Illinois Department of Transportation (IDOT) surveyors under the direction of Martin "Bud" Frey. In addition, IDOT District 8 Project Manager, George Lammers, was particularly helpful in resolving problems concerned with right-of-way changes and landowner permissions during the survey, testing, and mitigation phases. George also provided several useful insights into engineering principles related to keyhole structure construction and function. We would like to thank Curtis Henke Excavating and its operators, John Tevebaugh (1981) and Dave Vollmer (1982), who were responsible for the careful removal of plowzone from the Fish Lake site.

The 1982 excavations were directed by the senior author, assisted by Fred Finney, Chief Field Supervisor, who also authored the section on ceramics in this volume. Roger Williamson, Scott Detwiler, and John Duncan formed the nucleus of the 1982 field crew and were particularly helpful during the final hectic days of excavation. Richard Lacampagne also provided valuable assistance during the final days and perhaps more importantly, helped the senior author with the computerization of feature and material inventories and authored the section on lithics in this volume. Finally, we wish to thank Michael Morelock who worked as a supervisor in the field and organized and oversaw the water flotation process during 1981 and 1982. The dedication of all of these individuals to the completion of field and analytical goals is greatly appreciated by the senior author. The authors would like to thank Dr. John E. Kelly for releasing his crew for several days to assist in the excavation of this site. Their help came at a critical time and greatly expedited the completion of the work at this site.

The authors would like to thank Project Cartographers Guy Prentice and Scott Wade, who were assisted by Lawrence Kritis; Project Photographers Jeff Abrams and Dean Meador; and Project Illustrator Linda Alexander, who were responsible for the production of the illustrations and figures in this volume. The faunal analysis was completed by Lucretia Kelly, who would like to thank James R. Purdue of the zoology lab at the Illinois State Museum for the use of their faunal comparative collection. The ethnobotanical analysis was completed by Sissel Johannessen, who would like to thank Mike Lawrence and Richard Ennis for processing flotation samples, and Marilyn Weiss for producing Figure 62.

Finally, the authors gratefully acknowledge the work of the Project editorial staff. This volume was produced under the editorial supervision of Carolyn McElrath, assisted by Judith Jablonski. The typing and correction of the manuscript on the UIUC Cyber system using ICE (Illinois Central Editor) and RNF (formatter) were performed by Luann White, assisted by Scott Hatcher and Julie Prince.

The contents of this volume reflect the views of the authors who are responsible for the facts and accuracy of the data presented herein. The contents do not necessarily reflect the official views or policies of the Illinois Department of Transportation and/or the Federal Government.

Fish Lake Site Field Crews

1981	1982
Warren Wittry (Project Director)	Andrew Fortier (Site Director)
John Arnold (Supervisor)	Fred Finney (Supervisor)
Charles Witty (Crew Chief)	Michael Morelock (Supervisor)
Eric Berge	Cindy Balek
Tom Berres	Karen Callis
Brian Hosick	Scott Detwiler
Elizabeth Kassly	John Duncan
Larry Kritis	Richard Lacampagne
George Kutterer	Jackie Reichman
Bob Ord	Becky Schaefer
Debbie Page	Sharon Taube
Ester Read	Craig Volkert
Alan Volkert	Joyce Williams
	Roger Williamson

American Bottom Chronology

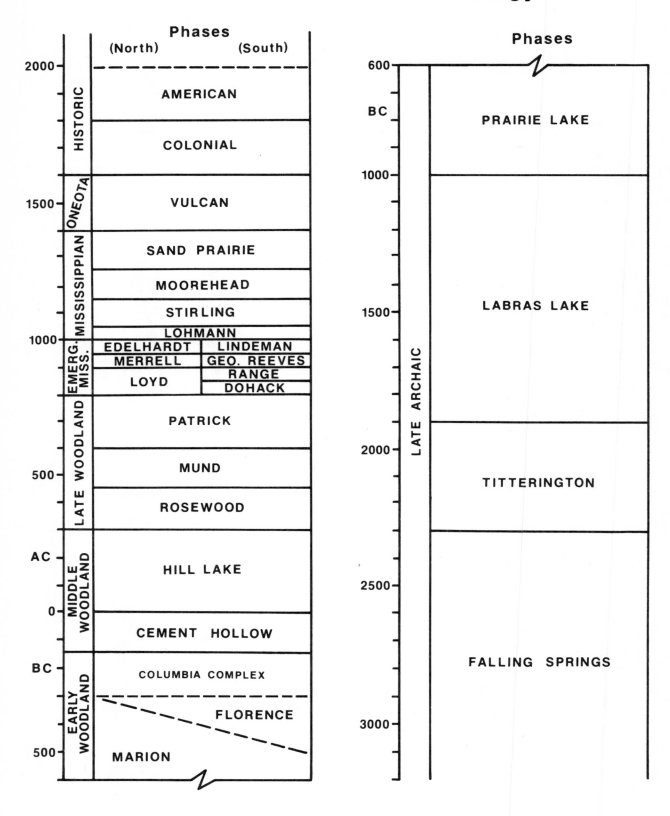

INTRODUCTION

by Andrew C. Fortier

This volume presents the results of archaeological investigations at the Fish Lake site (11-Mo-608) conducted by the University of Illinois at Urbana-Champaign (UIUC) FAI-270 Archaeological Mitigation Project. The site was situated on the Hill Lake meander point bar and Fish Lake meander bank in northern Monroe County (Figure 1). The Fish Lake site was originally defined in 1976 on the basis of prehistoric and historic debris recovered during pedestrian surveys of an area scheduled for construction along the FAI-270 highway. Included within the site area, which comprised ca. 11 ha at the time of investigations, were a house, road, and junkyard in the west and a borrow pit in the north (for Bypass 50) [Kelly et al. 1979:106-107; Bareis et al. 1977:95-96].

At the time of the first survey in 1976, ca. 0.95 ha (9% of the site area) was to be impacted by proposed highway construction. Preliminary test excavations were conducted in 1977. In 1981 the impacted area was expanded because of planning changes related to construction of a frontage road. Approximately 6.4 ha of the 11 ha site area were to be impacted. The site area to be affected was then tested. In 1982 the right-of-way limits were reduced to avoid the junkyard area on the western edge of the site. Areas previously tested fell outside the modified impact area. Eventually, as a result of extensive test excavations in 1981 and full scale excavations in 1982, ca. 8.2% of the originally defined site area was excavated. A total area of 8990 m2 was eventually exposed by heavy machinery.

The 1981 and 1982 excavations revealed a Late Woodland Patrick phase community consisting of 7 keyhole structures, 2 post structures, 134 pits, 2 fill areas, 1 hearth, 1 post row, and 52 nonstructural postmolds. Excavations also indicated that this community extended beyond the right-of-way limits to the west. The excavated portion of the Fish Lake site revealed a multioccupational, but single component, settlement. Several of the structures were superimposed, indicating that this settlement had been occupied, abandoned, and later reoccupied. Based on the homogeneity of cultural materials and features, it was apparent that a single group of Patrick phase people produced all of the prehistoric occupational remains.

Features and cultural materials from the Fish Lake community represent a significant contribution to American Bottom prehistory. This site is the first single component Patrick phase community with keyhole structures excavated in this area. Its nonmixed ceramic and lithic assemblage should provide a basis for interpreting Late Woodland Patrick phase assemblages that are either mixed or only partially represented at other sites.

The Patrick phase, which represents part of the older Early Bluff designation, dates from 600 A.C. to 800 A.C. It postdates the Late

2

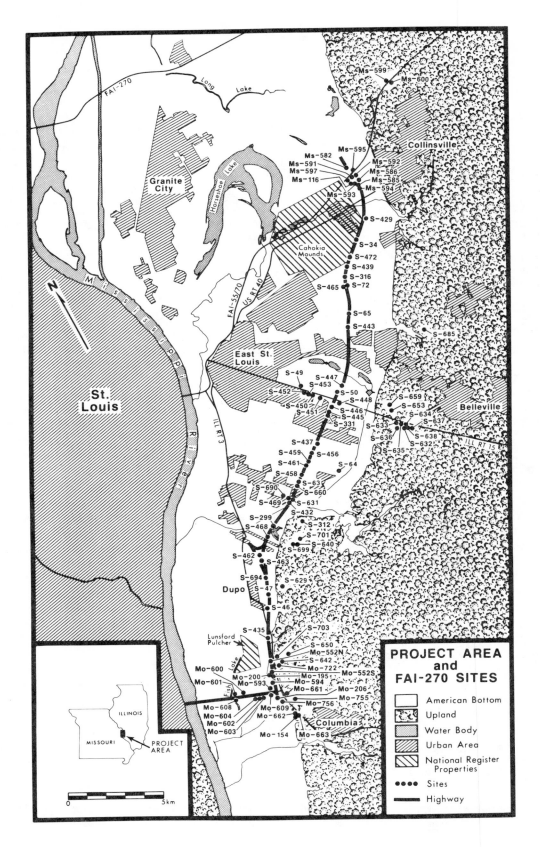

Figure 1. Project Area and FAI-270 Sites

Woodland Mund phase and predates the Emergent Mississippian Dohack and Loyd phases. Radiocarbon dates from the Fish Lake site range from 560 A.C. to 920 A.C., with a mean date of 726 A.C. This places the Fish Lake occupation in the middle of the Patrick phase (ca. 700 A.C.).

The Fish Lake site represents only one of two sites known in the American Bottom with keyhole-shaped structures. Keyhole structures have previously been reported at the Range site, where they were also associated with the Patrick phase (Bareis and Porter 1981:48; Kelly 1981a:14-23). Elsewhere in the Midwest they have been observed at the Hatchery West site in the Kaskaskia River drainage of Illinois (Binford et al. 1970) and at the Daugherty-Monroe site in the Wabash River drainage in Indiana (Pace and Apfelstadt 1978). At both sites, keyhole structures were associated with Late Woodland cultural materials. Keyhole structures are also known from eastern Pennsylvania, associated with the Late Woodland Susquehannock and Wyoming Valley cultures (Smith 1976). The Range site and Fish Lake site keyhole structures appear to represent the western limits of this unusual structural type in the Eastern Woodlands.

This volume has two primary objectives. The first is to describe Fish Lake site features and materials. The following sections describe the features, including pits, structures, and postmolds; the ceramic assemblage; the lithic assemblage; the worked bone assemblage; the floral remains; and the faunal remains. The second objective is to integrate the descriptive material into a coherent discussion of community duration and function, activity distribution, subsistence practices, and intrasite material assemblage variation.

ARCHAEOLOGICAL SIGNIFICANCE

by Andrew C. Fortier

One of the primary goals of the FAI-270 Project was to clarify the processes and the specific assemblage and subsistence changes that accompanied the transition from Late Woodland to Mississippian culture in the American Bottom. In order to accomplish this goal, it was necessary to establish the parameters of cultural variability within the Late Woodland and Mississippian periods. Thus, the excavation of single component communities with unmixed material and feature assemblages was of vital importance. Investigations at the Fish Lake site provided an excellent opportunity to study a relatively undisturbed and unmixed Late Woodland American Bottom community.

The Fish Lake site was significant for several reasons. It was the only site excavated by the Project within 2 km of the Mississippi River's present course. The site location was unique by virtue of its position at the western edge of the floodplain. Its distance from the natural resources of the surrounding bluffs and uplands resulted in an unusual material assemblage and subsistence inventory. This was reflected in the high degree to which lithic resources were efficiently utilized by the site inhabitants, by a predominance of floodplain pastes in ceramics, and by a heavy reliance on aquatic floral and faunal resources.

The Fish Lake site was also significant because of its Late Woodland feature types and community plan. Based on the number of features at this site, particularly structures, it was obvious that the Fish Lake community was not large, probably consisting of no more than four or five families at any given time.

The importance of an unmixed material assemblage cannot be over emphasized. Much of what was previously known about the Patrick phase was derived from surface collections. There are few undisturbed Patrick phase assemblages in the American Bottom or, indeed, the Midwest. The Fish Lake ceramic and lithic assemblage, although relatively small, consisted of typical Patrick phase artifacts, including diagnostic corner-notched and side-notched flake points and grog-tempered, cordmarked, subconoidal jars. The description of attribute variation within the Fish Lake ceramic assemblage represents an important contribution to information on ceramic variability in the Patrick phase. A heavy reliance on local lithic materials by the site inhabitants, particularly local chert types, fit the known pattern of Patrick phase lithic utilization. Both the ceramic and lithic assemblages recovered from this site indicated a reliance on locally available resources.

The following description of the Fish Lake keyhole and post structures fills a void in our knowledge of Patrick phase variation in structure type. The keyhole structures at this site were found in clear association with a large, square, community structure. Similar large community structures have also been found at the Range site, but because of the occupational activity in post-Patrick phase times that obscured community plans at that site, it could only be hypothesized there that community structures were contemporaneous with keyhole structures. The Fish Lake site serves as an important model for Patrick phase community organization in the American Bottom, supporting inferences made earlier at sites such as Range.

PHYSIOGRAPHIC SETTING

by Andrew C. Fortier

The Fish Lake site was situated at the southwestern end of the FAI-270 alignment in northern Monroe County. The site was located 2 km from the Mississippi River and Jefferson Barrack's Bridge, and ca. 5 km northwest of Columbia, Illinois. The Fish Lake site was located on the inner point bar ridge of the Hill Lake meander and on the eastern bank of the Fish Lake meander. Both meanders represent abandoned channels of the Mississippi River. The Fish Lake meander, after which the site was named, was oriented in a north-south direction. It truncated the east-west trending Hill Lake meander point bar ridge. Approximately 95% of the Fish Lake site was situated on the Hill Lake point bar ridge (Wittry 1981; White 1983) [Plate 1].

The Fish Lake site occupied an interesting physiographic position, since it lay along the western edge of the so-called Lunsford-Pulcher terrace (White 1983:9). This terrace is a raised portion of the floodplain that extends 2.5 km from the bluffs to the Fish Lake meander scar. This raised terrace appears to have originated as a result of tectonic uplift along the eastern portion of the American Bottom. The uplifting process and terrace formation appear to have been finalized sometime between 450 B.C. and 850 A.C. West of the Fish Lake scar and Lunsford-Pulcher terrace lies the Western Floodplain Proper (White 1983:9), which extends ca. 2 km from the Fish Lake scar to the Mississippi River. This western floodplain portion is 1 m to 3 m lower in elevation than the Lunsford-Pulcher terrace and is still subject to periodic inundation from Mississippi River overflows (Figure 2).

The terrace-floodplain dichotomy was present at the time of the Late Woodland occupation of the Fish Lake site. Settlement of the higher terrace edge no doubt provided protection from yearly inundation and provided ready access to lower floodplain aquatic resouces. At the time of the Late Woodland occupation, the Fish Lake community would have overlooked the Fish Lake meander as well as a series of alternating ridge and swale zones west of the meander. The Fish Lake meander probably was not active during the Late Woodland settlement. During times of extensive flooding, it is possible that the Mississippi River channel extended from the Fish Lake scar to the Missouri bluffs. The Hill Lake meander scar, however, was not an important source of aquatic resources during Late Woodland times. Although subject to periodic ponding, this scar had essentially been filled by sedimentary processes prior to the Patrick phase.

The point bar ridge on which the Late Woodland settlement was located trended east-west and sloped gradually downward to the north and sharply downward to the south. The ridge soils were sandy in texture with colors ranging from yellow-brown to white. The lower sands were extremely fine grained. The ridge may contain deposits as deep as 16 m at its apex. The sand ridge was capped by alluvial silts and clays that varied in depth from 0.5 m to 1.5 m. The northern and southern slopes contained dramatically different soil profiles; the southern slope consisted primarily of a thin silty cap over a fine sandy base, and the northern slope consisted of thick, dense clays over sand. Directly north of the Late Woodland community limits the clays were between 1.5 m and 2.0 m in depth. The depth of the clay cap became progressively greater to the north.

Prior to the Late Woodland settlement, the area immediately north of the ridge apex consisted of a low swale that, over a period of time, filled with overflow deposits from the nearby Fish Lake meander. During Late Woodland times, this area was a shallow, marshy environment

Plate 1. Aerial View of the Fish Lake site: a, Fish Lake meander; b, Mississippi River; c, Hill Lake point bar complex; d, the Fish Lake site

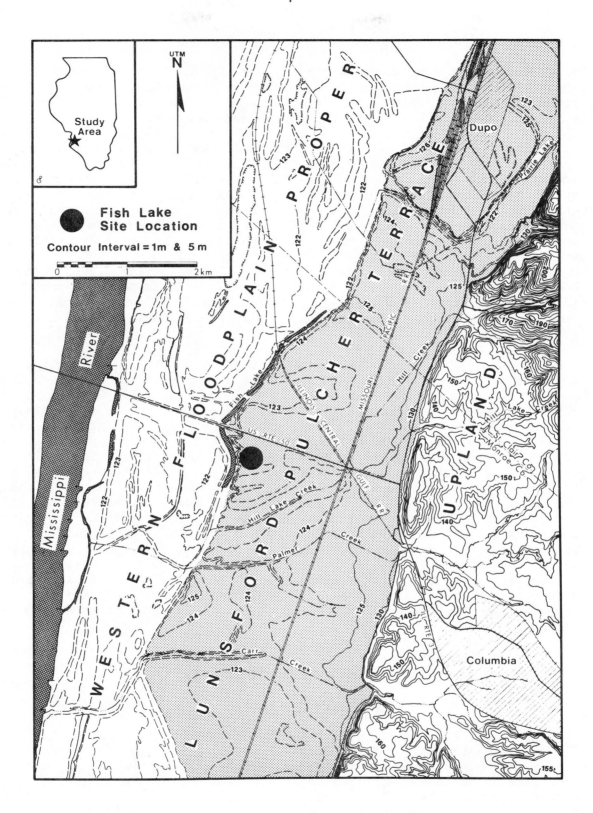

Figure 2. The Fish Lake Site in the American Bottom

characterized by wet, gumbo, backswamp deposits. Such an environment apparently served as an effective barrier to settlement. The northern boundary of the feature distribution, therefore, represents the real northern community limits, established by physiography.

Soil types played a significant role not only in establishing community limits, but in determining the distribution of feature types and pit depths. The occupants apparently avoided deep excavations into sandy soils, particularly along the southern slope. The northern pits, which were dug into clays, were nearly twice as deep on the average as pits excavated into sandy soils in the central and southern settlement areas. It is also apparent that the deeper pits were often reutilized, while the shallower pits to the south were utilized only once or for brief periods of time. In addition, the main keyhole structure concentration was located in the clay soils. It is probable that the pits and structures that were intended for longer use were constructed and excavated in clays because such soils were resistant to erosion and slumping (Figure 3).

The occurrence of a prehistoric occupation in this particular locality can only be explained by virtue of its close proximity to the aquatic resources of the Fish Lake meander and the nearby Mississippi River. There are no natural lithic resources in the immediate vicinity of the Fish Lake site. Chert, limestone, sandstone, and glacial till material, all of which were recovered, had to be transported from sources located 3 km or 4 km distant from the site. The primary attraction of this locality, therefore, must have been its accessibility to a wide variety of aquatic floral and faunal resources. In addition, the rich alluvial soils of the floodplain would have been ideal for horticulture. In fact, the faunal and floral remains from the site indicated a heavy reliance on both wild and cultivated resources. It is also obvious from the concentration of sites along the Lunsford-Pulcher terrace edge that this edge environment was heavily utilized by prehistoric peoples. Edge environments tend to attract a great diversity of animal life (Shelford 1963), so the Fish Lake locality and terrace edge would have been especially attractive to prehistoric Indians.

HISTORY OF INVESTIGATIONS

by Andrew C. Fortier

The Fish Lake site was located in March 1976 as a result of an Illinois Department of Transportation (IDOT) archaeological pedestrian survey, which was conducted to assess archaeological resources within the FAI-270 highway right-of-way. The site covered an 11 ha area and consisted of materials distributed over two major east-west trending point bar ridges. The ridges were separated by a swale. Three distinct concentrations of surface debris were defined and considered as three separate sites. However, subsequent examination of intervening areas

9

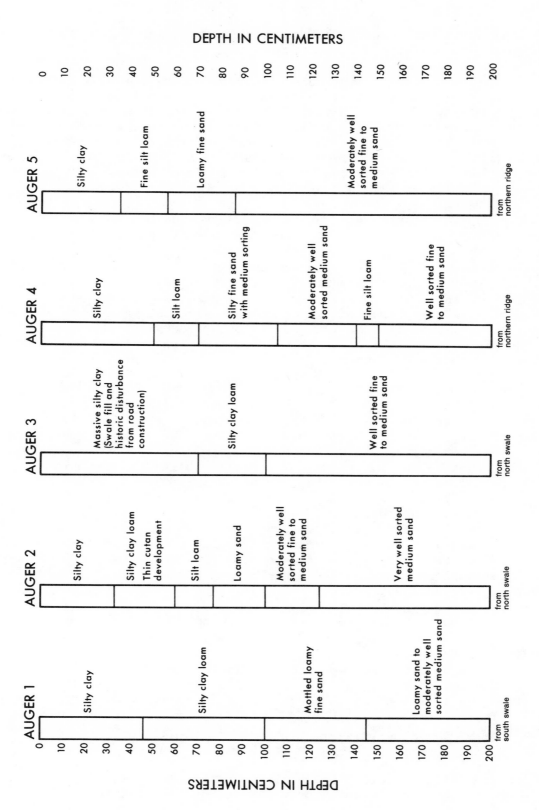

Figure 3. Selected Soil Profiles from Hand Auger Tests

produced additional materials, so the three material concentrations were combined into one site.

Over 3100 cultural items were recovered during the 1976 survey work, including diagnostic Early Woodland, Middle Woodland, Late Woodland, Emergent Mississippian, Mississippian, and Historic ceramic and lithic materials. Most of these materials were found in the southwestern and southeastern portions of the southern ridge. The northern ridge included only Late Woodland materials. A detailed description of cultural materials recovered during the 1976 survey can be found elsewhere (Kelly et al. 1979:106-107).

Part of the Fish Lake site has been disturbed by modern buildings. The western portion of the northern ridge includes ca. 5 acres of land owned by Mr. W.W. Jackson on which stands a 100 year old farm house, a mobile home, a junkyard, and various small work sheds. Approximately half of the five acres is periodically cultivated. In the southwestern portion of the southern ridge stands a modern home, barn, shed, and two grain bins. This property, which occurs in the midst of a major prehistoric material concentration, is occupied by Mr. Roy Ramsey. Much of the historical debris recovered from the Fish Lake site can be attributed to the Jackson and Ramsey occupations (Plate 2).

The Fish Lake site was first tested in 1977 by UIUC archaeologists. At that time ca. 0.95 ha of the site were to be impacted by proposed highway construction. Most of this area fell within the northern ridge area directly south of Bypass 50 and east of the Jackson property. Two test units, measuring 2 m by 2 m and 2 m by 3 m, were excavated in the central portion of the ridge. The smaller unit produced no feature or occupational material, while the larger unit revealed a deep, burned tree disturbance. In addition to these units, five soil probe transects were made in the northern ridge area. Soil probe cores were taken at 2 m intervals; they ranged in depth from 0.4 m to 1.5 m. No features were identified. The test units and soil probes produced negative results because they were placed in the deep, clay swale deposits, mentioned earlier, that marked the northern edge of the Late Woodland occupation (Figure 4).

Archaeological investigations were resumed in 1981 when it was learned that a frontage road connecting FAI-270 with a proposed industrial park would pass through much of the site. Approximately 6.4 ha of the 11 ha site area were to be affected by this road construction. Dr. Warren L. Wittry directed a controlled surface collection, which yielded 3614 items. This collection was made between January and March, 1981. The previously identified material concentrations were again found; evidence was also found of a previously unidentified Late Archaic component.

Under the direction of Wittry, extensive testing, involving large-scale machine excavation, was conducted between June 9 and September 16, 1981. A total of 6451 m2 in 13 excavation blocks were

Plate 2. Fish Lake Site Area: upper, view to the west; lower, view to the east

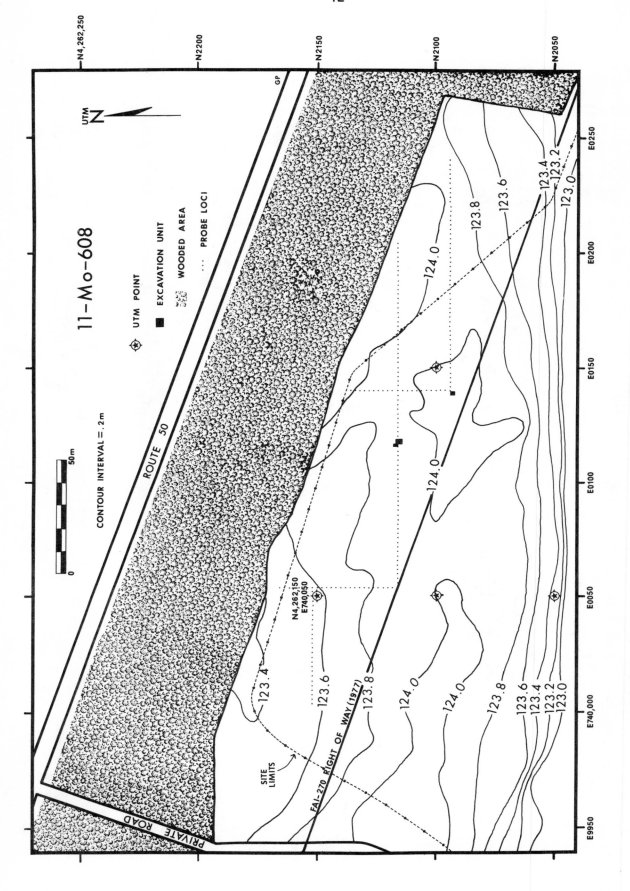

Figure 4. 1977 Test Excavation Units and Soil Probe Lines

cleared of plowzone (Figure 5). Most of these blocks were located in the northern ridge area; also excavated was a small area along the northern flank of the southern ridge. Despite the fact that the northern ridge area had previously produced the least amount of surface debris within the Fish Lake site and had produced no evidence of subsurface features during the 1977 testing, a rather significant Late Woodland community was exposed during the 1981 work. A total of 115 features were identified, of which 107 were excavated. This community was concentrated in the western half of the 1981 excavation area. Included among the features were six keyhole structures. Four were excavated, and two were partially excavated. The recovered materials were assignable to the Patrick phase.

Several test units were also placed in W.W. Jackson's junkyard, near the Fish Lake slough; they produced several pit features. Although these features were mapped, they were not excavated. The occurrence of these features indicated that the Fish Lake community extended from the Fish Lake scar ca. 200 m east through W.W. Jackson's property (Figure 6).

The initial results of the 1981 excavations were submitted as part of a budgetary request to the IDOT for final mitigation of the impact of the highway on the Fish Lake site. In 1982 new personnel were assigned to complete the site excavations.

Field investigations were resumed at the Fish Lake site in September, 1982, and continued to mid-October, 1982. The right-of-way limits were again altered to reduce the area of impact. Some areas tested in 1981 fell outside of the new right-of-way limits. Irregularly shaped excavation blocks along the western limits of the site reflect these right-of-way changes. The primary objective in 1982 was to delineate the northern and southern boundaries of the Late Woodland community.

Before the 1982 excavations were initiated, dense stands of ragweed, goosefoot, and other plants had to be removed by hand and heavy machinery. The 1981 grid system was reestablished, and the unexcavated features were relocated and remapped. The datum pin from the previous season was relocated and used to establish a new datum point nearer the excavation area. The old datum at E 0000, N 2200 was 123.65 m above mean sea level (amsl); the new datum was 124.34 m amsl.

During 1982, 2540 m2 of plowzone were removed by heavy machinery, bringing the total excavation area to 8990 m2 (8.2% of the 11 ha site) [Figure 7]. It was originally proposed that 10,000 m2 of excavation would be needed to complete the 1982 mitigation efforts, but this estimate was modified when it was learned that one of the target areas, which was located between Bypass 50 and the ridge apex, was an area of dense swale clays. Preliminary machine scraping and geomorphic coring in this area revealed no occupational debris or features. Excavations, therefore, were halted in this target area and shifted to portions of the ridge crest and slope.

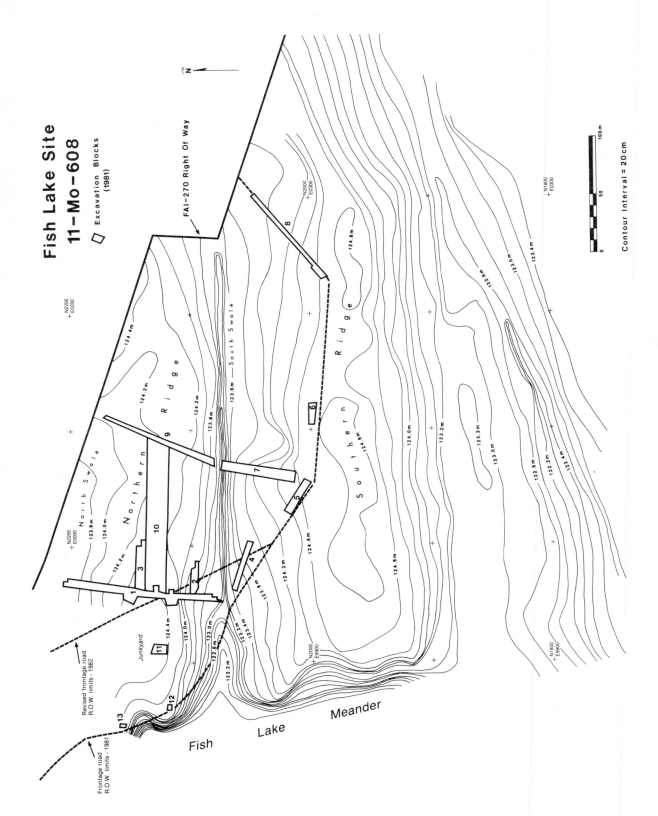

Figure 5. 1981 Excavation Blocks and Site Topography

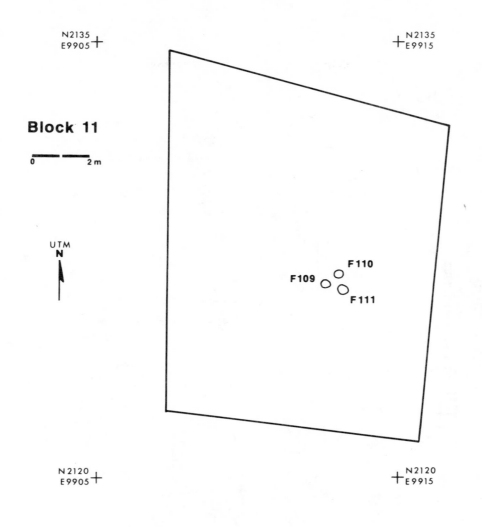

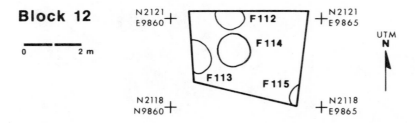

Figure 6. Feature Distribution in Blocks 11 and 12

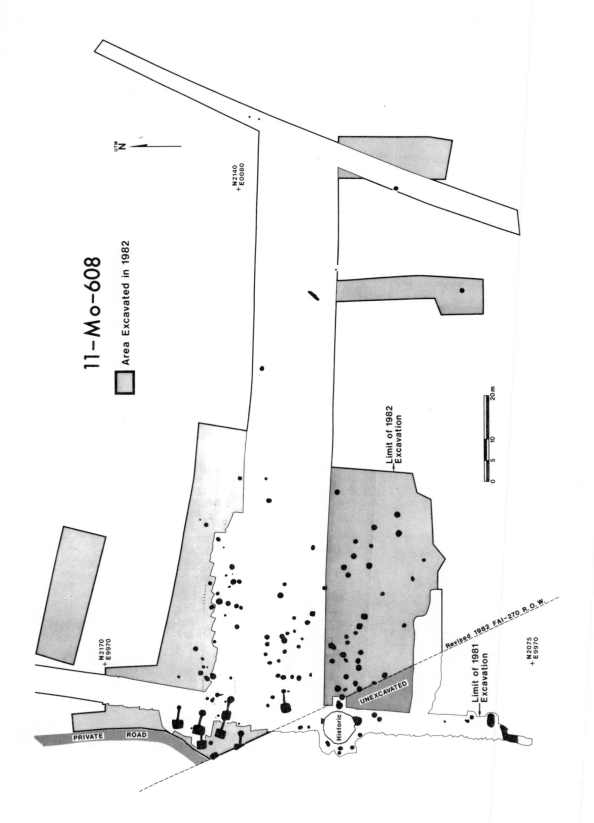

11-Mo-608

☐ Area Excavated in 1982

N
UTM

+ N2140
E0080

+ N2170
E9970

Limit of 1982
Excavation

0 5 10   20m

Revised 1982 FAI-270 R.O.W.

Limit of 1981
Excavation

+ N2075
E9970

UNEXCAVATED

Historic

PRIVATE   ROAD

Figure 7. 1981 and 1982 Excavation Areas

The 1981 and 1982 work resulted in the identification of 168 features. A total of 965 lot numbers were assigned during the two seasons to 516 material bags, 314 flotation samples, 102 soil samples, 29 radiocarbon samples, and 4 miscellaneous samples. Individual flotation samples normally consisted of 10 l of soil, but some were larger. One feature (Feature 161) was completely sampled, resulting in the collection of 3800 l of soil.

The exposure and mapping of features involved initial observation and marking with pin flags during machine scraping; shovel scraping in the immediate feature vicinity; definition of feature fill boundaries; mapping at a 1:20 scale; establishing profile points that transected the feature's long axis; setting a datum point outside each feature; and, finally, excavating the first half of the feature. The archaeological excavation techniques and sampling procedures were similar during both the 1981 and 1982 seasons. Vertical profiles that bisected the features were drawn at a 1:10 scale and photographed. Flotation samples were sometimes taken from soil zones in the first half of the feature excavated, but normally samples were only taken from the second half. These samples were taken based on zones observed in the feature profiles.

Large areas of the site did not need to be shovel scraped since features were readily visible following plowzone removal. Black feature fills contrasted sharply with the light brown sterile subsoil. The machine operations were closely supervised; observers were never more than several meters away from a backhoe blade or paddlewheel.

Excavations in 1982 were initially carried out on two keyhole structures (Features 116 and 117) located along the western limits of the site. These features had been partially exposed in 1981. Machine excavations along the northern and southern peripheries of the 1981 excavations followed shortly thereafter. Machine excavations were undertaken up to the limits of the right-of-way, an area with a high potential for producing additional structures. Parts of this area were still privately owned and included an access road used by W.W. Jackson and his business clients. Two features were exposed that extended partly outside the right-of-way; they were only partially excavated. These features, which were defined and excavated on the last day of the 1982 season, provided additional evidence that the Fish Lake Late Woodland community extended further to the west, toward the Fish Lake meander scar and bank.

FEATURE TYPES AND DISTRIBUTION

by Andrew C. Fortier

The Fish Lake site investigations resulted in the assignment of 169 feature numbers. These included 147 Late Woodland features and 6 historical disturbances. Fourteen features, which were given numbers in

1981, were later redesignated postmolds. These feature numbers, however, were maintained, and these postmolds appear on the maps with their original feature numbers. Materials acquired during machine excavation, shovel scraping, and backdirt removal were assigned to a generalized Feature 1 category. Feature number 103 was mistakenly assigned in 1981 to a previously identified feature (Feature 13); feature number 103 was not reassigned to another feature. A total of 38 postmolds were identified in the field in addition to those reassigned during analysis. The postmolds outlining structure walls and those in structure basins are not included in the total postmold figure.

The features identified in 1981, but not excavated during that season, were Features 2, 112, 113, 114, and 115. Features 112 to 115, located in Block 12, fell outside of the 1982 adjusted right-of-way and so were never excavated. Feature 2, which was located in a low depression immediately south of the northern ridge, remained under water during the entire 1982 field season, so it too was left unexcavated.

The Late Woodland settlement was composed of 147 features and 52 postmolds (Figure 8). This total included 7 keyhole-shaped structures, 2 post structures, 2 fill areas, 134 pits, 1 hearth, and 1 post row. These features were distributed primarily along the ridge crest and southern ridge slope, with most features falling within a 60 m by 60 m area. Features did, however, extend along the ridge nearly 150 m east of the western right-of-way limits. The presence of Features 112 to 115 nearly 85 m west of the western right-of-way limits indicated that the complete settlement may have covered an area measuring as much as 230 m by 60 m, or 1.4 ha. It was estimated that roughly 60% to 70% of the community area was exposed by the 1981 and 1982 investigations. It was impossible to calculate the total feature density in the 30% to 40% area that was not investigated, since the overall community plan was asymmetrical.

The Late Woodland community area was subdivided into four units, termed occupation areas. Most of the excavated features occurred within these occupation areas. Essentially the occupation areas represented spatially discrete concentrations of features. For example, the boundary between the northern area (Occupation Area 1) and the central area (Occupation Area 2) was defined by a gap of nearly 6 m in which no features occurred. The boundaries between the central area and the feature concentrations to the southwest (Occupation Area 3) and to the southeast (Occupation Area 4) were more diffuse and irregular. Occupation Areas 3 and 4, however, were distinct units separated by a gap of nearly 10 m. Occupation Areas 2 and 4 were spatially distinct except for the occurrence of pit Feature 79, located precisely half-way between the two areas. Except for that feature, a clear gap of 10 m existed between Occupation Areas 2 and 4 (Figure 9).

This division of the Late Woodland community into four units represented a preliminary construct, established to explore the possibilities of intrasite assemblage variation. It was hoped that

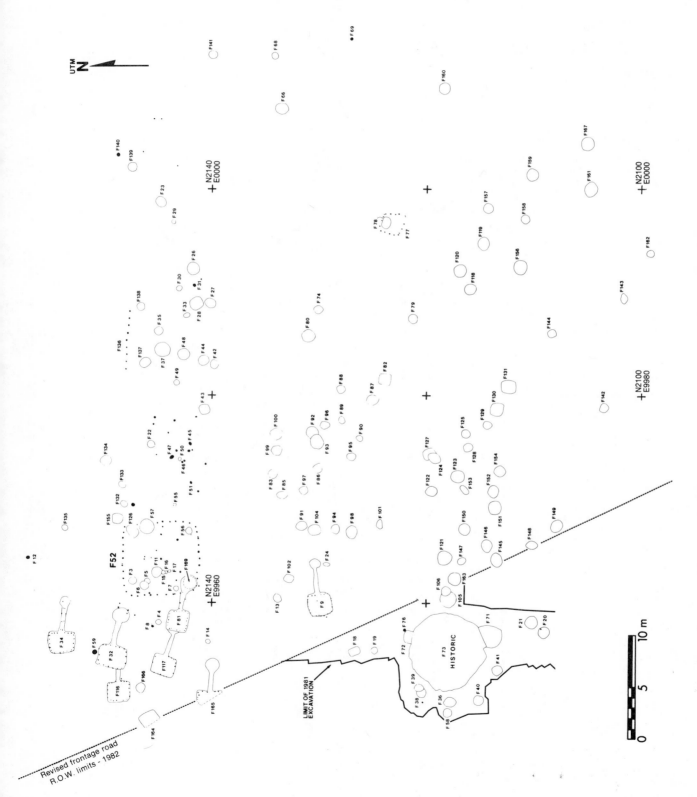

Figure 8. Main Patrick Phase Community Focus (see pocket map for all features)

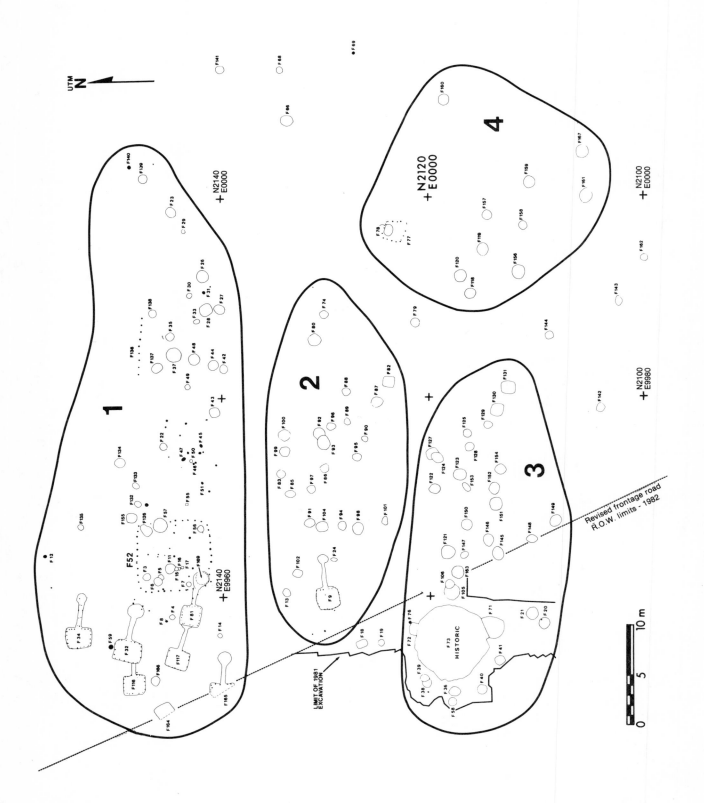

Figure 9. Occupation Areas 1, 2, 3, and 4

differences in lithic tool inventories, ceramic vessel forms and decoration frequencies, and feature type distributions could be discerned among the occupation areas. Given the occurrence of structural superpositioning in Occupation Area 1, to be discussed below, it was believed that various occupational episodes, evidenced by the superpositioning, might be distinguishable by assemblage variation. Some differences were apparent among the occupation areas, for example, in the differential distributions of various types of features. However, differences among the material assemblages recovered from the occupation areas were more difficult to discern, suggesting that, despite the superpositioning, the gaps between areas, and the differential distribution of feature types, all four occupation areas were formed as a result of intermittent occupation of this locality by a single group of people.

Structures and Overall Feature Distribution in the Northern Occupation Area

The northern occupation area, referred to as Occupation Area 1, was situated on the apex of the northernmost point bar ridge and extended from the western right-of-way limits to a point approximately 60 m to the east. The northern and southern boundaries were distinct, with a gap of 6 m occurring between this occupation area and the central occupation area immediately to the south. The northern extent of this area was defined by an absence of features and the presence of dense clay swale deposits. The western limits of the area were not defined due to the right-of-way limits. However, it was clear that the Fish Lake site, as well as this particular occupation area, extended further west, as evidenced by two features (Features 164 and 165) that were bisected by the right-of-way.

The northern occupation area represented the central focus of the Late Woodland occupation, since it included the main concentration of structures. This area yielded 6 keyhole structures, a large post structure (Feature 52), 39 pits, 1 post row, and 35 isolated postmolds. The keyhole structures were situated along the western edge of the occupation area and were distributed in a line along a northeast-southwest axis. All of the keyhole ramp extensions were oriented either due east (from grid north) or a few degrees to the southeast. The keyhole structures consisted of subterranean basins with internal postmolds, narrow ramp extensions, and shallow basin-shaped pits attached to the ends of the ramps.

Very few refuse pits were found in the immediate vicinity of the keyhole structures in Occupation Area 1. However, an extremely large pit (Feature 164) was uncovered just a few meters west of this structure cluster. This pit, over a meter deep and nearly 2 m in diameter, was the largest pit at the site. It may represent a communal pit used by the occupants of this structure area. It may also represent a central community pit. Unfortunately, the area directly west of this pit could not be investigated, so its central position could not be confirmed. If it was a central pit, another group of keyhole structures might be located directly to the west.

A large post structure (Feature 52) lay immediately east of the main keyhole structure concentration. This structure, which contained no basin fill, was oriented in a north-south direction. Several pits were found inside the structure and just outside its northeastern corner. The large size of this structure and its central position in Occupation Area 1 suggests that Feature 52 served a community function (Plate 3).

Approximately 5 m east of Feature 52 lay a concentration of 18 postmolds and 2 pits. The postmolds did not form any discernible pattern. Presumably, this concentration represents a specialized processing area, possibly for drying fish or tobacco, or for hide preparation. One of the two pits (Feature 43) contained the greatest number of tobacco remains found at the site.

Five meters east of the postmold concentration was a discrete cluster of features, including 13 pits, 2 postmolds, and a post row (Feature 136). The post row marked the northern extent of this concentration and was oriented in an east-west direction. It may have served as a wind screen for activities carried out in the pit cluster immediately to the south. Of interest is the fact that the post row lined up with the northern wall of the large post structure, located 15 m to the west. This may be fortuitous, but it seems more likely that the two were associated and that there was some attempt to maintain an east-west community symmetry. Presumably, the pits associated with the post row were also utilized at the same time as the structure.

Finally, three pits and six postmolds were found in a small cluster, which formed no particular pattern, ca. 10 m east of the post row. This cluster marked the eastern extent of Occupation Area 1. Like most pits and features of the northern occupation area, these features were located in dense clays.

Superpositioning was generally rare at the Fish Lake site. The one critical exception was its occurrence in the northern occupation area where both keyhole and post structures were involved in superimposed sequences of features. Four keyhole structures were superpositioned over other features. Keyhole structure Features 32 and 81 were constructed over keyhole structure Features 116 and 117, respectively. In addition, structure Feature 81 was superimposed over post structure Feature 52. Pit Feature 57 appeared to have been superimposed over the northeastern wall of structure Feature 52. Keyhole structure Feature 81 and pit Feature 57 obviously postdated the post structure. Features 32 and 81 also postdated Features 116 and 117. Feature 81 probably was superimposed through a collapsed post structure, since it does not seem likely that the builders of structure Feature 81 would have troubled themselves with dismantling the southwestern corner of Feature 52 just to accommodate the ramp pit of a keyhole structure. They did, however,

23

Plate 3. General Excavation: upper left, backhoe excavation in Occupation Area 1; upper right, shovel scraping around Features 52 and 81 in Occupation Area 1 (view to the north); lower left, western site limits in Occupation Area 1 and junkyard (view to the west); lower right, feature excavation in Block 10, Occupation Area 2 (view to the east)

probably notice the depression left by pit Feature 169 in the southwestern corner of the post structure. It was there that the ramp pit was placed.

The occurrence of superpositioning in Occupation Area 1 indicated that the Late Woodland occupation comprised minimally two settlement episodes. The interval between these episodes could only be conjectured, but the homogeneity of cultural materials from this occupation area indicated that the time span was short. For reasons given above, it appears that the large post structure had collapsed prior to the later occupational episodes. It is, of course, possible that the post structure had actually been dismantled and that structure Feature 81 had been built immediately after that event. It is suggested here, however, that a single community was responsibile for all occupational episodes at this site. This inference is based on the occurrence of a homogeneous material assemblage distributed uniformly across the entire site.

Structure Feature 32

Feature 32 was a keyhole-shaped structure located ca. 5 m south of structure Feature 34. Feature 32 was superimposed on Feature 116, a keyhole structure immediately west of Feature 32. Feature 32 superimposed the ramp and ramp pit of Feature 116. Both keyhole structures were oriented toward the east. Feature 32 was the largest keyhole structure at the Fish Lake site, measuring 2.66 m (north-south) by 2.1 m (east-west), as defined at the base of plowzone. Its 18 basin postmolds were the largest (mean diameter=10.0 cm), deepest (mean=34.18 cm), and most widely spaced (mean distance=44.59 cm) of any keyhole structure postmolds at the site. The total length of the structure, as measured from its western basin edge to its ramp pit, was 5.78 m (Figure 10).

Structure Feature 32 consisted of a basin that measured 40 cm in depth, a ramp measuring 2.28 m in length, and a ramp pit measuring 1.60 m by 1.32 m in plan view and 30 cm in depth. The 18 basin postmolds, comprising the four walls of the structure, had been placed vertically in the basin floor and were uniformly spaced. Six postmolds each formed the western and eastern walls, while three postmolds each formed the northern and southern walls. The east-west and north-south postmolds appeared to be directly opposed to one another. No postmolds for interior supports were identified nor was there any indication regarding the nature of the prehistoric roof construction. One postmold exterior support (Postmold 22) was uncovered in the northwestern corner above the basin floor. It was probably associated with Postmold 1, a postmold for a northwestern corner wall post. No evidence of post or basin floor burning was observed in this structure. Feature 32 was probably simply abandoned and left to decay.

The ramp was maximally 20 cm deep, with its greatest depth occurring

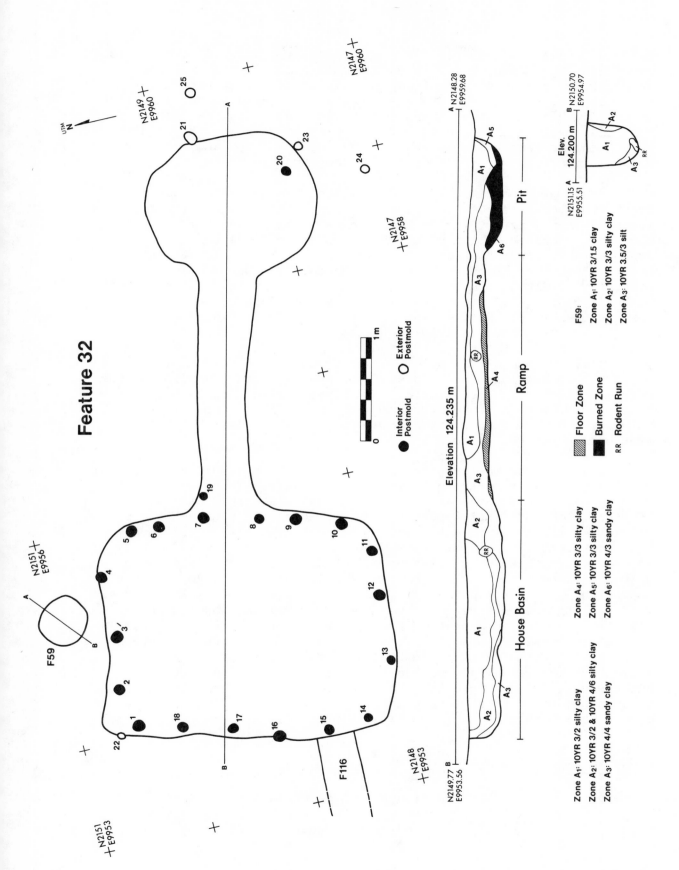

Figure 10. Keyhole Structure Feature 32, Plan and Profile Views

near the basin entrance. The ramp gradually decreased in depth as it approached the ramp pit. The maximum width of the ramp was 52 cm, making it the broadest ramp of any keyhole structure at this site. The ramp was constricted near its western end. A single postmold (Postmold 19) was found along the northern edge of the ramp at the entry point into the basin. The function of this post is unknown. No evidence of packing in the ramp was observed by the excavators, and only a few cultural materials were recovered from the ramp floor and fill.

The ramp pit described above was filled with three soil zones. The upper two zones represented secondary deposition and contained a great deal of cultural material. In fact, these zones produced more material than the combined fills of the ramp and basin. The basal zone in the ramp pit, however, contained no cultural materials. It consisted of a shallow layer of burned clay and charcoal fragments. This material apparently resulted from burning inside the pit itself. The ramp pit in Feature 32 closely resembled the ramp pit in Feature 165 in that both were obviously firepits. The functional implications of keyhole firepits are discussed in a following section.

A single postmold (Postmold 20) was found in the ramp pit, and four additional postmolds were identified nearby. The function of these posts is not readily discernible, but it seems likely that they served as supports for a superstructure covering the ramp pit. Similar postmolds around the ramp pit of Feature 34 suggest that the Feature 32 construction was not unique.

Of interest was the presence of a large, deep postmold situated only 20 cm north of the northern basin structure wall. This postmold, which was originally designated as Feature 59, was located outside of the structure. It did not appear to be related to the construction of the dwelling or to any particular feature of the structure. This postmold, which measured 47 cm by 46 cm, was 50 cm deep and conically shaped. It was classified, therefore, as a postpit. Cultural materials were not recovered from its fill. Charcoal flecks, however, were found at the base of the postmold, indicating that it may have burned. The function of this post can only be conjectured, but it may have been a marker for this structure or for a particular cluster of structures. A similar, but smaller, postmold was also found just north of structure Feature 81, and another postmold was identified just outside the northeastern portion of the large, square, post structure designated Feature 52. In this context, it is interesting that a rather large postpit was also found outside of a large rectangular post structure dating to the Mund phase at the Mund site (Fortier et al. 1982:151).

Structure Feature 34

Feature 34 was a keyhole structure located at the northern end of Occupation Area 1. It lay approximately 5 m north of keyhole structure Feature 32. Feature 34 consisted of a square subterranean basin, a ramp, and a shallow pit attached to the eastern end of the ramp. The total length of the structure was 5.45 m. The basin was 40 cm deep and measured 2.54 m (north-south) by 2.11 m (east-west). The ramp was 2.34 m long and was oriented toward the east. Its width ranged from 43 cm to 47 cm. The depth of fill in the ramp was 24 cm. Its maximum depth was reached near the junction of the ramp with the basin. It was only 14 cm deep near the junction with the ramp pit. The ramp pit, which was basin shaped, measured 96 cm by 99 cm and was 16 cm deep. Pottery, chert, burned clay, and wood charcoal were recovered from the ramp pit, with the heaviest concentrations of material occurring at its base (Figure 11).

A total of 41 postmolds were associated with this structure, including 20 postmolds which formed the walls of the basin along the basin floor, 11 postmolds that were associated with the basin but were located above it and outside of the basin wall line, 8 posts located in the ramp, 1 post located in the ramp pit, and 1 post situated just outside of the ramp pit. All of the basin posts had been burned, but the ramp and ramp pit posts had not. Evidence of post burning as well as a large area of burning on the basin floor indicated that this structure was destroyed by fire. The apparent lack of post burning in the ramp was, however, curious. Apparently, the structure conflagration did not extend into the ramp.

There were 20 wall postmolds in the basin floor. Six postmolds formed the eastern wall, with three postmolds on either side of the ramp entrance. A gap of 69 cm in the eastern wall marked the entrance of the ramp into the basin. The northern and southern walls had five postmolds each and the western wall contained four postmolds. The spacing between postmolds inside the basin, excluding the gap in the eastern wall, averaged 34.79 cm. The average postmold diameter was 9.97 cm, and the average postmold depth was 30.17 cm. All wall posts had been burned.

There were 11 postmolds above the basin floor and outside of the interior wall line. Seven of these appear to represent secondary supports for interior posts. For example, Postmolds 1, 2, 3, 7, 8, 9, and 11 were associated with wall Postmolds 22, 21, 19, 28, 27, 25, and 23, respectively. The four remaining postmolds outside and above the basin occupied the four corners and probably represent structural supports. This was the only keyhole structure at the Fish Lake site with exterior corner posts. The exterior postmolds, including the corner postmolds (Postmolds 4, 5, 6, and 10), were relatively small in diameter (mean=7.36 cm) and shallow in depth (mean=9.82 cm).

Eight postmolds were observed in the ramp itself. These were arranged in four pairs and occurred at intervals of 50 cm to 80 cm. They averaged 7.9 cm in diameter and 19.62 cm in depth. The ramp postmold pairs nearest the basin (Postmolds 32 to 33 and 34 to 35) occurred in the center of the ramp and were spaced about 20 cm apart in a north-south direction. The postmold pairs at the eastern end of the ramp (Postmolds 36 to 37 and 38 to 39) were spaced 40 cm and 15 cm

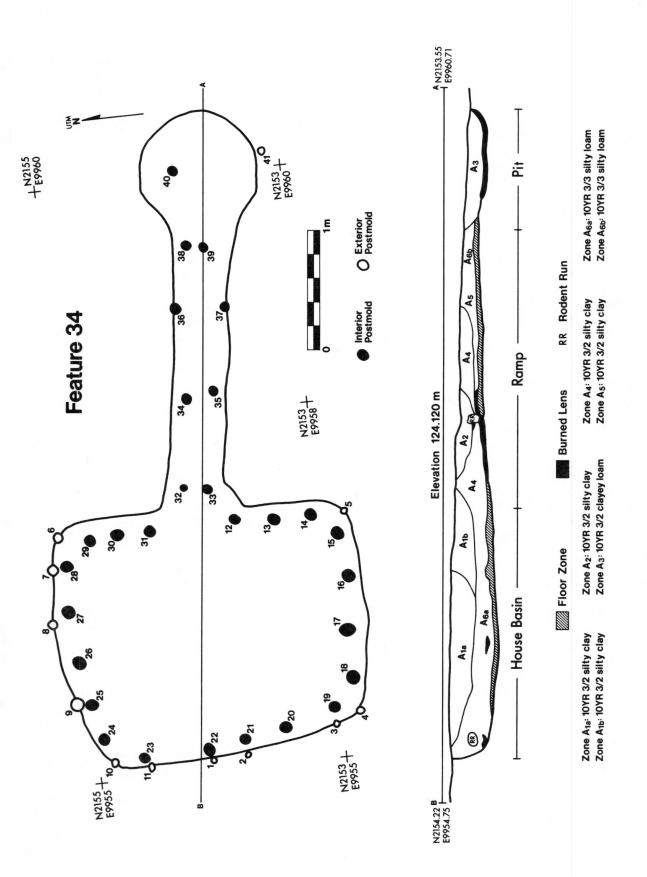

Feature 34

Interior Postmold

Exterior Postmold

N2155 E9960

N2153 E9960

N2153 E9958

N2155 E9955 E9955

N2153 E9955

UTM N

0 ____ 1 m

Elevation 124.120 m

A N2153.55 E9960.71

N2154.22 B E9954.75

A N2153.55 E9960.71

House Basin — Ramp — Pit

Floor Zone   Burned Lens   RR   Rodent Run

Zone A1a: 10YR 3/2 silty clay
Zone A1b: 10YR 3/2 silty clay

Zone A2: 10YR 3/2 silty clay
Zone A3: 10YR 3/2 clayey loam

Zone A4: 10YR 3/2 silty clay
Zone A5: 10YR 3/2 silty clay

Zone A6a: 10YR 3/3 silty loam
Zone A6b: 10YR 3/3 silty loam

Figure 11. Keyhole Structure Feature 34, Plan and Profile Views

apart, respectively, in a north-south direction. Postmold pair 36 and 37 occurred on the edge of the ramp while Postmold pair 38 and 39 was situated in the center and northern half of the ramp. The ramp posts that were not burned are interpreted as having been support posts for a domed ramp cover.

The structure basin exhibited two major fill zones and a burned basin floor, which was covered by an extensive area of wood charcoal. Burning was particularly evident in the central portion of the structure. In several places, burned areas appeared in a criss-cross fashion as if a meshed framework had fallen onto the floor. Cultural materials were found in association with the burned areas. In addition, several small concentrations of nut fragments were found with the wood charcoal. These nut remains probably represent original floor debris that became interspersed with the collapsed walls of the burned structure. A number of charcoal concentrations appeared to extend from a burned post outward along the wall, suggesting a fallen wall post. An additional burned area was found in the ramp near the basin. Since the ramp posts did not exhibit evidence of burning, it seems likely that this burning can be attributed to a fallen post or framework from the basin portion of the structure.

The fill zones above the burned floor level contained little evidence of burning and produced only a small amount of cultural material. The fills of these two upper zones appeared lightly mottled, suggesting secondary, natural filling of the basin and ramp areas following the fire.

Feature 34 represents a rare example of a burned keyhole structure. The burning preserved a relatively complete set of posts. The criss-cross pattern of burning on the basin floor indicated a structure with a wicker-work frame. That this was a relatively substantial structure was indicated by the number of support posts bolstering the primary wall line and the four corner posts that probably represent key support elements. This was also the only structure at the site with clear evidence for ramp posts. These posts had been set so close together that passage through the ramp would have been impossible, providing that these posts supported a superstructure. The depth of these posts indicates that they probably did serve as supports for a heavy superstructure, and that the ramp in Feature 34 was not a passageway.

Structure Feature 81

Feature 81 was a keyhole structure in the western portion of Occupation Area 1. It superimposed the ramp pit of another keyhole structure (Feature 117) to the west, and it also superimposed the southwestern wall of Feature 52. The ramp pit of Feature 81 also superimposed pit Feature 169, which was located in the southwestern corner of Feature 52. Feature 81 consisted of a basin, a ramp, and a ramp pit. The ramp and basin were oriented a few degrees to the southeast. Feature 81 provides clear evidence that at least one keyhole structure at the Fish Lake site postdated the large post structure (Feature 52) [Figure 12].

Feature 81 was the smallest keyhole structure at the Fish Lake site, measuring only 5.38 m in length and containing a basin fill area of only 4.08 m2. The floor area within the post walls, of course, was even smaller than 4 m2. The subterranean basin measured 2.06 m by 1.98 m, with its long axis oriented in an east-west direction. All other keyhole structures at this site had their longest axes oriented north to south. The basin was 39 cm deep. The ramp was 1.64 m in length, 40 cm wide, and 16 cm deep. Feature 81 contained the shortest ramp of any keyhole structure at the site. The ramp pit was 1.66 m by 1.46 m in plan view and 49 cm deep. This was the largest of the structure ramp pits. Its size was, in fact, difficult to determine, since this pit was superimposed over pit Feature 169.

The Feature 81 basin contained 20 postmolds organized in the following manner. Four postmolds made up the eastern wall, with two postmolds each on either side of the ramp entry into the basin. These postmolds were directly opposed by four postmolds comprising the western wall of the structure. The northern and southern walls contained five postmolds each and were also opposed. Postmold 12, situated in the southwestern corner, and Postmold 22, located in the northeastern corner, may represent opposed corner posts. Postmold 12 was slanted toward the interior of the structure, indicating that this corner post had been bent and attached at the center of the structure basin. The wall postmolds in this structure were spaced at irregular intervals, separated by an average of 31.63 cm. The western and northern wall postmolds were deeper and slightly larger in diameter than the other postmolds in the structure. A gap of 52 cm occurred in the eastern wall at the entry point of the ramp into the basin. A postmold was found in the middle of this gap, but it was not associated with the wall. Another interior postmold (Postmold 26) was situated ca. 25 cm west of this postmold; it probably held an interior support post.

The basin was composed of three fill zones that had been deposited in the basin after the structure was abandoned. Very little cultural material was found in any of these fill zones. The base of the basin was compacted and probably represents the original floor. No cultural materials, however, were found associated with this floor level. No evidence of burning was found on the floor, in the fill, or in the postmold fills. This indicates that the structure had been abandoned and had filled naturally.

The fill that covered the basin also filled the ramp. The original ramp fill, however, was observed at the base of the ramp and measured a maximum of 6 cm in depth. The ramp fill had apparently spilled into the basin while the basin was still open, since it occurred at the base of secondarily deposited basin fill zones. This fill also marked the base

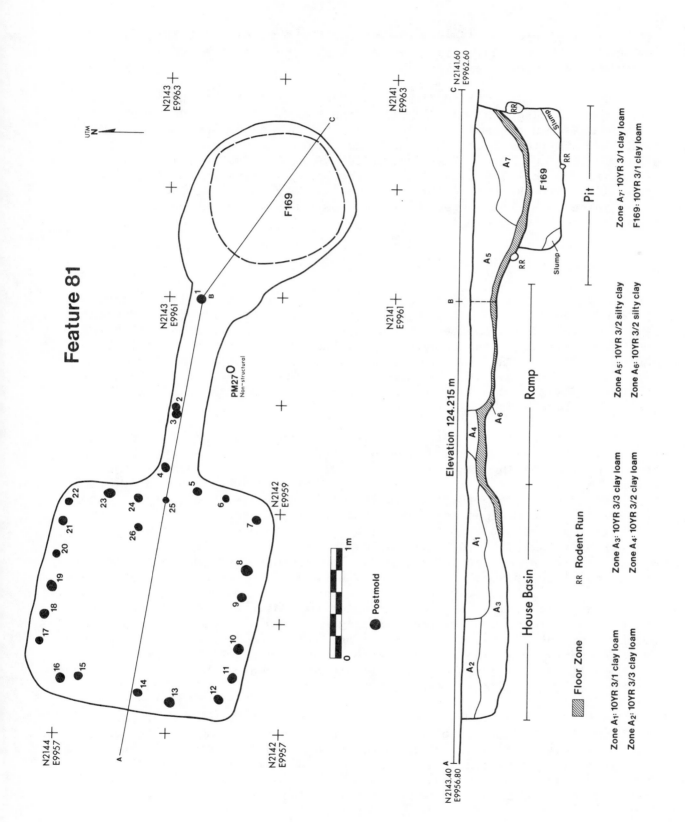

Figure 12. Keyhole Structure Feature 81, Plan and Profile Views

of the ramp pit and clearly demarcated the ramp pit fill from the pit feature (Feature 169) fill beneath it. The ramp pit was apparently basin shaped in cross section.

The ramp also contained four postmolds located at the base of the ramp and situated along its northern half. One of the postmolds (Postmold 4) was situated at the entry point into the basin. Its position was identical to the ramp postmold (Postmold 19) found in structure Feature 32. This postmold (Postmold 4) and a postmold (Postmold 25) that lay only 20 cm to the west, marking the center of the ramp entry into the basin, are functionally enigmatic, particularly if this space was a passageway. These posts would have obstructed entry from the ramp into the basin.

Structure Feature 116

Feature 116 was a keyhole structure located in the western portion of Occupation Area 1. It was superimposed by keyhole structure Feature 32. The structure consisted of a subterranean basin and a partial ramp. The ramp pit had been destroyed by Feature 32. The ramp was oriented almost due east. The basin measured 2.14 m (north-south) by 2.0 m (east-west) and was 45.5 cm deep. The length of the ramp to its point of superimposition was 1.20 m. The maximum width of the ramp was 38 cm, and its maximum depth was only 12 cm.

The basin of Feature 116 was slightly incurved and included 19 postmolds. The average spacing between postmolds was 34.44 cm. For the most part the spacing was relatively regular. However, there existed a gap of nearly 60 cm in the western wall between Postmolds 9 and 10, and a gap of 52 cm between the basin entry of the ramp and the basin. The eastern wall contained six postmolds, three each on either side of the entryway gap. Five postmolds comprised the western wall and, with the exception of the gap between Postmolds 9 and 10, the eastern and western wall postmolds were directly opposed. The northern and southern walls contained four postmolds each and were directly opposed. Thus, the Feature 116 wall pattern was very symmetric. All postmold fills exhibited charcoal flecking. No interior postmolds were found, nor were any postmolds found in the ramp. A single postmold (Postmold 20) was found just outside the ramp near the entryway into the basin. In terms of its relative position next to the entryway, this postmold was similar to the isolated postmolds found in structure Features 32 and 81. The function of such posts is unknown (Figure 13).

The basin floor exhibited signs of burning that consisted of patches of charcoal staining concentrated primarily in the center of the basin. Some large pieces of charcoal were recovered, and in several instances it appeared that pieces were intermeshed, as if a wicker-work wall had fallen inward toward the center of the basin. More perplexing was the presence of carbonized nut fragments mixed with the wood charcoal on the floor. This was also observed in structure Feature 34.

Feature 116

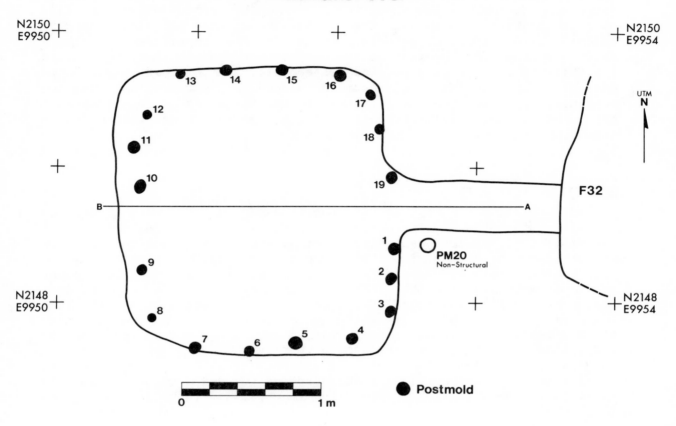

N2150
E9950

N2150
E9954

UTM
N

13 14 15 16

17

18

12

11

19

10

F32

B————————————————————A

1

PM20
Non-Structural

2

3

9

4

8

5

7   6

N2148
E9950

N2148
E9954

● Postmold

0   1 m

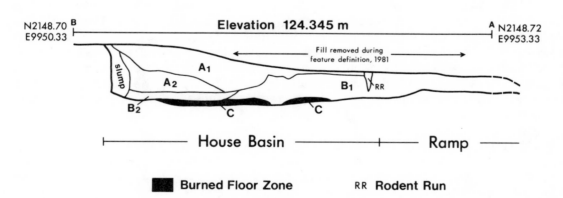

N2148.70
E9950.33 B

Elevation 124.345 m

A N2148.72
E9953.33

Fill removed during
feature definition, 1981

slump

A₁

A₂

B₁

RR

B₂

C   C

House Basin   Ramp

■ Burned Floor Zone   RR Rodent Run

Zone A₁: 10YR 3/2 clay loam   Zone B₁: 10YR 4/3 sandy loam   Zone C: 10YR 3/3 silty sand

Zone A₂: 10YR 3/3 clay loam   Zone B₂: 10YR 4/3 sandy loam   Slump: 10YR 4/3 silty sand

Figure 13. Keyhole Structure Feature 116, Plan and Profile Views

Covering the burned floor area of this structure were several fill zones. The basal zone was composed of a fill that extended from the ramp into the basin. The upper two zones represented a single fill episode that was confined to the basin. These zones contained the vast majority of the cultural materials found in the structure. A large rodent burrow in the west-central portion of the structure penetrated the fill and floor area along the western wall line. This disturbance accounts for the missing postmold along the western wall and the presence of some historical materials in the fill, including fragments of a Root Bitters flask probably dating to the late nineteenth or early twentieth century.

Structure Feature 117

Feature 117 was a keyhole structure located in the western portion of Occupation Area 1. It was superimposed by structure Feature 81. It consisted of a subterranean basin, a ramp, and a small portion of the western edge of a ramp pit. The basin measured 2.20 m (north-south) by 1.94 m (east-west) and was 28 cm deep. Feature 117 was the second smallest keyhole structure at the site, having a floor area of only 4.27 m2 and a fill volume of 1195.0 dm3. The ramp was 2.26 m long and was oriented several degrees to the southeast. The width of the ramp was maximally 40 cm, and its depth was 15 cm. A portion of the western ramp and ramp pit were excavated during the 1981 season. The 1982 excavations revealed a great deal of apparent erosion in this western area. Hence, the profile map that appears to show a sloping ramp only reflects the amount of fill eroded from the ramp surface in this area (Figure 14).

Only two major fill zones were observed in this structure. Both zones were also observed in the ramp. No floor area was discernible. The postmolds (N=15) were highly eroded and barely visible. A number of "postmolds" were later disregarded when their profiles could not be distinguished from the surrounding soil. The soil in the floor area was very sandy, and fill boundaries were very diffuse. The basin fill was homogeneous and contained very little debris. No evidence of burning was found in the structure or its ramp.

A total of 15 postmolds were defined in the basin area. The spacing between these postmolds was difficult to determine because of a large number of missing postmolds, although the spacing did appear to be highly irregular. In addition, the post pattern was not symmetric. That is, none of the postmolds appeared to be directly opposed by an opposite wall postmold. In this respect, Feature 117 was clearly distinctive. One explanation for the apparently missing postmolds in this basin is that the original posts may have been removed, possibly by the builders of structure Feature 81, which superimposed this structure.

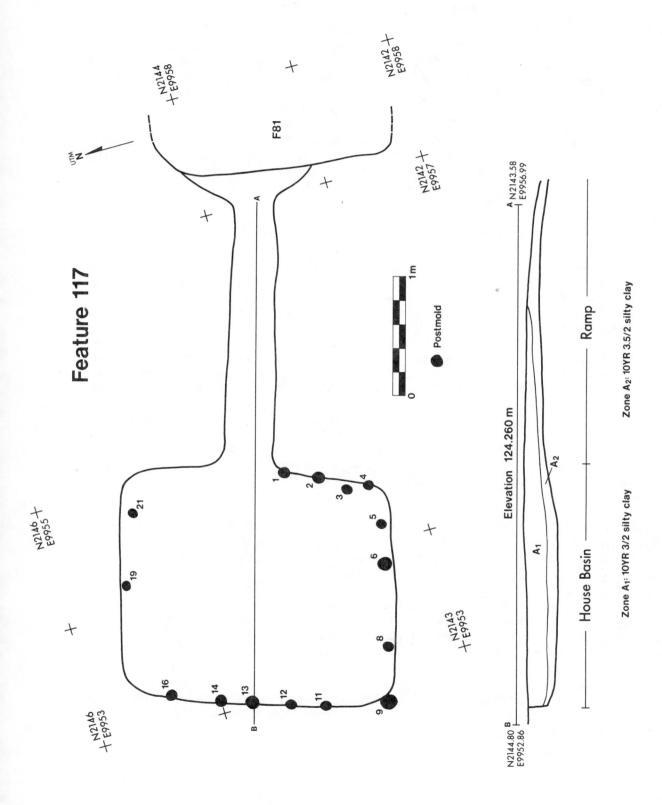

Figure 14. Keyhole Structure Feature 117, Plan and Profile Views

Structure Feature 165

Structure Feature 165 was a keyhole structure located in the southwestern corner of Occupation Area 1. The basin was intersected by the right-of-way. Only the ramp pit, ramp, and the eastern portion of the basin fell within the right-of-way limits. Only these sections of the structure were excavated. Therefore, measurements and construction details are incomplete. The basin measured 2.36 m in a north-south direction and was 38 cm deep. Its east-west extent is unknown. Only nine postmolds were found in the basin. In terms of postmold spacing and mean postmold depth, this feature most closely resembled structure Feature 9, which was located about 15 m southeast of this structure in Occupation Area 2 (Figure 15).

The basin contained only one soil zone, a black homogeneous fill containing occasional cultural materials, calcined bone, and charcoal flecks. This fill extended into the ramp and upper portion of the ramp pit. It was very compact and clayey in texture. The floor area contained a higher percentage of sand than did the remainder of the fill. The walls of the basin were nearly vertical, and there was little evidence of slumping.

The ramp was 1.82 m long, the second shortest ramp at this site, and it measured 19 cm deep at its maximum point. The ramp was deeper near the entry point into the basin. Some of the ramp fill had eroded into the basin floor and, in fact, was observed beneath the zone at which postmolds were defined. This indicated that the ramp fill had been deposited into a small depression within the floor. The origin of this depression is unknown, but it may have resulted from sloppy digging when the basin was first excavated by the inhabitants. It could also have resulted from an old post depression.

The ramp pit measured 1.32 m by 1.30 m and was 18 cm deep. It was basin shaped. The Feature 165 ramp pit exhibited clear evidence that it had been utilized as a fire pit. Indeed, most of the ramp pits associated with keyhole structures at this site produced some evidence of burning, usually in the form of small fragments of scattered charcoal or burned clay. Generally, however, in the other structures it was virtually impossible to distinguish actual burning in the pit from redeposited burned materials that had been simply thrown into the pit. The ramp pit of Feature 165 was burned at its base. This burned area was approximately half of the surface area of the ramp pit and was marked by a heavy concentration of oxidized clay and occasional pieces of charcoal. Cultural materials were absent at the base of the ramp pit, although several pieces of pottery and chert flakes were found in its upper portion. In short, it is obvious that this pit was used primarily as a fire basin.

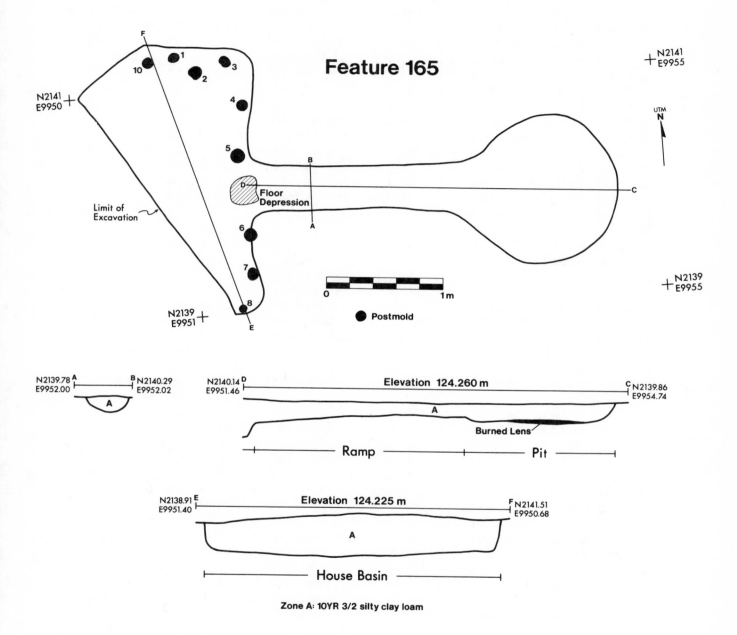

Figure 15. Keyhole Structure Feature 165, Plan and Profile Views

Structure Feature 52

Feature 52 was a large, square, post structure located in Occupation Area 1. It consisted of 40 wall postmolds, 11 interior postmolds, and 12 internal pits. The structure was superimposed by keyhole structure Feature 81 and pit Feature 57. Feature 52 measured 7.20 m (north-south) by 6.96 m (east-west) and contained a floor area of ca. 51 m2. The length and width measurements were calculated from the center of Postmold 32 to Postmold 14 (north-south) and from Postmold 20 to Postmold 3 (east-west) [Figure 16].

This post structure contained no discernible floor fill. For this reason it was not possible to directly associate most of the internal pits with the structure. Feature 57 was superimposed through the northeastern wall post line and clearly postdated the structure. The ramp and ramp pit of keyhole structure Feature 81 cut through the southwestern post line. In addition, the ramp pit was placed directly on top of pit Feature 169.

Forty postmolds comprised the four walls of the structure. These were distributed relatively evenly. For example, 11 postmolds comprised each of the northern, western, and southern walls, while 7 made up the eastern wall. However, in the case of the eastern wall it appeared that posts had been destroyed by the superpositioning of Feature 57. The southern wall contained ten primary wall posts and a single wall support post (Postmold 9). The western wall contained nine primary posts and two wall support posts (Postmolds 19 and 24). The northern wall and eastern wall contained 11 and 7 primary posts, respectively. The spacing between wall postmolds was extremely regular and averaged 62.5 cm (Table 1).

Despite the regularity in postmold intervals and the nearly perfect symmetry of the structure, several differences in the walls were observed. These differences are expressed in mean depth and diameter calculations. Postmolds in both the northern and western walls exceeded the southern and eastern walls in depth and diameter. The postmolds of the northern wall were nearly 6 cm deeper than those comprising the southern wall. The postmolds of the western wall were ca. 3 cm deeper on the average than those of either the southern or eastern walls (Table 1). It is apparent that the occupants of this structure purposely bolstered both the northern and western walls by placing larger posts in those areas and setting them in deeper. This structural adaptation was no doubt undertaken to shield the interior more effectively from prevailing winds (Table 2).

This structure also contained 11 interior postmolds. One of these (Postmold 36) probably contained a central support post, since it was located in the middle of the structure and was also the deepest (25 cm) [Table 3]. This postmold and Postmold 41 were also the largest in diameter. In addition, Postmolds 41 and 42 were located in the centers of the southeastern and southwestern quadrants, respectively. These

Feature 52

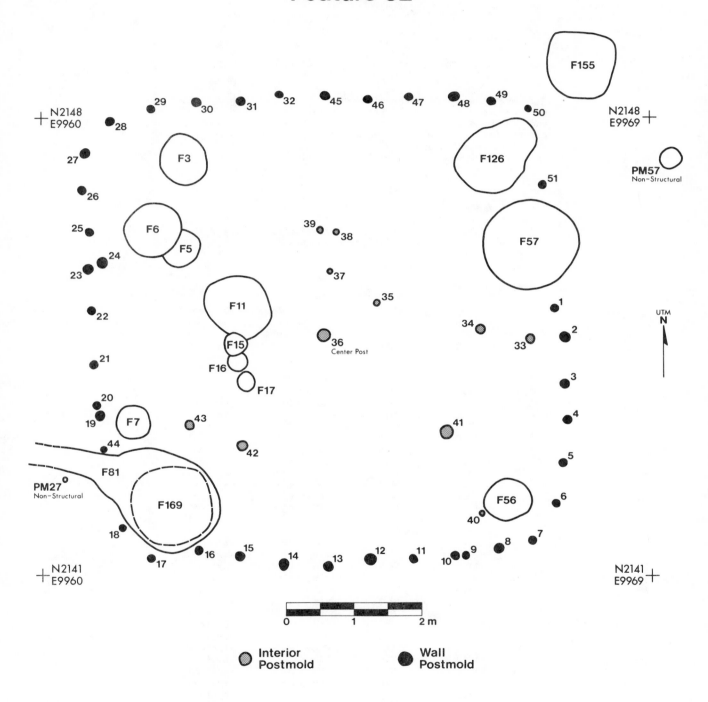

Figure 16. Post Structure Feature 52, Plan View

Table 1. Feature 52 Wall Post Attributes

Wall	N of Posts	Mean Dia. (cm)	Mean Depth (cm)	Mean Distance Between Posts (cm)*
east	7	12.43	13.43	60.60
west	11	12.59	15.73	63.40
north	11	12.86	18.82	62.00
south	11	11.45	12.95	63.20
total	40	12.32	15.41	62.50

* Intervals were not measured between posts where superpositioning occurred, e.g., between PM 44 and PM 18. In addition, PM 9, 19, and 24 were excluded, since these served as support posts to the primary wall. These posts, however, were included in the diameter and depth calculations.

Table 2. Attributes of Posts Comprising the Wall of Structure Feature 52

PM	Dia. (cm)	Depth (cm)	Wall	Shape	Orientation
1	12.5	21.0	east	conical	slanted
2	14.0	13.0	east	round	vertical
3	12.0	10.0	east	round	vertical
4	12.5	10.0	east	flat	vertical
5	12.0	14.0	east	flat	vertical
6	12.0	16.0	east	conical	vertical
51	12.0	10.0	east	round	vertical
18	9.0	18.0	west	conical	vertical
19	15.0	9.0	west	round	vertical
20	13.0	20.0	west	conical	slanted
21	14.0	17.0	west	flat	slanted
22	12.0	15.0	west	flat	vertical
23	14.0	15.0	west	flat	vertical
24	15.0	20.0	west	conical	vertical
25	11.0	14.0	west	conical	vertical
26	11.0	10.0	west	conical	vertical
27	13.5	14.0	west	flat	vertical
44	11.0	21.0	west	round	vertical
7	7.5	21.0	south	conical	vertical
8	12.0	20.0	south	conical	vertical
9	11.5	7.0	south	round	vertical
10	11.0	12.0	south	flat	vertical
11	11.0	11.5	south	irregular	vertical
12	12.0	12.0	south	flat	vertical
13	11.0	12.0	south	conical	vertical
14	12.0	12.0	south	conical	vertical
15	12.0	9.0	south	round	vertical
16	14.0	13.0	south	conical	vertical
17	12.0	13.0	south	flat	vertical
28	12.0	14.0	north	round	slanted
29	13.0	14.0	north	flat	vertical
30	13.0	23.0	north	round	vertical
31	14.0	22.0	north	round	vertical
32	11.5	22.0	north	round	vertical
45	14.0	20.0	north	conical	vertical
46	12.0	20.0	north	conical	vertical
47	12.0	16.0	north	conical	vertical
48	16.0	21.0	north	conical	slanted
49	14.0	14.0	north	round	vertical
50	10.0	21.0	north	conical	vertical

Table 3. Feature 52 Interior Floor Post Attributes

PM	Dia. (cm)	Depth (cm)	Shape	Orientation	Quadrant
33	12.0	9.0	irregular	vertical	SE
34	10.0	13.0	conical	vertical	SE
35	10.5	11.0	conical	slanted	NE
36	18.0	25.0	round	vertical	Center
37	9.0	18.0	conical	vertical	NE/NW
38	10.0	17.0	conical	vertical	NE
39	8.5	14.0	conical	vertical	NE/NW
40	8.0	8.0	round	slanted	SE
41	18.0	16.0	round	vertical	SE
42	15.5	12.0	round	vertical	SW
43	12.0	15.0	flat	vertical	SW

Table 4. Post Attributes for Post Cluster
in Occupation Area 1

PM	Dia. (cm)	Depth (cm)	Shape	Orientation	Burning
11	8.5	26.0	conical	vertical	Yes
12	8.0	20.0	conical	vertical	Yes
13	18.0	6.5	round	vertical	No
14	14.0	10.0	flat	vertical	Yes
15	14.0	17.0	round	vertical	Yes
16	21.0	15.0	round	vertical	Yes
17	19.0	20.0	flat	slanted	No
18	15.0	18.0	round	vertical	Yes
19	18.0	19.0	round	vertical	Yes
20	19.0	10.0	round	vertical	No
21	15.0	15.0	round	slanted	No
22	13.0	13.0	round	slanted	No
23	19.0	9.0	triangular	vertical	Yes
45*	32.0	19.0	round	vertical	Yes
46*	25.0	10.5	round	vertical	No
47*	40.0	55.0	round	vertical	Yes
50*	37.0	15.0	round	vertical	No
51*	24.0	17.0	flat	vertical	Yes

* These numbers represent feature numbers. These features were redesignated as postmolds but their original numbers were maintained.

large postmolds apparently once held major support posts. Similar postmolds were not found in the northern half of the structure. Postmolds 33, 34, 35, 37, 38, and 39 were located in the northeastern quadrant, and together they formed a curved line dividing the northeastern quadrant of the structure from the southeastern quadrant. Therefore, these posts probably functioned as partitions rather than as support posts.

No entryway to the structure was apparent. There were no discernible gaps in the structure walls, except in the northeastern corner, where superpositioning by Feature 57 may have obliterated wall posts. It is interesting that just outside the northeastern corner of the structure were several pits and a large postmold (Postmold 57). This postmold measured 34 cm by 33 cm and was 18 cm deep. The size of this postmold suggests a specialized function, perhaps as a marker post for either the structure or the northeastern corner entrance.

As previously explained, the association of many internally located pits with the structure is tenuous. Feature 57 was superimposed through the eastern wall; therefore, it was not associated with the structure. It is also possible that Features 6 and 15 were associated with keyhole structure Feature 81 and pit Feature 57. Presumably, Feature 169, which lay under the ramp pit of keyhole structure Feature 81, was associated with the post structure, but this cannot be confirmed.

Each of the four corners of the post structure contained a pit. The remaining eight pits in the structure were distributed in no discernible pattern, although it is perhaps noteworthy that nine of the twelve pits, including Feature 57, occurred within the western half of the structure. In addition, a 2.5 m wide area containing no features existed in the central portion of the structure that extended between the northern and southern walls. One may conclude that the western half of the structure was utilized primarily for activities such as cooking and food processing, while the relatively open eastern and central portions of the structure served as sleeping or general use areas. It is interesting that the main open area in the south-central portion of the structure was marked by three main support postmolds (Postmolds 36, 41, and 42), which formed an isosceles triangle. The purpose of this arrangement is unknown, but it is possible that additional support was desired in this section of the structure or that extra care was taken to provide a stronger superstructure for a primary sleeping or activity area.

Since none of the internal pits could be directly associated with the structure, the pit contents could not be used to reconstruct possible activities conducted in the structure. Nevertheless, it is noteworthy that a variety of tools were found in these pits, including three hammerstones, two grinding stones and a celt fragment. Such tools were not abundant at this site. In addition, a sandstone abrader, a denticulate, 28 retouched flakes, and chert debitage were found in these same pits. The chert types in these pits were distributed uniformly, with white Burlington varieties comprising the largest percentage.

Several pit types were represented in the post structure including deep cylindrical (Feature 57), basin-shaped (Features 7, 15, 16, and 17), deep bell-shaped (Features 3, 5, 6, 11, and 56), and irregular (Feature 126) pits. Another pit (Feature 169) could not be assigned to a specific pit type since it was superimposed by Feature 81. Features 6, 11, and 126 contained several major fill episodes, but most of the other deep pits exhibited only minor filling episodes. Limestone was found in all but five pits (Features 5, 7, 15, 16, and 17), while sandstone, in much smaller quantities than limestone, was found in all but four pits (Features 5, 7, 15, and 16). All of the limestone and sandstone was burned and occurred most frequently in fill zones that exhibited burning. Most of the cultural materials recovered from the internal pits were derived from those in the northwestern quadrant of the structure. If those pits were truly associated with the structure, then it was there that the majority of cooking and processing activities were performed.

Special Features

This section describes two special features and an unusual configuration of posts located east of structure Feature 52. The two special features included Feature 164, a large communal pit on the western edge of Occupation Area 1, and Feature 136, a row of postmolds at the eastern end of that occupation area. The postmold configuration occurred between Feature 52 and the post row, and was not given a specific feature number since the postmolds did not form a recognizable pattern. This unit is referred to as a post cluster.

Pit Feature 164

Feature 164 was the largest prehistoric pit at the Fish Lake site. It was located on the western edge of Occupation Area 1 ca. 3 m to 5 m west of structure Features 116 and 117. Nearly half of the pit lay outside of the right-of-way limits, so only the northeastern half was excavated. In plan view this pit was rectangular, with its long axis oriented in a northwest-southeast direction; it measured 1.73 m in extent. Its short axis measured 1.24 m. Owing to its large size, rectangular shape, and dark, homogeneous fill, this feature was initially regarded as a possible keyhole structure. Subsequent excavation, however, revealed a deep (1.14 m), multizoned, slightly bell-shaped pit. The volume for the excavated portion of this pit was 1973.46 dm3. This figure represents roughly half of the volume of this pit. The pit containing the next highest fill volume (Feature 37) was almost half the size of Feature 164 (Figure 17).

Feature 164 contained several distinct fill zones, indicating that this pit had been utilized several times. The basal zone consisted of a shallow fill containing little debris and only slight indications of burning. This zone had lain open long enough for extensive slumping to

Feature 164

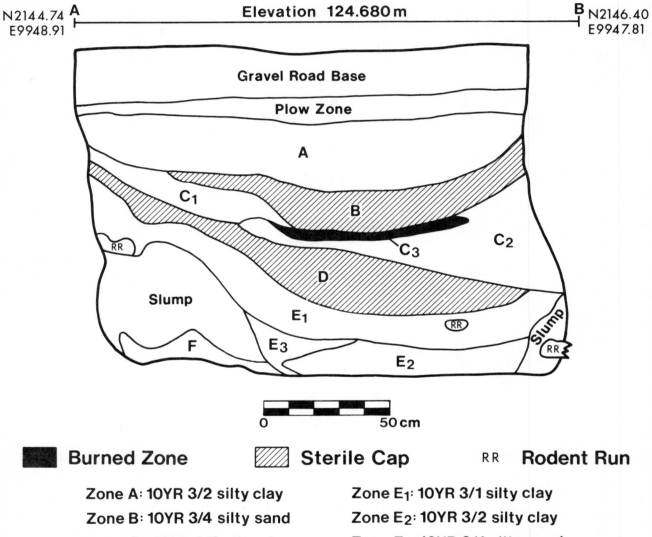

Figure 17. Pit Feature 164 in Occupation Area 1, Profile

cover the sides of this zone. Directly above this zone was a dark homogeneous fill containing a moderate amount of debris and no evidence of burning. It represented a refuse-filling episode that covered the slump and initial fill zone. This zone dipped downward to the north as did a sterile cap zone that covered it. The cap zone was light brown in color, very compact, and contained no cultural materials. It was probably an intentional cap, since no slumping was observed around its edges. Directly above this zone was a burned and heavily oxidized area. A narrow lens of burning appeared at the base of this zone. Most of the faunal remains recovered from this pit occurred in this lens and the associated zone of burning. At the time of burning, the pit was 60% filled. Above the burned zone was another sterile cap containing neither debris nor traces of burning. Above this cap was a final fill zone, which contained a moderate amount of cultural material, burned clay, and charcoal. This was also a refuse fill zone.

In summary, four major fill episodes were observed in this pit. The first was covered by slumping, while the next two fill zones were covered, probably intentionally, by sterile caps. The final fill zone was covered by recent alluvium that was partially disturbed by plowing and the construction of a private road leading into Mr. W.W. Jackson's yard. The pit had been utilized primarily as a refuse facility but the burned zone also indicated its possible use as a cooking or roasting pit for a brief period of time.

The large size of this pit and its location near the main concentration of keyhole structures indicated that this facility probably served as a communal pit. Since it was not possible to investigate the area immediately west of this pit, it is not known whether it occupied a central position in the community. A large refuse facility near the keyhole structures may explain why so little material was found in the keyhole structures, particularly in the closest two structures (Features 116 and 117) [Plate 4].

Feature 136

Feature 136 consisted of a row of nine postmolds oriented in an east-west direction that were situated in the north central portion of Occupation Area 1. This row lay immediately north of pit Features 137 and 138, and also north of a cluster of pits marking the eastern section of Occupation Area 1. The postmolds were spaced at regular intervals averaging 70 cm, as measured from postmold midpoint to midpoint. The postmold row measured 5.64 m in length.

The postmolds were relatively shallow, ranging in depth from 6.5 cm to 18 cm (mean=11.8 cm). In diameter they ranged from 9 cm to 18 cm (mean=12.7 cm). Their profile shapes varied from narrow, conical, and rounded, to flat bottomed with outflaring walls. The fills were relatively homogeneous, consisting of a 10YR 3/1 and 10YR 3/2 silty clay loam. Postmolds 2 and 8 contained small flecks of charcoal and burned

46

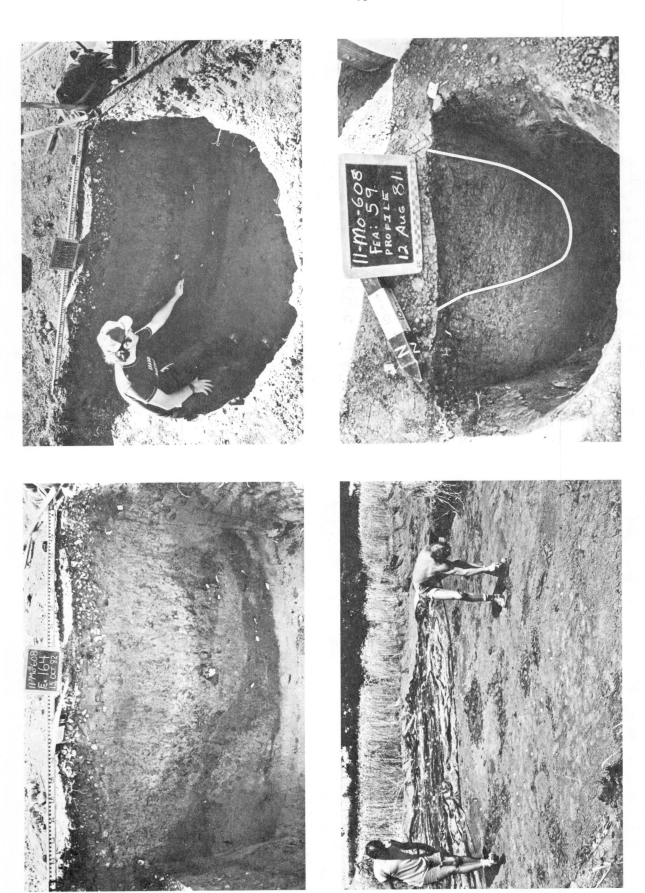

Plate 4. Features in Occupation Area 1: upper left and right, profile of Feature 164; lower left, west wall of Feature 52, post structure; lower right, post profile of Feature 59

clay, indicating that they may have been burned. None of the postmold fills yielded cultural materials.

The Feature 136 postmold row paralleled the northern wall of post structure Feature 52. In fact, it was originally believed that this postmold row might represent a wall of another large building. However, careful shovel scraping over this entire area failed to produce additional connecting posts. It appears, therefore, that this postmold row was a special feature unlike the structure postmold arrangements at this site. Feature 136 may represent either a special processing rack, perhaps for drying fish, or it may have served as a wind screen. Its location directly north of a dense cluster of pits does not seem fortuitous, so it was probably directly related to the activities carried out near those pits. Its similar orientation to that of post structure Feature 52 suggested that this postmold row and its associated pits were constructed at the same time that Feature 52 was occupied. Postmold rows such as this have been observed at other sites in the area, with several examples occurring at the Range site (John E. Kelly, personal communication). The function of post rows at that site is equally enigmatic.

Post Cluster

A cluster of 18 postmolds occurred in the area between structure Feature 52 and the post row (Feature 136). Two pits (Features 22 and 43) were identified on the northwestern and southeastern edges of this cluster, respectively. The postmolds did not form any discernible pattern although several may have been paired. The diameters and depths of these postmolds varied considerably, ranging from 8 cm to 40 cm in diameter and from 6.5 cm to 55 cm in depth. Postmold profile shapes were rounded, conical, flat, and triangular. Only three postmolds (Postmolds 17, 21, and 22) were slanted. The largest postmold was 40 cm in diameter and 55 cm deep. This postmold was originally designated as pit Feature 47, but was later redesignated as a postmold because of its conical shape, absence of cultural material, and homogeneous black fill. Four additional features in this cluster were also initially classified as pits (Features 45, 46, 50, and 51), but later redesignated as postmolds. Postmold Feature 45 resembled in size and shape the large postmold (Postmold 57) found just outside of structure Feature 52. Postmold 57 was 34 cm in diameter and 18 cm deep. Postmold 57 appears to have been directly associated with the structure. Eleven of the postmolds exhibited some evidence of burning in their fills, but these postmolds formed no apparent pattern (Table 4).

It is probable that this postmold cluster served as a specialized processing area, although the nature of the processing activities can only be conjectured. Its location near the large post structure may be significant as may its position near the postmold row and its associated pits. Possible functions for this post cluster include drying racks for food or hide stretching.

Structure and Overall Feature Distribution
in the Central Occupation Area

The central occupation area was situated just south of the ridge apex on a relatively level surface. This occupation area extended ca. 35 km in an east-west direction and was no more than 11 m wide at its maximum north-south width. This area, also referred to as Occupation Area 2, consisted of a single keyhole structure (Feature 9), 25 pits, and 3 postmolds. All but three pits were situated east of the keyhole structure. The basin of structure Feature 9 was oriented a few degrees to the northeast. Most of the features of this occupation area had been excavated into clayey soil. The soil texture gradually became more sandy in the southern portion of the occupation area.

The association of Feature 9 with the cluster of pits located to the east is problematical. This was the only keyhole structure at this site located south of the main structure concentration in Occupation Area 1. In addition, the association of pits in Occupation Area 2 with the pits of the remaining occupation areas to the south was impossible to establish. While the central occupation area was distinguished from the others by vacant areas, an argument could be made for alternative spatial groupings. For example, pit Features 91, 94, 98, 101, and 104 in Occupation Area 2 appeared to form a continuous arc with pit Features 122, 123, 124, 125, 127, 128, 129, 130, 131, and 153 in Occupation Area 3. On the other hand, the orientation of pits along a northwest-southeast axis in Occupation Areas 2 and 4 indicated a possible association between these two occupation areas. In short, the various pit cluster possibilities are endless and highlight the difficulties in determining occupational activity boundaries within site areas, particularly in instances such as this where variation is lacking in the material assemblage.

Structure Feature 9

Feature 9 was a keyhole structure located along the western limits of Occupation Area 2. It lay ca. 10 m southeast of Feature 165, a keyhole structure in Occupation Area 1. Feature 9 consisted of a square subterranean basin, a ramp, and a shallow pit attached to the eastern end of the ramp. The total length of the structure was 5.47 m. The basin, which was 50.5 cm deep, measured 2.25 m (north-south) by 2.20 m (east-west). The ramp, which measured 2.30 m in length, varied in width from 28 cm to 43 cm. Its maximum width of 43 cm was reached at the midpoint of the long axis. In depth the ramp varied from 3 cm to 18 cm, with its maximum depth occurring near the juncture with the basin and its minimum depth occurring at the midpoint of the long axis. Hence, the ramp was slightly raised at its midpoint and sloped from that point downward toward both the basin and ramp pit. The ramp pit, which was basin shaped, measured 1.06 m by 0.90 m and was 23 cm deep. This pit produced very little debris and exhibited no evidence of burning (Figure 18).

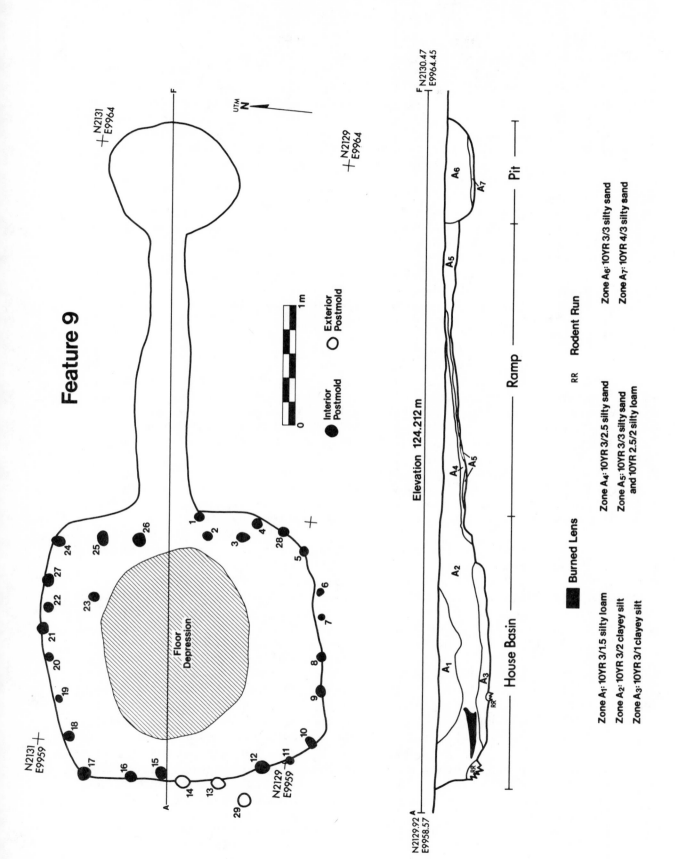

Feature 9

Zone A1: 10YR 3/1.5 silty loam
Zone A2: 10YR 3/2 clayey silt
Zone A3: 10YR 3/1 clayey silt

Zone A4: 10YR 3/2.5 silty sand
Zone A5: 10YR 3/3 silty sand
and 10YR 2.5/2 silty loam

Zone A6: 10YR 3/3 silty sand
Zone A7: 10YR 4/3 silty sand

Burned Lens   RR   Rodent Run

Elevation 124.212 m

Figure 18. Keyhole Structure Feature 9, Plan and Profile Views

Twenty-nine postmolds were associated with the structure basin. With three exceptions (Postmolds 13, 14, and 29), all postmolds were found on or near the basin floor. Postmolds 13, 14, and 29 were located near the central portion of the western wall, but were discovered 10 cm to 15 cm above the basin floor. Postmold 29, in fact, occurred ca. 20 cm outside of the wall line and limits of the basin fill. This postmold and Postmolds 13 and 14 probably represent external supports, and may even mark a possible western entryway into the basin. None of the postmolds had burned fills.

Twenty-five postmolds comprised the main wall around the basin. Postmold 1 marked the juncture of the ramp with the basin and may not have been associated with the primary wall, although it is possible that it was paired with a nearby wall postmold (Postmold 2). Postmold 4, which lay 50 cm due south of Postmold 1, may have been associated with the wall as a secondary support and may have been paired with a wall postmold (Postmold 3). A single interior postmold (Postmold 3), whose function is unknown, was located on the floor in the northeastern quadrant of the basin.

The 25 wall postmolds, including Postmolds 1 and 4, were spaced at somewhat irregular intervals (mean distance=30 cm). These postmolds averaged only 10.36 cm in depth and were the most shallow and most closely spaced wall postmolds found in keyhole structures at this site. Six of the wall postmolds exhibited interior slants, suggesting posts that had been bent inward. Included were Postmolds 5, 7, and 9 in the southern wall, Postmolds 11 and 15 in the western wall, and Postmold 18 in the northern wall. Along both the southern wall and the southern portion of the western wall, every second postmold slanted toward the interior of the basin, i.e., slanted Postmolds 5, 7, 9, and 11 were separated from one another by vertical Postmolds 6, 8, and 10.

Three distinct soil zones comprised the basin fill. The uppermost zone (A1) was restricted to the central portion of the basin and consisted of a black (10YR 3/1.5) silt loam with frequent burned clay fragments and charcoal flecks. In profile, this zone was roughly basin shaped with an irregular bottom, and it varied in depth from 13 cm to 20 cm. It appeared to have been deposited in a primary fill zone that extended from the present surface at which the basin was defined to its floor. This primary fill zone (A2) was clayey silt in texture, compact, and lighter in color (10YR 3/2) than the upper zone. It was generally free of charcoal flecking and burned clay, but contained two concentrated areas of burning near its base in the northern portion of the southwestern quadrant of the basin. Burned silt (5YR 4/3) and heavy concentrations of charcoal comprised both burned areas. The burning did not appear to have occurred in the basin, but was probably later deposited into the basin along with this fill zone. A final, basal zone (A3) occupied the central portion of the basin. It was a shallow (7 cm to 13 cm), circular depression extending ca. 5 cm below the floor level. This zone consisted of a dark clayey silt (10YR 3/1) in which only a few charcoal flecks were observed. This circular depression may represent the central living or sleeping area of the dwelling (Plate 5).

Plate 5. Keyhole Structure Feature 9: upper left, plan view; upper right, profile view; lower left, upper basin fill, southwestern quarter; lower right, central floor depression and excavated basin

A significant quantity of material was recovered from the basin fill, but materials were not recovered from the central depression or from the burned areas in the second fill zone. Most of the basin debris originated in the upper two zones and appeared to be distributed throughout the fill. Materials were piece-plotted in the southwestern quadrant, but this operation was not continued in the other quadrants when it became apparent that materials in the fill had been redeposited. No specific floor could be identified, as evidenced by either soil compaction or material distribution.

The ramp consisted of a dark fill that was subdivided into three distinct zones. No compaction was observed in any of the zones, and no so-called ramp floor could be distinguished. The upper zone (A2) appeared to be related to the primary fill zone in the basin. It was nearly 15 cm thick in places, and it extended from the basin to the apex of the humped area at the midpoint of the ramp. The second zone (A4) was an extremely thin lens, varying from 1 cm to 5 cm in thickness, which extended from the ramp midpoint and emptied into the basin at the junction of the ramp and basin. This ramp fill had apparently eroded into the basin while it was open and before the deposition of basin fills. Ramp erosion was also observed at other keyhole structures at this site, e.g., Feature 165. The third zone (A5) extended across the entire ramp and actually comprised all of the ramp fill east of the humped central portion. This ramp fill and the fill of the ramp pit were virtually indistinguishable.

A basin-shaped pit at the entry of the ramp consisted of two zones (A6 and A7), the lowermost of which possibly represented a bleed zone. As previously mentioned, neither debris nor evidence of burning were observed in this pit fill. It seemed to be related to the basal fill zone of the ramp and, as such, was probably filled at the same time.

Feature Distribution in the Southwestern Occupation Area

The southwestern occupation area, also known as Occupation Area 3, consisted of a dense concentration of pits located immediately southwest of the central occupation area. These pits were situated on the sloping sandy portion of the ridge. Approximately 40% of them fell outside the present right-of-way limits. These features were exposed during the 1981 season when the right-of-way extended further to the west. An irregular area, which was not exposed during 1981, intruded through the feature concentration. Additional pits probably lay within this area.

The southwestern occupation area extended ca. 35 m in an east-west direction and 15 m in a north-south direction. A total of 33 pits, 1 large historical disturbance, and 3 postmolds were defined and excavated in this area. No structures were identified. The pits were situated in sandy portions of the ridge and, for this reason, were generally shallow and highly eroded. They contrasted strongly with the deep cylindrical pits of the northern occupation area but were similar to the pits in the southeastern and southern portions of the central occupation area.

A historical feature (Feature 73) that was found in this occupation area was somewhat of an enigma. It superimposed two prehistoric pit features and no doubt also obliterated other features associated with the Late Woodland occupation. Feature 73 was a deep, circular, historical disturbance measuring 7.55 m in diameter and 4.18 m in depth. Owing to the great depth of this feature and the fact that it was relatively recent, only 25% of the feature was excavated. In one quarter section of excavation, over 1500 kg of limestone debris were recovered, including one slab that weighed nearly 90 kg. The limestone pieces consisted primarily of broken slabs and appeared to be either part of a dismantled foundation or, perhaps, siding associated with the deep excavation. Historical materials recovered from this feature included small pieces of corroded iron, broken glass, and bones of domesticated animals. In addition, several pieces of Patrick phase ceramics and chert flakes were recovered from the fill of the excavation. The function of this historical feature is unknown. It may have been an old cistern or well, or possibly the base of a silo. It probably dates to the first farmstead in this locality, i.e., ca. 100 years ago.

Structure and Overall Feature Distribution in the Southeastern Occupation Area

A small cluster of ten pits and one small post structure formed the southeastern occupation area (Occupation Area 4). This area was situated southeast of the central occupation area and appeared to be an extension of a group of pits in the central occupation area that were oriented in a northwest-southeast direction. It is perhaps significant that if Occupation Areas 2 and 4 were combined, the pits of these areas would account for nearly 65% of the straight-sided, flat-bottomed pits at this site and nearly 85% of the same category of pits found in Occupation Areas 2, 3, and 4. However, enough of a gap existed between Occupation Areas 2 and 4 to consider them as two distinct occupation areas.

Post structure Feature 77 and an isolated pit (Feature 160) were included in Occupation Area 4, although they lay outside the main feature concentration. The relationship of this post structure to the pits in this area is problematical, particularly since no cultural materials were found in the structure. A small hearth (Feature 78) was found in the structure.

Occupation Area 4 was oriented in a northwest-southeast direction and included an area of 18 m by 13 m, excluding Features 77 and 160. The pits were situated on a sandy slope of the ridge and appeared to be somewhat eroded. The fills of pits at the northwestern end of the area were very dark and clearly visible in the yellowish-brown sandy soil. Pits at the southeastern end, on the other hand, were indistinct and shallow. They contained few cultural materials. In terms of fill type and depth the pits of Occupation Area 4 most closely resembled those in

Occupation Area 3. In contrast to the other occupation areas, no postmolds were found in this area, except those associated with Feature 77.

Structure Feature 77

Feature 77 was a square post structure located ca. 10 m to 15 m east of Occupation Area 2, and 10 m north of the northernmost pits of Occupation Area 4. Feature 77 may be associated with either Occupation Area 2 or 4. This structure consisted of 18 postmolds and extended 2.06 m in a north-south direction and 2.10 m in an east-west direction. It was oriented slightly to the northeast. The overall plan was slightly irregular with the northern end measuring 1.60 m and the southern wall measuring 2.10 m. The corners were rounded. The postmolds were spaced at irregular intervals ranging from 10 cm to 73 cm apart (mean=41.1 cm). The postmolds were relatively deep, averaging 26.2 cm. Most had either conical or round profiles, and only Postmolds 9 and 15 had slanted orientations (Table 5). None contained material in their fills, and only Postmold 5 produced evidence of burning (Figure 19).

A large (112 cm by 84 cm) oval fill zone was found in the north-central portion of the structure and was given a feature number (Feature 78). This irregular area was excavated as a pit feature. The fill measured only 4 cm in depth and was slightly basin shaped. No material was recovered, but some small fragments of burned clay were observed. There are two possible interpretations of this feature. Feature 78 may represent a remnant basin fill of a highly eroded subterranean pit house, possibly even a keyhole structure. On the other hand, it may represent a shallow hearth, as evidenced by the burned clay fragments in the fill. It does not appear to have been a pit, however, particularly since the feature edges were diffuse and the fill was extremely shallow.

There may have been three sets of paired postmolds along the structure walls. These pairs would have included Postmolds 5 and 6 in the northeastern corner, Postmolds 10 and 11 in the southeastern corner, and Postmolds 14 and 15 in the southwestern corner. These postmolds are thought to have been paired because of the extremely close spacing between them and the fact that the pairs occurred only in the structure corners. These pairs probably related to the construction of the superstructure, although it has not been determined why there was no pair in the northwestern corner. The postmold arrangement suggested a wigwam style of construction.

The function of this post structure can only be conjectured. Its location away from major feature concentrations, particularly from other structures, was noteworthy. The absence of cultural materials in the structure area indicated that this feature was neither a work shed nor a focus of cooking, food processing, or tool manufacturing activities.

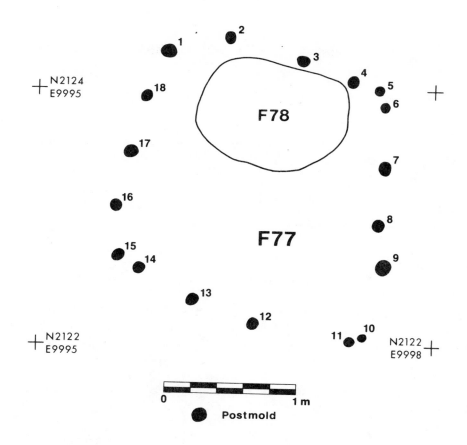

Figure 19. Post Structure Feature 77, Plan View

Table 5. Post Attributes for Structure Feature 77

PM	Dia. (cm)	Depth (cm)	Shape	Orientation	Position
1	11	30	round	vertical	NW corner
2	9	22	round	vertical	N wall
3	9	24	round	vertical	N wall
4	10	22	conical	vertical	N wall
5	8	23	round	vertical	NE corner
6	8	25	conical	vertical	E wall
7	9	24	round	vertical	E wall
8	8	30	unknown	vertical	E wall
9	11	24	conical	slanted	E wall
10	7	26	conical	vertical	SE corner
11	10	27	conical	vertical	SE corner
12	10	25	conical	vertical	S wall
13	11	27	round	vertical	S wall
14	10	24	conical	vertical	S wall
15	10	25	round	slanted	SW corner
16	10	34	round	vertical	W wall
17	11	30	conical	vertical	W wall
18	9	30	conical	vertical	W wall
Mean	9.5	26.2			

Perhaps such small structures served functions related to community life. This structure was located somewhat distant from the central area of the community, suggesting an exclusionary activity. Perhaps it functioned as a menstrual hut, although this can not be supported by any direct evidence. A circular post structure at the Hatchery West site has been interpreted as a possible menstrual hut (Binford et al. 1970:41). Small structures such as these may have served alternatively as sweat lodges, drying sheds, or possibly as specialized ceremonial dwellings. For example, Lowie (1983:292) mentions in reference to the Crow the use of miniature sweat lodges near garden beds. Such structures were viewed as ceremonial sweat lodges for tobacco; the internal fire was intended to encourage the growth of tobacco seedlings in nearby garden beds.

Miscellaneous Features

A number of features and postmolds were not affiliated with the four occupation areas discussed above. These features fell into three general categories, including those situated between two occupation areas, such as Features 18, 19, 79, 142, 143, 144, and 162; those located east or south of the main occupation areas, forming no recognizable patterns, such as Features 2, 25, 53, 54, 60, 61, 63, 66, 67, 68, 70, 107, 108, 141, and 168; and those features in the small 1981 test units located west of the present right-of-way limits, such as Features 109 to 115 (see Figure 6). A total of 27 pits, 4 historical disturbances, 11 postmolds, and 2 fill areas (Features 2 and 107) were not associated with specific occupation areas.

The features located east of the main occupation area demonstrated how difficult it is to establish precise boundaries for archaeological communities. These features were scattered in isolated locations along the entire ridge east of the main occupation, and their locations could never be predicted. They were presumably related to the main occupation areas, but their occurrence so far away from the main foci of settlement is difficult to explain. The pit shapes, fills, and material contents were in no way unusual or indicative of specialized functions.

A concentration of six postmolds and an unusually shaped feature (Feature 67) was identified over 60 m east of the central occupation area. Feature 67 was a long (3.19 m), narrow (81 cm), oval-shaped, trench-like feature, measuring 82.5 cm in depth. It was flat-bottomed, multizoned, and contained no cultural materials. Small pockets of burning, evidenced by lenses of burned clay and charcoal occurred in the upper zones. The fill was quite compact and clayey. Six postmolds that formed no recognizable pattern were located in the vicinity of Feature 67. The function of Feature 67 is unknown and its association with the six postmolds is problematical. If this was a specialized processing pit or trench, the processed remains either were not redeposited into the pit or were not preserved.

Located ca. 25 m south of the southwestern occupation area was Feature 2. This feature was partially exposed in 1981, but it was not excavated in 1982 because it fell outside of the altered right-of-way limits. It was located just south of pit Features 25, 53, 54, 107, and 108. It was thought that this feature might represent a structure.

The fill area of Feature 2 extended 3.60 m in a northeast-southwest direction, and was maximally 3.20 m wide. Its east-west extent was not determined. The fill was dark, homogeneous, and reminiscent of the dark fills in the keyhole structures. However, this fill occupied too large an area to be a keyhole structure basin and its downslope location in the lowest portion of the swale, dividing two point bar ridges, suggested that it was actually an organically enriched swale or backswamp deposit. The fill area was not probed to determine its depth. Three cultural items were recovered from its surface, including two grog-tempered, cordmarked rims and a chert scraper. These materials had probably washed into this area. No other evidence of cultural occupation, such as burned clay or charcoal, was observed in the fill. Another fill area was later identified several meters north of Feature 2. This area was designated as Feature 107, and it was excavated in 1981. It was oval, measuring 3.18 m in length and 1.60 m in width. The fill extended 14.5 cm in depth, and the profile was basin shaped. No cultural materials were recovered, nor were charcoal or burned clay observed. This feature probably resulted from the same natural depositional processes that produced Feature 2.

Pit Features and Postmolds

Pit Types and Functions

Pits were the most numerous features at the Fish Lake site. A total of 134 pits were exposed, and 130 of these were excavated. Features 112 to 115 were identified and mapped during 1981, but due to the 1982 shift in right-of-way these features were not further investigated.

Pits were categorized on the basis of profile shape. Three general profile shape categories were recognized, including basin-shaped, flat-bottomed, and indeterminate. Flat-bottomed pits were the most numerous, constituting 61.5% of the total. Basin-shaped pits comprised 33.1% of the total, while indeterminate pits comprised the remainder. The three general profile shape categories were further divided into several varieties. In the types described below, the first digit refers to profile shape, while the second digit refers to characteristics of both wall shape and pit size. The basin-shaped pits included small (Type 11), large (Type 12), and irregular-shaped (Type 13) varieties. The flat-bottomed pits included shallow, outslanted (Type 21); medium, outslanted (Type 22); deep, outslanted (Type 23); straight-sided (Type 24); shallow, inslanted (Type 25); deep, inslanted (Type 26); and irregular-sided (Type 27) varieties. Indeterminate (Type 31) pits were not subdivided. For basin-shaped pits, the varieties reflected primarily different plan view sizes; for flat-bottomed pits, the varieties reflected differential depths and wall orientations (Figure 20). Tables 6, 7, 8, and 9 list the metric attributes of each pit type as well as the distribution of these types by occupation area (Appendix 1).

Six metric attributes were utilized to measure variation among the pit types and to explore possible differences in pit type distribution between the four major occupation areas. These attributes included maximum length and width of pits in plan view, maximum depth, volume (pit capacity), total weight of cultural materials, and density of material in pit fills. Pit volume was calculated on the basis of mathematical formulae utilized for three dimensional shapes. Such calculations are, of course, only estimates; prehistoric pits rarely conform to ideal shapes, such as perfect basins or cylinders. However, these formulae have been utilized in analyses of other American Bottom sites and, therefore, they have comparative significance (Fortier et al. 1982; McElrath and Fortier 1981).

Pit capacity was expressed in cubic decimeters (dm3). For example, the mean capacity of pits at the Fish Lake site was 278 dm3. In contrast, the mean capacity of 161 Late Woodland pits from the Mund site was 389.7 dm3 (Figure 21). Pit fill density was simply the total weight of debris divided by the pit volume. Density figures represent a general quantitative measure of the intensity of occupation. For example, the mean density for Fish Lake site pits was 5.12 g/dm3. Late Woodland Mund phase pits at the Mund site, however, produced a density figure of 9.49 g/dm3 (Fortier et al. 1982:155).

The formulae utilized to calculate pit volumes are shown in Figure 22. To calculate the area of the surface, the maximum length and width radii were averaged; this figure was then squared and multiplied by π. Estimating the basal area required additional computations. The basal length measurement was derived from the profile, and the basal width radius was assumed to be proportional to the surface width radius. For example, if the maximum surface length was 50 cm and the maximum surface width (taken at a right angle from the maximum length) was 25 cm, and the visible width of the base (seen in profile) was 20 cm, then the basal width was estimated to be 10 cm. For computational purposes, the average basal width, therefore, would be 15 cm, a number which was squared and multiplied by π, giving the area of the base.

No attempt has been made to assign functional categories to specific pit profile types. Theoretically, the function of an individual pit could be determined from its overall size, profile shape, texture, color, fill mottling characteristics, number and thicknesses of fill episodes, material contents, and plant and animal remains. In reality, however, a pit's function was usually not obvious. The difference between a shallow flat-bottomed pit and a shallow basin-shaped pit, for example, may be the product of idiosyncratic rather than functional behavior.

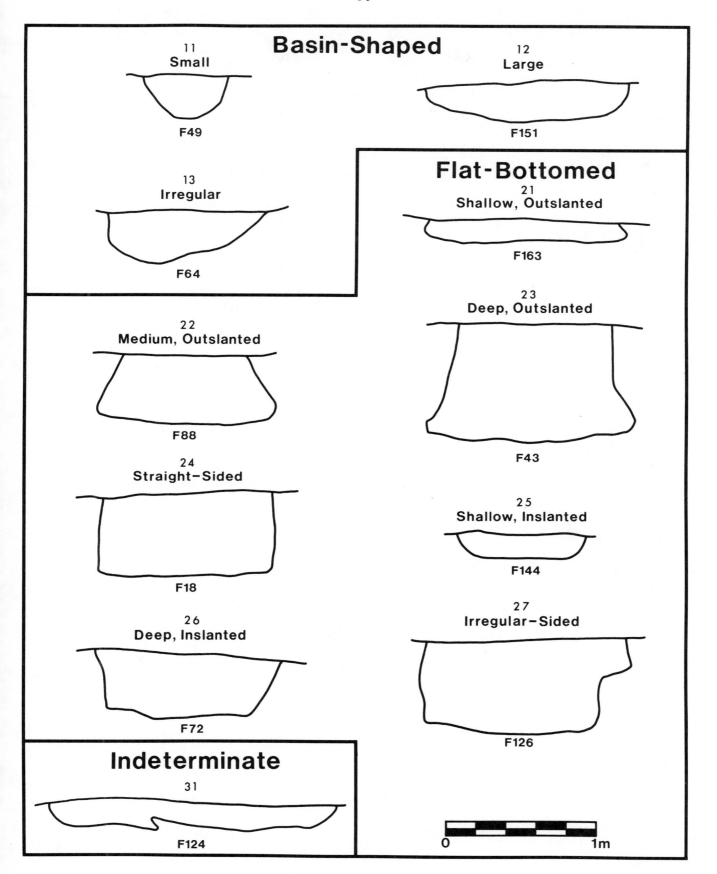

Figure 20. Pit Morphological Types

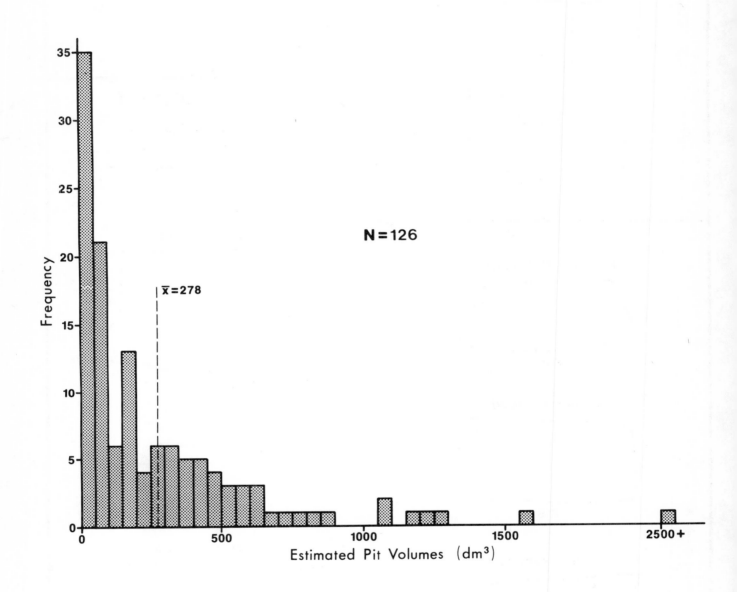

Figure 21.   Frequency Distribution of Pit Volumes

Portion of a cone

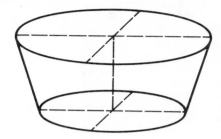

$$V = \frac{h}{2}(a_1 + a_2)$$

a_1 = area of base (πr^2)
a_2 = area of surface (πr^2)
h = height (depth)

Circular or eliptical basin

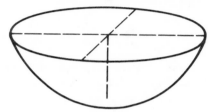

$$V = .16\pi h(3ab + h^2)$$

a = maximum length of surface radius
b = maximum width of surface radius
h = height (depth)

Cylinder

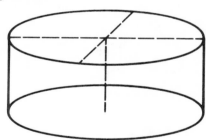

$$V = \pi r^2 h$$

r = surface radius
h = height (depth)

Compound pit

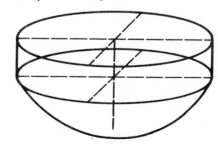

**V = volume of cylinder
plus volume of basin**

Figure 22. Pit Volume Formulae

Table 6. Pit Type Attributes

Type*	Mean Length (cm)	Mean Width (cm)	Mean Depth (cm)	Mean Vol. (dm3)	Mean Material Wt(g)	Mean Material Density (g/dm3)
11	46.44	41.06	13.89	14.26	12.72	0.69
12	101.26	91.47	14.00	60.14	360.20	6.36
13	104.29	82.71	18.86	83.86	226.46	3.83
21	99.17	91.83	25.83	191.78	1636.10	7.62
22	93.14	84.14	50.77	375.20	2133.57	6.29
23	127.75	122.75	88.75	1258.09	4401.50	4.07
24	112.82	99.18	40.47	408.08	2088.56	5.02
25	97.75	82.17	21.42	102.21	1122.99	6.58
26	104.75	91.25	37.00	188.91	1709.75	7.80
27	116.20	106.20	50.40	442.81	1951.76	3.84
31	171.00	119.83	38.43	411.61	866.17	2.73

*see Figure 20

Table 7. Comparison of Pit Attributes by Occupation Area

Occupation Area	Mean Length (cm)	Mean Width (cm)	Mean Depth (cm)	Mean Vol. (dm3)	Mean Material Wt(g)	Mean Material Density (g/dm3)
1	86.08	79.45	48.36	437.62	1372.13	2.69
2	96.50	85.48	28.88	215.59	1527.07	4.52
3	112.64	105.12	25.54	204.41	2070.41	10.73
4	120.90	109.60	24.10	238.66	658.89	3.14
Miscellaneous Features	88.26	66.52	29.61	192.90	673.13	3.04
Total Mean	97.76	87.22	33.64	277.49	1400.65	5.12

Table 8. Pit Type Frequency Distribution by Occupation Area

Type	Occupation Areas 1	2	3	4	Misc. Features	Total
11	8	1	1	0	7	17
12	0	3	11	1	4	19
13	0	1	3	1	2	7
21	3	3	4	2	0	12
22	11	4	3	0	4	22
23	7	0	1	0	0	8
24	3	8	1	3	2	17
25	2	4	3	2	1	12
26	1	0	1	1	1	4
27	2	0	2	0	1	5
31	2	1	3	0	1	7
Total	39	25	33	10	23	130*

* Features 112-115 were not excavated and do not
  appear in this table.

Table 9. Distribution of Feature Attributes by Occupation Area

Occupation Area 1

Feature	Depth (cm)	Length (cm)	Width (cm)	Volume (dm3)	Wt(g) of Material	Density (g/dm3)	Pit Type
3	69	80	70	362.07	2173.7	6.0	22
4	31	57	52	87.55	281.7	3.2	21
5	47	60	56	147.36	40.4	0.3	22
6	71	85	82	562.85	2430.7	4.3	22
7	8	51	48	7.60	0.0	0.0	11
11	84	99	90	761.32	6495.6	8.5	23
14	9	45	44	7.05	0.0	0.0	11
15	11	34	32	9.69	0.0	0.0	11
16	5	30	28	1.64	0.0	0.0	11
17	9	32	28	3.39	1.0	0.3	11
22	30	72	72	156.42	56.5	0.4	21
23	54	106	92	450.39	68.8	0.1	22
26	46	124	117	553.37	1507.2	2.7	22
27	47	112	90	376.37	3321.5	8.8	24
28	73	128	126	1064.55	1380.9	1.3	23
29	16	42	38	11.62	0.0	0.0	11
30	20	54	53	25.46	9.9	0.4	11
33	18	64	47	42.36	262.9	6.2	30
35	55	85	83	343.07	3314.1	9.7	22
37	92	144	143	1577.87	1757.1	1.1	23
42	24	90	80	99.75	52.7	0.5	25
43	81	104	102	834.04	4345.0	5.2	23
44	41	103	102	386.28	1541.5	4.0	27
48	62	116	114	643.66	528.5	0.8	22
49	30	57	54	48.13	97.1	2.0	11
56	32	71	64	115.30	92.6	0.8	21
57	81	143	137	1246.27	610.7	0.5	24
126	65	130	95	511.58	1793.4	3.5	27
132	49	70	60	162.51	1028.5	6.3	22
133	19	71	55	59.20	0.0	0.0	24
134	111	106	106	1170.27	5921.3	5.0	23
135	34	58	53	65.78	0.0	0.0	26
137	89	108	90	684.75	1279.4	1.9	23
138	49	81	75	290.58	800.9	2.7	22
139	60	87	86	450.89	1268.7	2.8	22
155	54	102	101	436.71	523.2	1.2	22
164	114	173	173	2678.35	3192.6	1.2	23
166	41	97	81	193.38	2058.0	10.6	25
169	55	-	-	-	5277.1	-	30

Table 9. Continued

Occupation Area 2

Feature	Depth (cm)	Length (cm)	Width (cm)	Volume (dm3)	Wt(g) of Material	Density (g/dm3)	Pit Type
13	21	83	75	53.65	64.3	1.2	24
24	15	62	34	13.54	0.0	0.0	11
74	42	91	80	241.02	203.5	0.8	24
80	40	128	122	435.28	868.5	2.0	24
82	33	111	110	329.45	10352.0	31.4	21
83	12	83	80	62.57	0.0	0.0	24
85	10	106	72	29.12	13.5	0.5	25
86	41	86	82	254.22	212.6	0.8	22
87	20	117	102	93.50	83.5	0.9	25
88	49	81	80	361.60	2564.7	7.1	22
89	21	66	63	71.29	675.5	9.5	21
90	15	68	54	22.34	200.2	9.0	25
91	20	98	88	119.40	257.3	2.1	24
92	27	-	112	-	91.5	-	30
93	63	143	124	881.40	9031.1	10.2	24
94	50	91	77	304.58	887.1	2.9	22
95	17	87	76	69.15	384.4	5.5	12
96	15	92	72	38.95	56.1	1.4	12
97	14	80	78	61.22	118.0	1.9	25
98	66	128	106	709.23	9910.9	14.0	24
99	7	99	92	24.08	1.3	0.1	13
100	32	117	116	340.93	241.9	0.7	21
101	10	88	60	20.30	35.8	1.8	12
102	36	94	80	204.29	56.1	0.3	22
104	46	117	102	432.97	1866.9	4.3	24

Table 9. Continued

Occupation Area 3

Feature	Depth (cm)	Length (cm)	Width (cm)	Volume (dm3)	Wt(g) of Material	Density (g/dm3)	Pit Type
20	6	111	106	26.58	205.2	7.7	12
21	16	124	120	91.33	538.6	5.9	12
36	60	116	94	627.61	7346.1	11.7	22
38	53	93	88	386.81	7865.1	20.3	22
39	17	84	76	43.15	93.8	2.2	11
40	19	93	93	65.05	730.3	11.2	12
41	16	102	96	60.80	619.3	10.2	25
58	25	88	78	184.03	3465.6	18.8	22
71	51	–	238	–	145.1	–	30
72	50	118	78	304.84	7558.7	24.8	25
105	66	160	152	1293.59	10840.1	8.4	23
106	27	91	90	173.59	4968.7	28.6	24
121	38	140	134	444.38	599.2	1.3	27
122	14	110	98	57.97	352.7	6.1	12
123	54	128	120	606.20	5463.2	9.0	27
124	22	130	109	122.23	235.6	1.9	30
125	13	86	80	34.64	1212.3	35.0	12
127	14	–	132	–	41.0	–	30
128	22	95	86	72.73	1028.9	14.1	21
129	13	83	78	32.66	22.1	0.7	12
130	24	126	122	289.68	1322.9	4.6	21
131	17	140	129	117.59	833.1	7.1	13
145	12	133	110	66.70	2.3	0.1	12
146	13	122	104	62.95	1835.0	29.1	12
147	14	86	63	29.82	296.1	9.9	13
148	29	106	79	208.95	4173.4	20.0	21
149	32	133	110	191.94	3256.0	17.0	26
150	16	113	108	131.00	25.4	0.2	12
151	29	133	122	188.65	1030.4	5.5	12
152	22	126	103	177.07	1821.0	10.3	25
153	13	100	60	30.49	189.0	6.2	13
154	10	100	98	37.25	164.0	4.4	12
163	16	122	115	176.37	43.3	0.2	21

Table 9.   Continued

Occupation Area 4

Feature	Depth (cm)	Length (cm)	Width (cm)	Volume (dm3)	Wt(g) of Material	Density (g/dm3)	Pit Type
118	20	110	105	175.62	836.5	4.8	24
119	46	130	112	299.83	2258.9	7.5	26
120	35	134	123	453.67	800.0	1.8	24
156	21	135	123	285.17	298.5	0.1	21
157	17	99	88	95.87	927.0	9.7	25
158	10	90	84	47.86	3.8	0.1	25
159	10	120	109	86.88	20.8	0.2	12
160	19	112	100	167.58	1066.0	6.4	21
161	37	146	128	545.15	302.8	0.5	24
167	26	133	124	229.01	74.6	0.3	13

Miscellaneous Features

Feature	Depth (cm)	Length (cm)	Width (cm)	Volume (dm3)	Wt(g) of Material	Density (g/dm3)	Pit Type
18	59	117	76	431.30	2372.4	5.5	24
19	19	68	60	61.09	189.6	3.1	13
25	11	56	44	10.83	0.5	0.1	11
53	9	33	25	3.15	0.0	0.0	11
54	10	75	75	21.59	0.0	0.0	12
60	49	102	94	467.82	1828.4	3.9	22
61	17	41	40	12.91	3.8	0.3	11
63	14	37	35	8.17	0.0	0.0	11
64	36	104	51	94.93	1.5	0.1	13
65	8	35	31	3.51	22.9	6.5	11
66	53	123	105	540.70	90.4	0.2	24
67	82	319	81	1070.23	10.0	0.1	30
68	9	66	62	23.30	0.0	0.0	11
70	59	108	88	595.91	1090.9	1.8	22
75	16	40	40	11.65	0.0	0.0	11
79	41	92	83	300.63	5271.0	17.5	22
108	14	92	78	39.05	0.0	0.0	12
141	54	80	80	265.60	361.5	1.4	27
142	17	89	80	47.85	171.4	3.6	12
143	38	102	71	163.52	2666.2	16.3	22
144	18	80	70	40.72	20.2	0.5	25
162	12	73	71	24.19	57.1	2.4	12
168	36	98	90	198.10	1324.1	6.7	26

Yet, there were probably functional differences between the deep, flat-bottomed pits, and the large basin-shaped pits at this site. Both pit types no doubt served as primary food processing and cooking facilities but differed in terms of heating techniques. The deep, flat-bottomed pits contained a slightly higher percentage of limestone in their fills than the basin-shaped pits. Of the 24 pits containing 1000 g or more of limestone, only two were basin-shaped. The remainder were all deep, flat-bottomed pits. A similar close association between limestone and deep, flat-bottomed pits was also observed at the Mund phase occupation at the Mund site (Fortier et al. 1982:124-128). It was believed that heated limestone provided the primary heat for an indirect steam cooking process at the Mund site. A similar phenomenon was noted at the Hatchery West site where such features were referred to as "earth ovens" (Binford et al. 1970). Deep, flat-bottomed pits at the Fish Lake site were probably used in the same way.

It is interesting that limestone lenses were not nearly as common in pits at the Fish Lake site as they were at the Mund site or, apparently, at the Hatchery West site. More efficient use of limestone was probably made at the Fish Lake site, since the site was located in the floodplain far from the limestone bluffs. Limestone may have been repeatedly used for lining pits at the Fish Lake site. Archaeologically this resulted in two phenomena. The first was the occurrence of ash lenses composed of completely or almost completely disintegrated limestone. Examples of such lenses occurred in Feature 43 in Occupation Area 1 and Feature 72 in Occupation Area 3. The second phenomenon involved the general dispersal of limestone through several fill episodes and the absence of distinct limestone linings or prepared hearths at the bases of fill zones.

It should be added that all of the deep, flat-bottomed pits were also used as refuse containers. In fact, the thicknesses of fill zones were the direct result of refuse accumulation and were not related to the pits' primary use as earth ovens or cooking facilities. Apparently, a typical pit of this type was first used as an earth oven. Refuse was subsequently dumped over the actual fire area (or heated rock area). Often the pit was again used as an earth oven or shallow hearth. More refuse was then dumped over the fired zones. Most of the floral and faunal remains retrieved from the pits occurred in the refuse deposits and not in the fired zones. Sometimes sterile caps were intentionally deposited over fire zones or refuse layers. Finally, many of the deep pits may have served as storage containers, but direct evidence for this is lacking. Feature 164, a very large pit, was surprising since it lacked thick refuse-laden zones, despite its great depth, large volume, and location near the structures. This feature may have been a large, communal storage unit in addition to its obvious function as a refuse facility. The nature of the materials stored is unknown. Presumably they were removed prior to pit use as a refuse facility.

The small and shallow basin-shaped pits and probably the shallow, flat-bottomed pits served as open, sunken hearths. Presumably, these were cooking facilities. They contained as a group fewer cultural materials than other types of pits; therefore, they did not function as refuse facilities. They were rarely multizoned and they appeared to represent a single episode of use. They generally lacked limestone concentrations, although occasional limestone fragments did occur in their fills. Food appears to have been cooked or prepared over open fires. Bones tended to be more calcined in these pits than they were in the deep earth ovens (Plate 6).

A few pits with square or rectangular plan shapes were identified at this site, including Features 18, 72, 82, 108, 130, 131, and 164. All of these pits, except for Features 108 and 131, were flat-bottomed. Feature 108 contained no cultural materials, but the remaining pits produced relatively high percentages of limestone by weight and a variety of other cultural materials. For example, Features 18, 72, and 82 yielded 10 nonchert tools, comprising ca. 18% of the total number of nonchert tools from the site. A unique turtle effigy pipe fragment was recovered from Feature 18. Such features may have been important activity foci within occupation areas. The rectangular or square plan shape of these features is puzzling and does not seem related to pit function. Such pits tended to occur on the edges of occupation areas or between occupation areas. Thus, they may have marked central places between occupation or main activity areas.

Pit Type Distribution

It was suggested previously that two primary functional pit types occurred at the Fish Lake site: the earth oven and the shallow hearth. The distributions of these general pit types were not uniform. The deep, often multizoned, earth ovens occurred almost exclusively in Occupation Area 1, while the shallow hearths occurred predominantly in Occupation Areas 2, 3, and 4 (Figure 23). Certain pit profile shape categories related to these functional types appear to have had relatively exclusive distributions. For example, 73% of the large, basin-shaped pits (Type 12) were found in Occupation Area 3. Nearly 62% of the medium-sized, outslanting flat-bottomed pits (Type 22) occurred in the same area. In addition, 73% of the straight-sided, flat-bottomed pits (Type 23) were found in Occupation Areas 2 and 4. Perhaps the most obvious distribution was the high percentage (70%) of earth ovens in Occupation Area 1 and the high percentage (73%) of large, basin-shaped hearths in Occupation Area 3. The highest percentage of reutilized pits also occurred in Occupation Area 1 (Figure 24).

Various hypotheses can be proposed for the differential pattern of pit type distributions observed at this site. The occurrence of deep, flat-bottomed pits in Occupation Area 1 and shallow, basin-shaped pits in the southern occupation areas may reflect two distinct activity foci. For example, indirect processing or cooking techniques perhaps were undertaken primarily within Occupation Area 1 and shallow, open hearth processing and cooking took place in Occupation Areas 2, 3, and 4. This

Plate 6. Flat-bottomed Pits: upper left, shallow, outslanted (Type 21); upper right, straight-sided (Type 24); lower left and right, deep outslanted (Type 23)

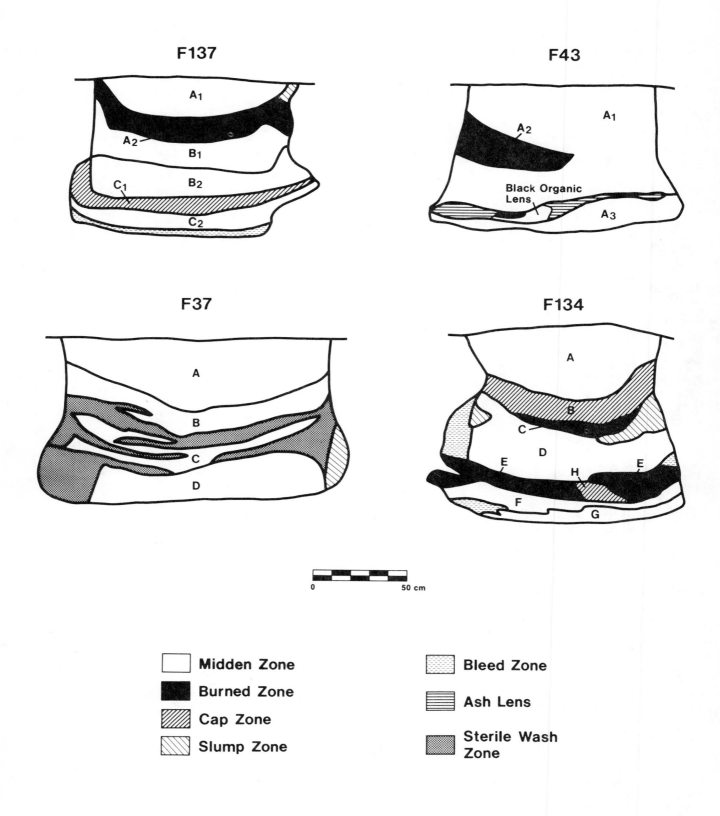

Figure 23. Multizonal Pits in Occupation Area 1

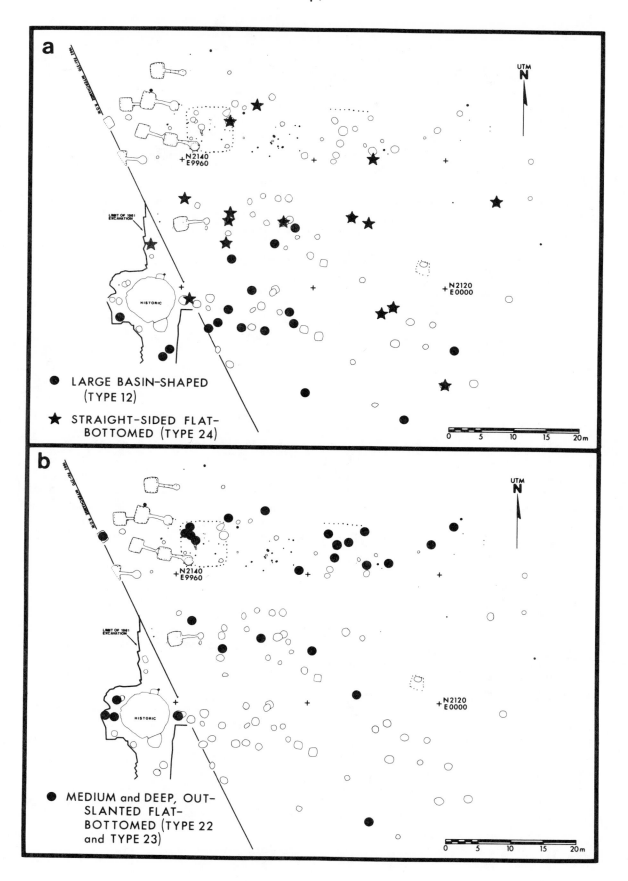

Figure 24. Distribution of Selected Pit Morphological Types

division may reflect differences in soil texture, i.e., the occurrence of dense clays in the north and of sandy soils in the south. Perhaps deep pits were placed intentionally in the dense clays of the ridge apex because clay-walled pits were more stable, capable of withstanding long use.

A second explanation for differential pit distribution may be related to distinct occupational episodes at the site. Perhaps there were seasonal differences, with the shallow, basin-shaped hearths being utilized during particular seasons and the deep pits being used continuously. Unfortunately, analysis of pit contents failed to reveal definite evidence for specific seasons of use for any of the pits.

A third hypothesis for this uneven distribution is that deep pits occurred in Occupation Area 1 because it was the primary living area and the most important focus of activity at the site. The fact that at least two separate occupational episodes occurred in this area indicated that it was viewed by the Late Woodland inhabitants as the primary focus of the community. It was not possible, however, to associate specific fill episodes in pits with particular structures or particular occupational episodes. Cultural materials were simply too uniform from feature to feature to establish such associations.

One of the chief difficulties in recognizing the spatial distribution of pits at this site lay in the fact that the material assemblage did not vary much among the pit type categories. While limestone was associated almost exclusively with the deep earth ovens, other materials did not have such exclusive distributions. Curiously, the highest density of materials occurred in the shallow pits of Occupation Area 3. This suggests that activities undertaken in Occupation Area 3 were just as intense and perhaps as diverse as those undertaken in Occupation Area 1, which encompassed many structures and deep pits.

One drawback in this analysis is that Occupation Areas 1 and 3 were perhaps only incompletely defined. It is not known whether structures also existed just west of Occupation Area 3 outside of the present right-of-way limits. It is also possible that the northeast-southwest distribution of keyhole structures visible in Occupation Area 1, and partially exposed in Occupation Area 2, extended further south. If so, then the occupation areas and areas of pit concentration defined by the excavations might be related to other, as yet unidentified structure clusters. Hence, final interpretations of community differentiation must await additional exposure of the western community limits. Yet, the Fish Lake site investigations have exposed a large enough area to suggest that activity areas were a definite feature of Late Woodland communities. While it is not possible to explain how these various activity areas related to one another in time and function, their presence provides a useful model for understanding the size and organization of Late Woodland communities in the American Bottom.

Isolated Postmolds

In addition to the postmolds associated with structures, the post row feature (Feature 136), and the postmold cluster in Occupation Area 1, a number of isolated postmolds were found scattered over the entire site area. A total of 35 isolated postmolds were identified, including 17 in Occupation Area 1, 3 in Occupation Area 2, 3 in Occupation Area 3, and 12 postmolds that did not occur in any of the designated occupation areas. Nine of these postmolds had been assigned as pit features in 1981, but were redesignated as postmolds during subsequent laboratory analysis. Attributes for these postmolds are presented in Table 10.

The function of these isolated posts is problematical. There was great variation in the size and shape of postmolds, but little evidence to suggest their function. Approximately 54% of the postmolds exhibited some evidence of burning in the form of charcoal flecking or burned clay in their fills. Some postmolds were located near or on the edges of pits, and these were probably associated with food processing or preparation activities undertaken in connection with pits. At least two postmolds (Feature 59 and Postmold 57) and possibly Features 8 and 12, in Occupation Area 1, may have served as markers. These postmolds were large, deep, and positioned near structures. The Feature 12 postmold, for example, was 60 cm deep.

An alternative interpretation for these postmolds, as suggested in the ethnographic literature, is that they represented "wooden mills" instead of posts. The following account of wooden mills pertains to the Skidi Pawnee.

> Just north of the area occupied by the sweat-lodge was reserved a space for the corn mill, which may be regarded as a permanent fixture . . ., and which consisted of a hackberry log firmly implanted in the ground and hollowed in its upper half. The corn was crushed by means of a long pestle of the same material . . . (Dorsey 1904:XVI)

If mill posts were placed firmly in the ground, they would have left postmold impressions indistinguishable from those of any other posts. It is conceivable that the lack of grinding tools at the Fish Lake site may stem from the use of nonpreservable wooden seed mills.

Keyhole Structure Characteristics and Functions

The main features of the Fish Lake site keyhole structures included subterranean basins; basin wall posts; narrow and shallow ramp extensions; and shallow, basin-shaped ramp pits containing little or no

Table 10. Isolated Postmold Attributes

PM	Occupation Area	Dia. (cm)	Depth (cm)	Shape	Orientation	Burning
1	1	14	12.0	round	vertical	no
2	1	14	23.0	flat	vertical	yes
3	1	18	24.0	flat	vertical	no
4	1	20	29.0	irregular	vertical	no
5	2	18	1.0	flat	vertical	yes
6	2	11	5.0	round	vertical	yes
7	3	12	7.0	round	vertical	no
8	ind	22	34.0	round	vertical	yes
9	1	12	16.0	irregular	vertical	yes
10	3	14	24.0	irregular	vertical	no
24	2	8	3.0	round	vertical	no
25	ind	16	16.5	round	vertical	yes
26	ind	19	16.0	round	slanted	yes
27	1	6	18.0	conical	vertical	no
28	ind	11	3.0	round	vertical	no
29	ind	20	19.5	round	vertical	no
30	ind	20	25.0	flat	vertical	no
31	ind	10	5.0	conical	vertical	no
32	ind	21	21.0	round	vertical	no
33	ind	7	4.5	round	vertical	no
34	ind	29	13.0	round	vertical	no
38	1	10	9.0	round	vertical	yes
39	1	10	22.0	round	vertical	yes
40	1	10	5.0	round	vertical	yes
41	1	12	10.0	round	vertical	yes
57	1	34	18.0	round	vertical	yes
8*	1	24	13.0	irregular	slanted	no
10*	1	26	38.0	irregular	slanted	no
12*	1	34	60.0	conical	vertical	yes
31*	1	26	22.5	round	vertical	yes
59*	1	47	50.0	round	vertical	yes
69*	ind	30	14.0	round	vertical	yes
76*	3	26	12.0	round	vertical	yes
84*	ind	31	28.0	round	vertical	yes

* These are feature numbers of pits that were redesignated as postmolds during analysis.

cultural materials. The structures lacked internal hearths and well-defined floors. Some of these structures had been destroyed by fire; others had been simply abandoned (Plate 7).

The term "keyhole structure" was borrowed from Binford et al. (1970) who, at the Hatchery West site, first recognized the occurrence of such structures in Illinois. Recently, three additional midwestern keyhole structures have been identified at the Daugherty-Monroe site in western Indiana (Pace and Apfelstadt 1978:56). Similar structures have been identified by Dragoo (1955) and others in western Pennsylvania and described as "ping-pong paddle" or "turtle" structures (Smith 1974, 1976). The keyhole structures identified to date in Indiana, Illinois, and Pennsylvania have all been associated with the Late Woodland period.

The keyhole structures at the Fish Lake site also bore a striking resemblance to the Basketmaker III and Pueblo I phase pithouses of the American Southwest (Bullard 1962). The subterranean basins, passage entrances, and so-called ventilator shafts of those pithouses are said to have originated in southeastern Arizona and spread northward at around 700 A.C.

There were seven keyhole structures at the Fish Lake site. Four were completely excavated; the remainder were missing various portions of their structural anatomy. Missing portions included ramp extensions and ramp pits in Features 116 and 117 and part of a basin in Feature 165. Tables 11 and 12 present attributes of the Fish Lake site keyhole structures and their posts.

Two orientations were calculated for keyhole structures at the Fish Lake site. Orientations are presented as azimuth degrees read clockwise from grid north. One orientation was along the long axis of the ramp extension. All of the ramp extensions were oriented to the east with the average orientation ranging between 84 degrees and 109 degrees. The second orientation involved the direction of the basin with regard to the ramp extension. Basins were generally oriented to the northeast if the ramp extended to the southeast, and to the northwest if the ramp pointed to the northeast. Basin orientations varied by 11 degrees; they ranged from 0 degrees to 349 degrees. It is interesting that most of the keyhole ramp extensions in the Midwest were oriented to the east. This may have had cosmological significance (orientation toward the morning star or the rising sun) or may simply have reflected an avoidance of the prevailing westerlies in this area (Figure 25).

The structure basin floor areas ranged in size from 4.08 m2 to 5.69 m2. The mean basin length measurement was 2.31 m; the mean width measurement was 2.06 m. In only one structure (Feature 32) did the maximum basin length exceed the maximum width by more than 25%. Both length and width measurements were taken from fill edge to fill edge when the structures were first defined. The basins generally had curved corners and slightly outslanting or nearly vertical walls. Basin depths varied from 28 cm to 50.5 cm. Very little wall slumping was observed,

Plate 7. Keyhole Structures in Occupation Area 1: upper left, plan views of Features 32, 34, and 116; upper right, excavation of Feature 32; lower left, plan view of Feature 116; lower right, burned floor in Feature 116 basin

Table 11. Attributes of Keyhole Structures

Feature	Total Length (m)	Basin Length (m)	Basin*** Orientation (degrees)	Basin Width (m)	Floor+ Area (m2)	Basin Depth (m)	Basin Volume (m3)	Ramp Length (m)	Ramp*** Orientation (degrees)	Ramp Width (m)	Ramp Depth (m)	Ramp Pit Plan Size (m x m)	Ramp Pit Depth (m)
9	5.47	2.25	349	2.20	4.95	0.505	2.500	2.30	86	0.43	0.18	1.06 0.90	0.23
32	5.78	2.66	13	2.14	5.69	0.400	2.277	2.28	84	0.52	0.20	1.60 1.32	0.30
34	5.45	2.54	0	2.11	5.36	0.400	2.144	2.34	89	0.47	0.24	0.99 0.96	0.16
81	5.38	2.06	11	1.98	4.08	0.390	1.591	1.64	103	0.40	0.16	1.66 1.46**	0.49
116	3.21*	2.14	0	2.00	4.28	0.455	1.947	-	91**	0.38	0.12*	-	-
117	4.46*	2.20	19	1.94	4.27	0.280	1.195	2.26	109	0.40	0.15*	-	-
165	3.89*	2.36	4**	-	-	0.380	-	1.82	94	0.40	0.19	1.32 1.30	0.18

* partial measurement
** estimated measurement
*** orientations represent azimuths - read clockwise from grid UTM north
+ floor area is calculated as the product of the basin length and width. A slightly smaller floor area figure is obtained by calculating only the area within the wall posts.

Table 12. Attributes of Keyhole Structure Posts

Structural Features	Total N Basin Posts	Mean Interval Between Posts (cm)	Mean Diameter of Wall Posts (cm)	Mean Depth of Wall Posts (cm)	Ramp-Entry Gap in Post Wall (cm)	Total N External Posts	Mean Diameter of External Posts (cm)	Mean Depth of External Posts (cm)	Total N Interior Ramp Posts	Mean Diameter of Ramp Posts (cm)	Mean Depth of Ramp Posts (cm)
9	25	30.00	8.76	10.36	53.00	3	11.00	8.67	0	-	-
32	18	44.59	10.00	34.18	52.00	1	7.00	17.50	1	7.00	22.50
34	20	34.79	9.97	30.17	69.00	11	7.36	9.82	8	7.94	19.62
81	20	31.63	7.85	17.60	52.00	0	-	-	4	8.25	14.00
116	19	34.44	7.84	13.74	52.00	0	-	-	0	-	-
117	15	35.00**	9.67	12.00	-	0	-	-	0	-	-
165	9*	30.86	9.89	11.89	70.00						

* this includes only the east wall and a portion of the north wall
** this interval is based on only 13 posts which form the southeast, south, and west walls

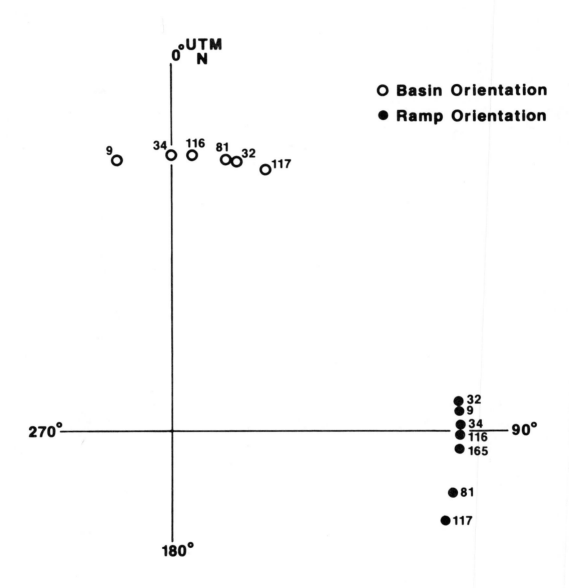

Figure 25. Orientations of Keyhole Structure Ramps and Basins

probably because the basins were excavated in dense clay. Finally, it can be noted that the maximum basin length was, except in two structures (Features 9 and 117), greater than the length of the ramp extension. The ramp extension was measured from the point of intersection with the basin to the point of contact with the ramp pit. The maximum length of the basin was oriented roughly perpendicular to the ramp extension. Keyhole structures at the nearby Range site (Kelly 1982:8-10) were similarly shaped. Keyhole structures in Pennsylvania, however, tended to have basins that were oriented parallel to the ramp extension (Smith 1976:4).

An interesting aspect of keyhole structure variation at the Fish Lake site related to the organization of wall postmolds within basins. Three general patterns of postmold organization were recognized. One consisted of wall postmolds that were directly opposed, i.e., one postmold could be matched with an opposing postmold. This wall pattern was symmetrical, and postmold spacing was regular. Features 32 and 116 were examples of this pattern.

The second pattern was similar to the first, except for the occurrence of two and four corner postmolds, as exemplified in Features 81 and 34, respectively. In Feature 81 the two corner postmolds were set inside the basin. The four corner postmolds in Feature 34 occurred above the basin, just outside the wall line. Feature 34 also exhibited a double set of postmolds in the northern and western walls. These postmolds, which lay above the basin, appeared to be paired with an internal basin postmold and probably provided additional wall support.

The third pattern involved wall postmolds that were not opposed and were spaced at irregular intervals. Structures exhibiting this pattern included Features 9, 117 and, possibly, 165, although in the last structure not enough of the floor area was exposed to determine the complete post pattern.

The wall postmold patterns suggested a wigwam type of construction. Internal postmolds were absent, so it is likely that the wall posts had been bent and lashed at the center of the structure. Feature 9 was the only keyhole structure with a consistent pattern of slanting postmolds, but even in that structure slanting postmolds only occurred along one wall. The structure walls were probably of wickerwork construction as evidenced by the grid-like arrangement of a burned, collapsed wall in Feature 34. No evidences of burned daub or wall plaster were found inside the structures that exhibited burning. Grass or hides probably covered the walls and roof.

The keyhole ramp extensions and ramp pits were unusual. Their function, particularly in relationship to the basins, was debatable. Various functional interpretations have been proposed for these elements as well as for keyhole structures in general. The ramp extensions may have served as covered entryways with the ramp pits functioning either as storage units or as ventilators to keep air flowing through the structure. In such a model the keyhole structure would have functioned as a domicile that was specially adapted for winter conditions (Binford et al. 1970; Dragoo 1955).

A second interpretation, developed by Smith (1976) for the Pennsylvannia keyhole structures, was that the ramp extension functioned as a specialized heat duct for channeling steam heat into the basin from a ramp pit furnace. In Pennsylvania the ramp pits contained piles of limestone. These rocks were presumably heated and water poured over them. The resulting steam would then have passed down the narrow ramp extension, which was covered, into the basin. Keyhole structures, therefore, were viewed as sweathouses, not domiciles (Smith 1976:11-12). Such sweathouses, needing frequent repair, would have been utilized all year round. Smith argued further that the evidence suggested that such structures were not utilized as domiciles since the basins lacked cultural debris, and both internal features and basins were small. Smith cited several ethnographic examples in the Northeast and Southwest where sweathouses had rampways and associated rock pits.

A third interpretation is proposed here for the Fish Lake site structures. Since keyhole structures represent the predominant structure type at this site and since they also were focal elements in community plans at the Range site, it is unlikely that they functioned only as sweathouses. Although keyhole structures were relatively small and contained few cultural materials, they were still large enough to have accommodated several individuals. The absence of cultural materials does not mean that a structure could not have been used for sleeping. Therefore, keyhole structures are here interpretated as domiciles and not as specialized sweat-lodges.

The function of the ramp extensions and ramp pits is more problematical. Rock piles did not occur in the ramps or in the pits at the Fish Lake site. The ramp pits did, however, exhibit evidence of intense burning in the form of charcoal and burned clay. They did not contain cultural materials nor did they contain faunal or floral remains. Thus, they probably did not serve as storage or refuse pits. Unlike the keyhole structures at the Hatchery West site, which apparently contained internal hearths (Binford et al. 1970), the Fish Lake site dwellings lacked evidence for a heat source, except in the ramp pits. In this respect the Fish Lake site keyhole structures resembled those from Pennsylvania. The ramp pits, therefore, were interpreted as fire pits. The ramp extension was regarded as a duct for conducting heat from the heat source to the basin. The narrow Fish Lake keyhole ramps and the presence of posts in the ramps would have effectively blocked access to anyone attempting to utilize these passageways as crawlways. This was not the case at the Hatchery West site where the ramps were twice as wide as the Fish Lake site ramps. At the Hatchery West site the ramps may very well have served as entryways. This seems even more likely since the Hatchery West site keyhole structures lacked ramp pits at the ends of the ramp extensions and contained hearths within the structure basins (Binford et al. 1970).

The Fish Lake site keyhole structures probably served as specially heated domiciles. Heat would have passed into the basins as radiant heat, not as steam. Low, but intense, fires rather than heated rocks may have served as primary sources of heat. Presumably, heat would have been drawn down the ramp extensions into the basins by vents in the basin roof. To prevent smoke from entering the basins, ramp pit coverings may have had small vents. Several of the keyhole structures lacked any evidence of burning in the ramp pits, suggesting that such pits may have been cleaned out periodically, perhaps after every use.

Entrance into the keyhole structures could have been gained through the walls surrounding the basins. Feature 9, for example, contained a gap in the western wall that could have been an entryway. Feature 116 produced a similar gap in the western wall, but in that structure the gap may have resulted from a later feature's intrusion into the wall. The remaining keyhole structures did not exhibit any clear gaps in their walls.

Keyhole structures at the Fish Lake site probably represent winter habitation units. It is significant that the Range site, in addition to producing keyhole structures, produced a number of square, basin-shaped structures that lacked ramp extensions but dated to this same time (John E. Kelly, personal communication). The additions of heat ducts and furnaces for winter use would not have involved major structural modifications of such basin structures.

Historical Features

Six features were designated as historical disturbances: Features 55, 62, 73, 109, 110, and 111. Each feature, except Feature 73, was defined, mapped, and excavated. Only 25% of Feature 73 was excavated due to its large size and obvious recent cultural affiliation. The remaining features were excavated in their entirety. All of the features appeared to be less than 100 years old although diagnostic material was too scarce to indicate a more precise age.

Feature 55 represents a recent post impression with a black, homogeneous sterile fill. This postmold measured 26 cm by 25 cm and was 15.5 cm deep. It was square in plan view and flat-bottomed in profile. Feature 55 was located ca. 2 m east of the eastern wall of structure Feature 52 in Occupation Area 1.

Feature 62 appeared to be a recent tire track depression. It was rectangular in shape, measuring 60 cm by 30 cm, and was only 8 cm in depth. The fill was black and sterile. Feature 62 was located in Block 8 southeast of the main Late Woodland occupation. Such disturbances occurred as a result of tractor tires becoming mired in the soil during plowing and cultivation. Two similar rectangular disturbances were also observed at the nearby Carbon Monoxide site (Fortier 1981b). Such disturbances probably date to the last plowing of the field prior to the archaeological excavations.

Plate 8. Excavation of Historical Feature 73: upper left, plan view; upper right and lower left, limestone concentrations; lower right, mapping the quarter-section profile

Feature 73, in Occupation Area 3, was probably a recent well or cistern. It measured 7.55 m in diameter and extended 4.18 m in depth. In profile it was conical, with a rounded base. Excavation of only a quarter section of the feature produced a large amount of recent limestone and concrete, bones of domesticated animals, heavily corroded iron pieces, fragments of glass, and a small amount of prehistoric material. This well or cistern may date to the original farmstead in this locality. Some of the glass appeared to date to the turn of the century (Plate 8).

Features 109, 110, and 111 were located in Block 11, which was located west of the present right-of-way limits in the vicinity of several modern buildings and junkyard debris. These features represent small, irregular to regular, basin-shaped depressions containing both historic and prehistoric materials. The origin of these depressions is unknown.

CERAMIC ASSEMBLAGE

by Fred A. Finney

Ceramic materials, including vessels, nonvessel items, burned clay, and daub, accounted for nearly one quarter by weight of the materials recovered from Fish Lake site feature contexts. Ceramic vessels were represented by 7638 sherds weighing 40,536 g (Appendix 2). This was the largest material category recovered from the site, with the exception of limestone. The ceramic materials clearly identified the Fish Lake site assemblage as belonging to the Late Woodland Patrick phase. This ceramic analysis describes the vessel forms and attributes, as well as the manufacture, use, and distribution of vessels. This approach follows that previously used for Late Woodland ceramics recovered from the Mund site.

The initial description of the ceramic assemblage involved the tabulation for each feature by count and weight of exterior vessel surface treatments and temper categories. Next, the rim sherds were separated from body sherds.

The rim sherds were designated by rim and feature numbers, e.g., the fourth rim in Feature 165 is referred to as 165-4. Next, the minimum number of vessels in each feature was determined. Within each feature, rims that could be fitted together or related to a common vessel by macroscopic observation were counted as a single vessel. Systematic attempts were made to find rim sherds from the same vessel in different features. If portions of a single vessel were distributed in more than one feature, the rims were counted as a single vessel. During analysis, the search for ceramic fits between features was extended to include body sherds. Vessel numbers corresponded to rim numbers; however, a vessel represented by multiple rims, e.g., 104-3, 104-4, and 104-5, was designated 104-3. Thus, vessels listed under any given feature in

Appendix 2 may skip numbers, e.g., 146-1, 146-3. The Fish Lake vessel assemblage contained 151 distinct Patrick phase vessels.

Four metric and ten nonmetric vessel attributes were recorded. The metric attributes included orifice diameter, percent of orifice present, lip thickness, and rim sherd weight. Generally, the diameter and percent of orifice present could be recorded for vessels having at least 5% of the estimated vessel orifice present. Some vessel orifices were asymmetric, so different rim segments of the same vessel gave different estimated vessel orifice sizes; in these instances, the estimated orifice diameters of the different rim segments were averaged, and the resulting mean diameter was used in analysis. Nonmetric attributes included vessel form, rim form, exterior surface treatment, rim cordmark orientation, cordmark twist, lip form, lip treatment, lip appendages, vessel paste, and vessel temper. These data were coded for computer analysis with SPSS (Nie et al. 1975) subprograms. In addition to ceramic attributes, the vessel number, feature cluster, and feature class (structure or pit) data were also coded for each vessel.

The rim profile illustrations in this report include several descriptive conventions to record various attributes. A key to these conventions is given in Figure 26. Information recorded on the left side of the profile includes the vessel orientation line (marking the vessel interior), vessel number, and orifice diameter and percentage, if known. Dashed lines across the interior or superior lip surface indicate lip impressions. The lines reveal the relative position, depth, length, and angle of these impressions. Solid lines on the exterior lip surface demarcate several treatments; most significant are lip appendages such as lugs, spouts, and zoomorphic effigies. Also shown on the exterior lip surface are rippled lips, resulting from the application of interior lip impressions. The most useful ceramic variables for intra-assemblage comparison were lip impressions. Fifty-four percent of the Fish Lake vessels exhibited lip impressions. Exterior surface treatments are indicated on miniature vessel rim profiles since both cordmarked and plain surfaces were present. All of the remaining specimens, both bowls and jars, were cordmarked.

Vessel Form

Nearly all vessels from the Fish Lake assemblage were classified as jars, bowls, or miniature vessels. Several vessels were represented by rim sherds too small to be reliably placed in these categories. These specimens were included in a jar/bowl category. These morphological distinctions probably reflect gross functional differences, e.g., for cooking, serving, or storage.

Rim Orientation

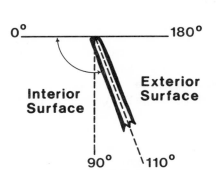

Rim Profile Key

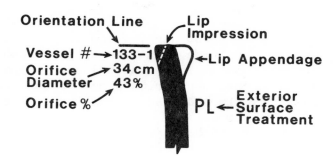

Jar Rim Forms

Inslanting

Vertical

Flaring

Bowl Rim Forms

Vertical

Outslanting

Miniature Vessel Rim Form

Vertical

Lip Forms

Rounded

Squared Interior

Flattened Interior

Squared Vertical

Flattened Exterior

Squared Exterior

Figure 26. Key to Rim Orientations, Rim Profiles, and Lip Forms

Jars

There were 108 jars, which accounted for 72% of the assemblage. Jars had orifice diameters smaller than their maximum vessel diameters (Shepard 1956). The jars included Shepard's (1956) simple-restricted and independent-restricted categories. Since complete vessels were not recovered, rim and base sherds formed the basis for analyzing jar form.

Jar rims formed a continuum, with inslanting rims at one end and flaring rims at the other (Figure 27). Rim orientation was used as the basis for category divisions, since other characteristics of vessel shape, for the most part, were unknown. Many rim sherds had been broken above the shoulder. Rim orientations were measured at the superior end, i.e., the portion of the rim nearest the lip. Three rim categories were established: inslanting, vertical, and flaring. While many rims were distinctly shaped, a number of specimens in the 95 degree to 110 degree orientation range would fall comfortably into either the inslanting or the vertical rim form categories.

A variety of additional jar forms, absent from the Fish Lake assemblage, are known from Patrick phase assemblages. These include "squarish" orifice jars recovered from the Dohack (Ann Stahl, personal communication) and Range (Steven J. Ozuk, personal communication) sites, and jars with peaked or castellated rims, recovered from the Schlemmer site (Thomas Berres, personal communication).

Inslanting Jar Rims

Inslanting rims represent the most constricting rim form category. Such rims had orientations ranging from 105 degrees to 130 degrees (Figure 27). The majority of the specimens appeared to have incurving

Table 13. Rim Form Categories and Vessel Distribution

Vessel Category	Rim Form						Vessel Distribution Per Occupation Area					
	Inslanting	Vertical	Flaring	Outslanting	Ind.	Total	1	2	3	4	N/A	Total
Jars	45	62	1	-	-	108	44	21	19	5	19	108
Bowls	-	20	-	5	-	25	8	4	7	1	5	25
Miniature Vessels	-	9	-	-	-	9	7	1	-	-	1	9
Jar/Bowl Ind.	-	-	-	-	9	9	3	2	2	1	1	9
Total	45	91	1	5	9	151	62	28	28	7	26	151

Ind.-Indeterminate
N/A -Nonoccupational affiliation

necks and shoulders. At least one shoulderless jar (138-1) was reminiscent of similar jars with constricting rims found in the preceding Mund phase (Fortier et al. 1982). Jars with Patrick phase inslanting rims (N=45, 42% of jars) comprised the second most frequently occurring jar category at the Fish Lake site (Table 13; Figures 28 and 29). All rim profiles are presented in Figures 28 and 29 to give a visual impression of the variation that existed in rim orientation, lip form, and lip thickness. The rim orientations had a continuous distribution from 105 degrees to 130 degrees. Most of the inslanting rims exhibited flattened interior lips. Variation in lip thickness within a single rim category is perhaps best observed in Vessels 169-1 and 132-1 (Figure 29).

Vertical Jar Rims

Vertical rims represent the most frequently occurring rim form in the Fish Lake vessel assemblage (N=62, 57% of jars). Vertical rim specimens include examples with distinct incurving necks and pronounced shoulders, as well as a few specimens that apparently lacked these features (Figures 30 and 31). Differences in rim height were pronounced in this category. Vertical rim orientations ranged from 85 degrees to 100 degrees. This range is somewhat arbitrary, particularly for vertical rims with relatively short rim heights.

The vertical rim jars were typical of the Late Woodland (Early Bluff) jar that served as the basic utilitarian vessel at Patrick phase sites in the American Bottom area. They represent part of a developmental sequence from constricting, shoulderless Mund phase jars to vertical, sharply shouldered Emergent Mississippian (Late Bluff) jars. All but two of the vertical rim jars at the Fish Lake site were grog tempered. Distinct red paste jars that were infrequent at the site were restricted to the vertical rim category. This may indicate a common manufacturing origin for these jars, perhaps at a nearby site. Vertical rim jars at the Fish Lake site were invariably associated with squared vertical lips. The contours of the uppermost rim and lip areas of several jars had been altered by the application of lip impressions (e.g., 79-8, 9-1, 134-1).

Flaring Jar Rims

Only one rim (28-1) in the Fish Lake assemblage was placed in the flaring rim category. This rim, which was from Occupation Area 1, was distinguished from the vertical rims on the basis of rim orientation (Figure 32). This vessel did not conform to the general vessel shape configuration at the Fish Lake site. It may simply reflect variation in ceramic manufacture at the site, or it may be indicative of manufacture elsewhere in the American Bottom.

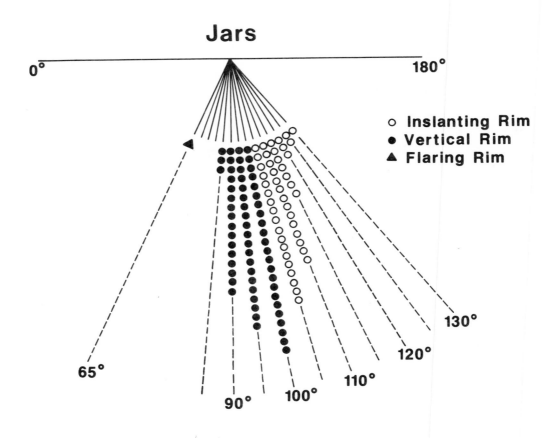

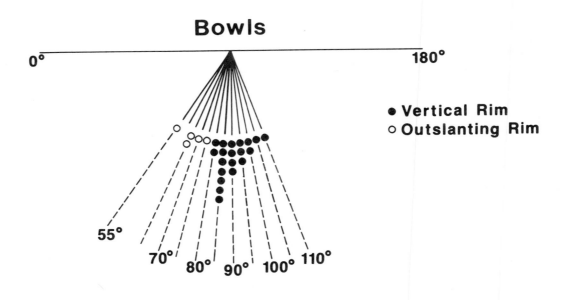

Figure 27. Rim Orientations of Jars and Bowls

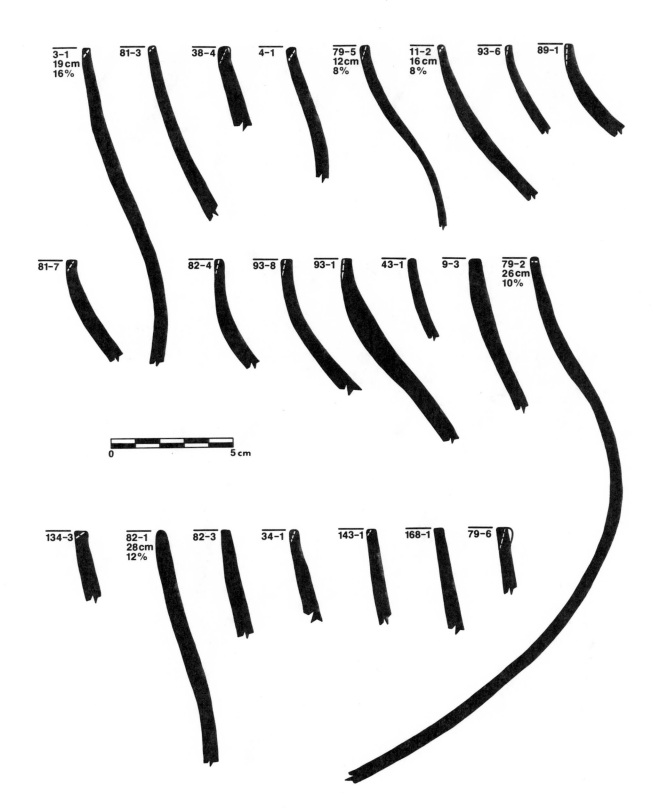

Figure 28. Rim Profiles of Inslanting Jars

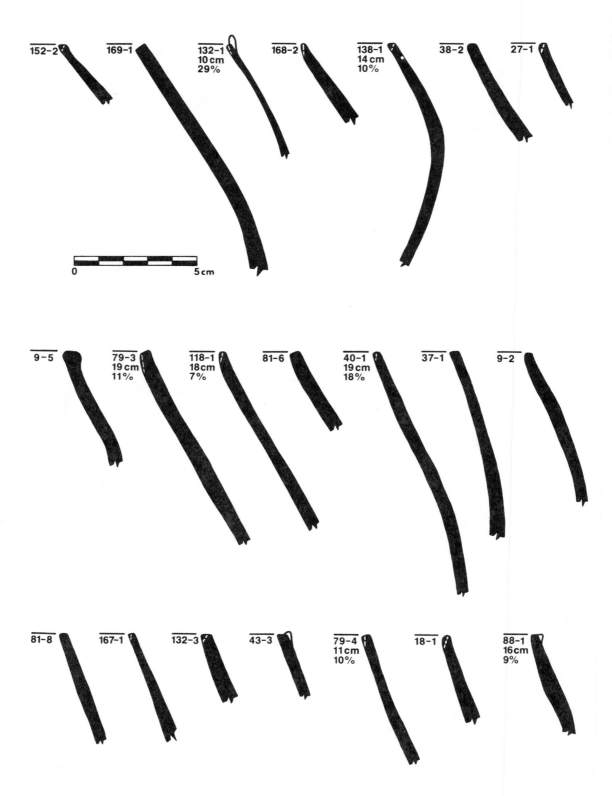

Figure 29. Rim Profiles of Inslanting Jars

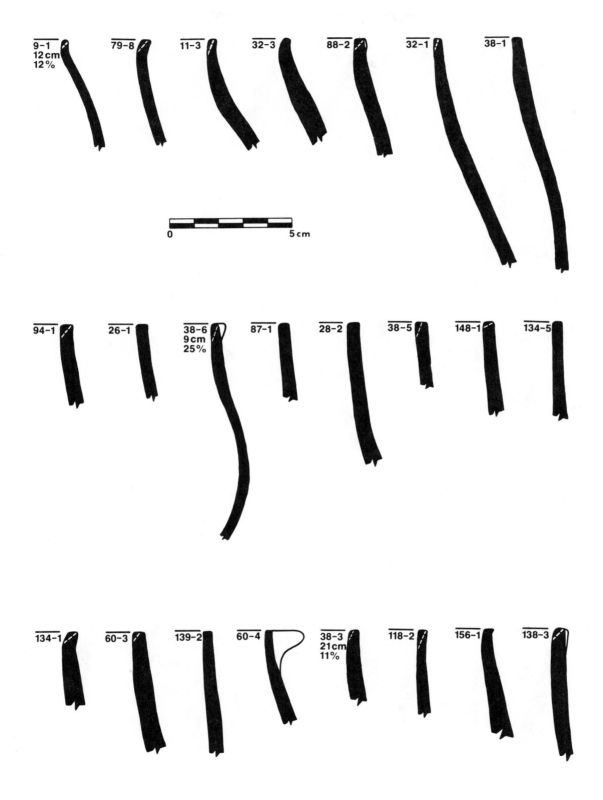

Figure 30. Rim Profiles of Vertical Jars

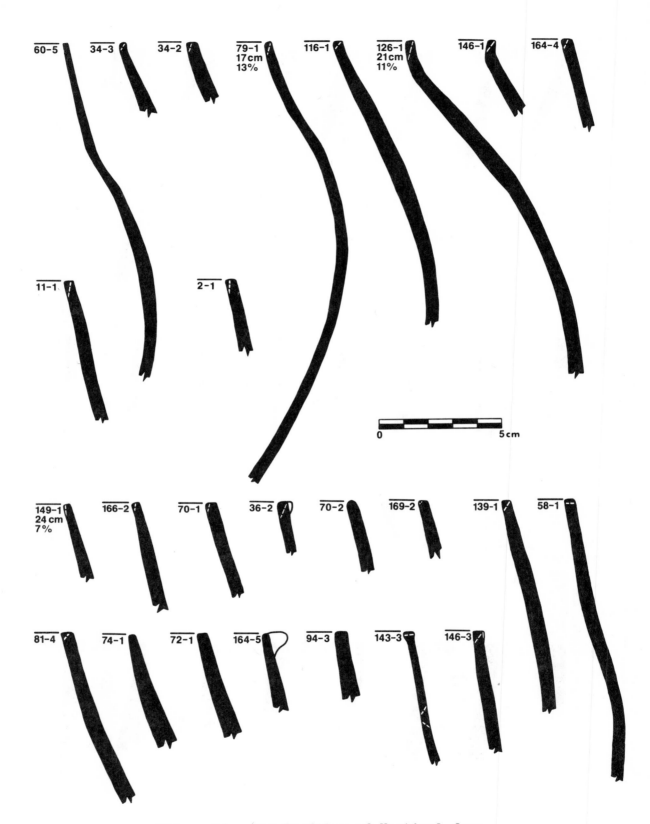

Figure 31. Rim Profiles of Vertical Jars

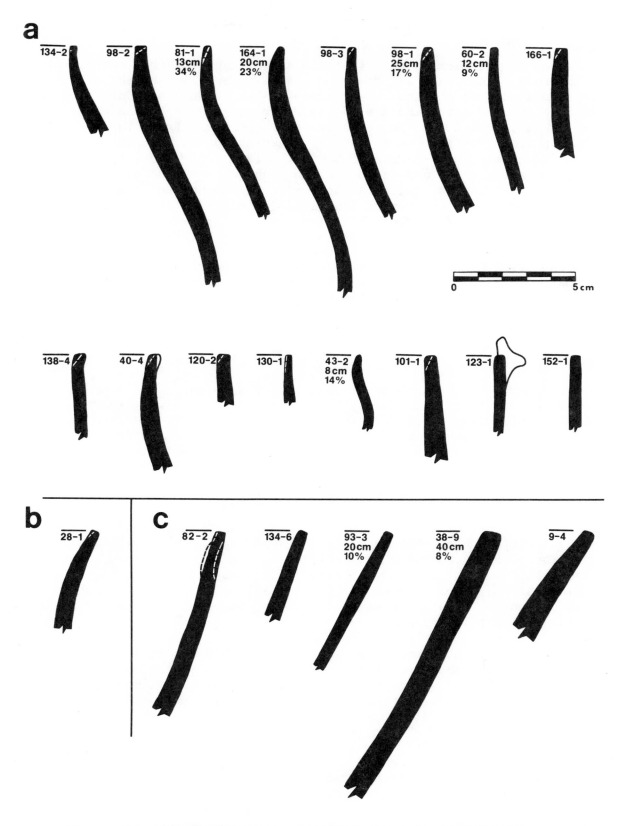

Figure 32. Rim Profiles: a, vertical jars; b, flaring jar; c, outslanting bowls

Jar Bases

None of the jars in the Fish Lake assemblage could be reconstructed completely from the lip to the base. Overall jar shape has been extrapolated from rim and base sherds. The base form of jars was subconoidal. The thicknesses of the recovered base sections ranged from ca. 10 mm to ca. 20 mm, approaching the range known from the preceding Mund phase (Fortier et al. 1982). Base sherds at the Fish Lake site were recognized on the basis of two criteria: they were thicker than body and rim sherds, and there was a noticable curvature on base sherds. These two attributes always co-occurred. All known base fragments were grog tempered. The number of identifiable individual base sections was far less than the number of rims in the assemblage. Jar bases represented ca. 20% of the Fish Lake jars. This phenomenon was also observed at several nearby Late Woodland sites (Fortier et al. 1982). At the Fish Lake site, the missing jar base sections may indicate that primary use (and later breakage) of the vessel occurred outside of the pits. It also likely reflects the comparatively small portion of a vessel surface that displays recognizable base characteristics.

Bowls

Bowls were vessels whose maximum vessel diameters were about equal to their orifice diameters. The orifice diameter was always greater than vessel height. The Fish Lake site bowls fell into Shepard's (1956) unrestricted vessel category. A total of 25 bowls were identified, representing 16% of the total vessel assemblage. Analysis of the bowl rim sherds indicated two distinct forms, which have been referred to as vertical and outslanting (Figure 26). Rim orientations formed the basis for assigning these vessels to distinct categories.

The presence of bowls in the Fish Lake vessel assemblage was notable since bowls occurred only as miniature vessels in preceding phases. The addition of bowls to vessel assemblages during the Patrick phase was also observed at the Range (Kelly 1981b), Dohack (Ann Stahl, personal communication), and Schlemmer (Szuter 1979) sites. Following the Patrick phase, bowls became common in Emergent Mississippian and Mississippian phase assemblages.

One significant distinction was found between the Fish Lake jars and bowls. Sixty-eight percent of the jars had lip impressions, while only 8% of the bowls had them. The frequencies of lip appendages were virtually the same for jars (7%) and bowls (8%).

Vertical Bowl Rims

Twenty specimens were included in the vertical rim bowl category, representing 80% of the Fish Lake site bowls (Figure 33). Considerable variation, particularly in metric attributes such as lip thickness and

95

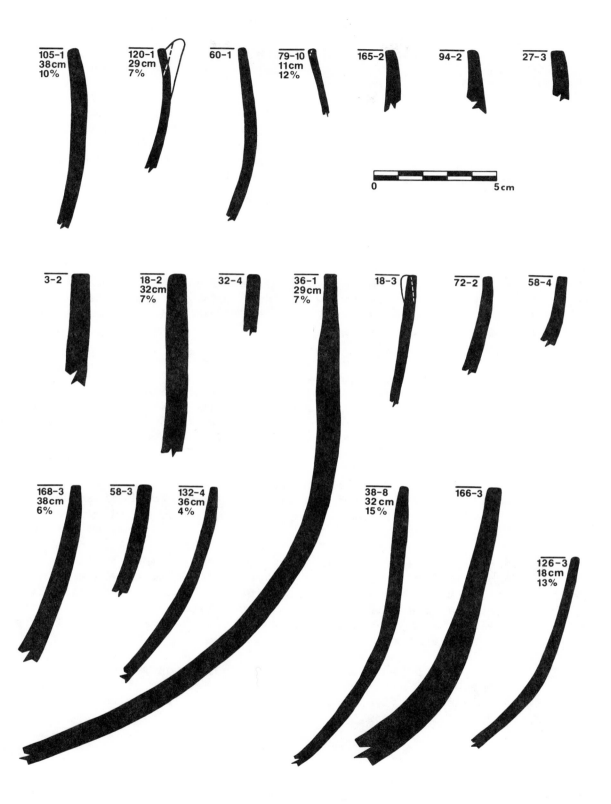

Figure 33. Rim Profiles of Vertical Bowls

orifice diameter, was indicated. The vertical rim bowls had rim orientations of 80 degrees to 110 degrees. Several of these vertical rims were comparatively small, extending down only 2 cm to 3 cm from the lip (79-10, 165-2, 94-2, 27-3, and 32-4).

One of the vertical bowls (36-1) was intermediate in shape between bowls and jars. The ratio between its vessel height (estimated at 23 cm) and its vessel orifice diameter (29 cm) was much higher than that of any other Fish Lake bowl. This specimen was comparatively deep. It was superficially similar to and probably represents a derivative of the Mund phase shoulderless jars.

The remaining Fish Lake site bowls were comparatively short in relation to their orifice diameter, forming a class of shallow bowls. The vertical and outslanting rim bowls were, however, among the larger Fish Lake vessels. For example, most of the bowl orifice diameters ranged from 29 cm to 40 cm. These bowls comprised a vessel size category distinct from that of the jars. Only one Fish Lake jar fell into this bowl size category. Two vertical bowls and one outslanting bowl were much smaller, having orifice diameters of only 11 cm, 18 cm, and 20 cm, respectively.

The 11 cm diameter vertical bowl (79-10) was notable for its interior lip impressions, one of only two Fish Lake bowls with this treatment. Vessel 120-1, a large bowl, exhibited a lip spout; its orifice contour was exaggerated or pinched outward at the spout, giving the impression of a squarish orifice. The orifice contour distortion on this bowl probably occurred during the forming of the lip spout.

Eighty-five percent (N=17) of the vertical bowls were grog tempered, while the remaining 15% included one limestone-tempered specimen and two grog/limestone-tempered specimens. Lip forms associated with the vertical bowls included flattened interior (N=29), squared vertical (N=14), and flattened exterior (N=4). Most vertical bowl rims had squared vertical lips. Considerable variation was present in the lip thicknesses of vertical bowls, which ranged from 3.0 mm to 7.0 mm. Many bowls appeared to have a vessel wall thickness comparable to their lip thickness; only a few specimens exhibited thicker basal portions, including Vessel 166-3. Vessels 36-1 and 168-3 had lips that were slightly thinner than the vessel walls.

The vertical bowls were concentrated in Occupation Areas 1 (N=7) and 3 (N=6). Only one vertical bowl each was identified from Occupation Areas 2 and 4. Another five vertical bowls came from features with nonoccupational affiliations, e. g., Features 18 and 79.

Outslanting Bowl Rims

Five bowls (20% of all bowls) were classified as having outslanting rims. Their orientations ranged from 55 degrees to 75 degrees (Figure

27). The outslanting bowl rim profiles, illustrated in Figure 32, were very distinctive. Outslanting rim bowls from the Patrick phase are apparently without local antecedents in the American Bottom area. One bowl (82-2) possessed both interior lip impressions and a pumpkin effigy, also on the lip. None of the remaining outslanting bowls showed any alteration of the vessel lips.

The two known orifice diameters were 20 cm and 40 cm, which probably accurately reflects the size range for outslanting bowls. Lip thicknesses ranged from 4.0 mm to 9.0 mm. Only one outslanting bowl, 38-9, had a comparatively thick lip. Another bowl (9-4) was thinned abruptly at the interior surface just below the lip. Not including Vessel 38-9, the lip thicknesses only ranged from 4.0 mm to 5.0 mm. The associated lip forms were flattened exterior (N=2) and squared exterior (N=3). The outslanting bowls were distributed in Occupation Areas 1 (N=1), 2 (N=3), and 3 (N=1).

Jar/Bowls

Nine rims (6% of total) could not be accurately assigned to either the jar or the bowl category. It is clear, however, that these rims were not from miniature vessels. These nine rims were comparatively small. One of them (93-2) is included in the lip appendage discussion since it had a lip spout.

The jar/bowl specimens included Vessels 6-1, 26-2, 40-5, 48-1, 72-3, 80-1, 93-2, 143-2, and 161-1 (Appendix 2). Attributes such as vessel form, rim form, lip form, orifice diameter, and orifice percentage could not be recorded because of the small size of these sherds. Two lip appendages and five lip impressions were the only notable characteristics on these rims. The specimens with lip impressions were most likely jars, and the specimen with a split pumpkin effigy lip appendage was most likely a bowl.

Rim sherds that could not be accurately assigned to either a jar or bowl category have occurred at nearly all known Patrick phase sites. As mentioned above, they accounted for 6% of the Fish Lake site vessels, a percentage less than that reported at other sites. Unlike other analyses, in the Fish Lake site analysis, rim sherds less than 2 cm wide and 2 cm long were not included in the vessel counts. This probably accounts for the comparatively low percentage of jar/bowl vessels in the Fish Lake assemblage.

Miniature Vessels

Nine miniature vessels (6% of total) were present in the Fish Lake assemblage. The vessels had comparatively thick walls, and 78% had plain, unsmoothed exterior surfaces, which were crude in appearance (Figure 34). There was a one-to-one correspondence between the

98

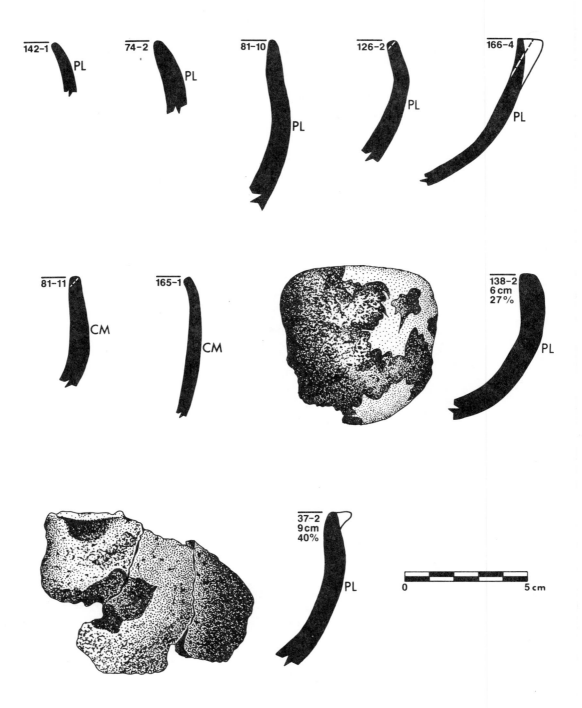

Figure 34.   Rim Profiles of Miniature Vessels

occurrence of tan-colored pastes and miniature vessels. Since the paste categories in this analysis represented the most subjective attribute recorded, the remaining two characteristics of the miniature vessels, vessel size and plain surface treatment, confirmed the definition of this vessel form.

Known orifice sizes for the Fish Lake miniature vessels were 6 cm and 9 cm. They are, therefore, among the smallest of the Fish Lake site vessels. With regard to size, miniature vessels are the smallest known Late Woodland ceramic vessels, presumably representing a functional variant. The miniature vessel class probably included both jar and bowl forms. Their small size distinguished them from all other vessels found at this site.

The only plain sherds in the Fish Lake assemblage belonged to miniature vessels. Seven (78%) of the nine specimens had plain exteriors, apparently smoothed by hand molding. Some tool marks were present on the plain interior surfaces, probably from scraping the surface during molding. Two had somewhat uneven surfaces exaggerated by spalling. Vessel 138-2 was unique in having an interior and exterior reddish tan slip over the plain surface. Since slipped vessels remain unknown or unreported for the Late Woodland period, this vessel probably represented trade ware, or the slip was a residue from the vessel contents. The remaining two miniature vessels (81-11, 165-1) were cordmarked. These specimens exhibited lighter, less dense cordmarking than the larger jars and bowls. The exterior surfaces of these cordmarked miniature vessels lacked the unsmooth, crude appearance of the plain-surfaced specimens. The application of cordmarking had produced a secondary effect of a comparatively smooth vessel surface.

The average miniature vessel lip was only 3.94 mm thick, a thickness only slightly larger than the jar lip mean of 3.79 mm and less than the bowl lip mean of 4.64 mm. Two miniature vessels (81-11, 126-1) had interior lip impressions. These were plain dowel impressions that were oriented vertically. Another two miniature vessels (37-2, 166-4) had lip appendages, both variants of lip spouts. Vessel 37-2 was notable for its two lip spouts; 40% of this vessel's orifice was present.

Vessel Size

Orifice Diameter

The orifice diameter could be determined for 27 jars (25% of the jars), 11 bowls (44% of the bowls), and 2 miniature vessels (22% of the miniature vessels), representing 26% of all vessels. For each rim, the orifice diameter was determined from the interior lip surface using a standard rim board. Generally, the orifice diameter could be determined for vessels with at least 5% of the vessel lip intact. Specifically, the jars with measurable orifice diameters were associated with orifice percentages that ranged from 7% to 34%, and the corresponding figures for bowls were 4% to 15%. There was an inverse linear relationship between orifice diameter and orifice percentage. Vessels with small orifice diameters tended to have large orifice percentages and those with larger orifice diameters tended to have smaller orifice percentages. The bowls exhibited a smaller orifice percentage range due to their generally greater orifice size.

The mean orifice diameter for the 27 Fish Lake jars was 17.5 cm, ranging from 8 cm to 28 cm. The distribution (Figure 35) was nearly continuous from 8 cm to 28 cm, with a cluster from 16 cm to 21 cm. Only four nonjar specimens fell within the jar orifice size distribution. The orifice diameter distribution illustrated in Figure 35 showed a general pattern of size differentiation among the vessel forms. The miniature vessels formed the smallest size class, being less than 10 cm in diameter. The jars were the next size class, and bowls comprised the largest class, with an orifice diameter range of 29 cm to 40 cm. However, three bowls were exceptions to this general pattern; they ranged in size from 11 cm to 20 cm.

Height and Capacity

Vessel height and capacity were estimated for three large vessel sections, representing two jars (79-1, 79-2) and a bowl (36-1). These estimates were based on the observed vessel sections in relation to the metric attributes recorded for three complete Late Woodland vessels from the Mund site (Fortier et al. 1982). The orifice diameters were known for these Fish Lake specimens. All three vessel sections extended from the lip to what appeared to be several centimeters short of the base centers. Estimated vessel heights were 29 cm, 22 cm, and 23 cm for 79-1, 79-2, and 36-1, respectively. Approximate vessel capacities for these vessels were 7 l, 8 l, and 9 l. The Fish Lake site capacity estimates fit into the known range for Late Woodland vessel capacities (Fortier et al. 1982).

Vessel Wall Thickness

Vessel wall thickness was not systematically recorded for the vessels or body sherds in the Fish Lake collection. Although not quantified, several observations were made regarding vessel walls. They tended to be quite similar in thickness to the lips (mean=3.96 mm). In fact, the wall thickness was characteristically uniform from the lip to just above the base. This was particularly true of jars. Although most vessel rims and lips essentially represented a continuation of the vessel wall thickness, thicker or thinner rims and lips did occur in the assemblage, especially among the bowls. The most commonly occurring variants were jar rims that gradually thinned in the final few centimeters below the lip.

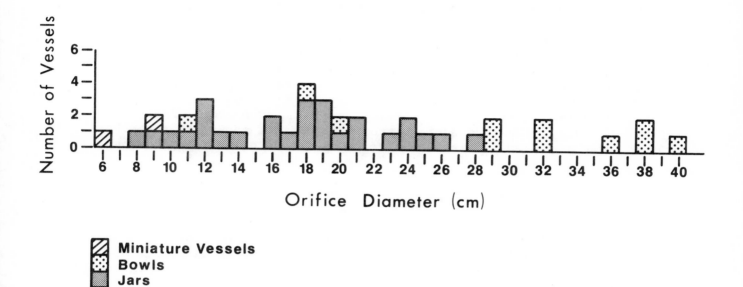

	JARS	ALL VESSELS
N	27	40
Mean	17.5 cm	20.3 cm
s	5.5 cm	8.9 cm

Figure 35. Frequency Distribution of Vessel Orifice Diameters

Vessel Attributes

Exterior Surface Treatment

Both jars and bowls exhibited cordmarked exterior surfaces and plain interior surfaces. Cordmarking was present from the vessel lip to the base, as is typical of Late Woodland jar and bowl treatments in the American Bottom. A variety of cordmarked surfaces were apparent, ranging from a few with distinct cord impressions (e.g., 79-2) to a majority with less distinct individual impressions (e.g., 81-1). Individual threads were often visible in the cord impressions. While some vessels had less distinct cordmarking than others, none of the specimens were classified as having smoothed-over cordmarking. In general, the cordmarked surface treatment did not appear to be as bold or as deeply applied as was the cordmarking in the preceding Mund phase.

Cordmark Orientation

The Fish Lake site Patrick phase vessels exhibited a consistent cordmark orientation on the uppermost 5 cm to 10 cm nearest the vessel orifice. The variation observed in orientation patterns was reduced to five categories (Figure 36). The consistent rim cordmark orientations were apparently caused by applying the cordmarking through a rolling method. Below the uppermost 5 cm to 10 cm of each vessel, the cordmarking appeared to have been applied by rolling and paddling methods. This cordmark orientation was invariably different from that of the upper rim area. Only a few examples (e.g., 3-1) had fairly consistent cordmark orientations extending all the way from the lip to the base (Figure 37).

Table 14 summarizes the occurrence of each rim cordmark orientation category. Fifty-eight percent of the vessels had vertical cordmark orientations. No other cordmark orientation category included more than 22% of the vessels. The left-to-right oblique and right-to-left oblique categories, with 22% and 15% of the jars respectively, were distinctive variants in the assemblage. There was no appreciable distinction in the occurrence of these three categories between the jar and bowl vessel forms. Only one jar each was placed in the oblique crisscross and vertical-horizontal crisscross categories. These latter two stylistic variants are better known from earlier Late Woodland contexts, such as the Mund phase at the Mund site (Fortier et al. 1982).

Cordmark Twist

Researchers in the American Bottom have used frequencies of S-twist and Z-twist cordmarked vessels as general horizon markers. Specifically, S-twist vessels have been associated with the Late Woodland (Early Bluff) period, and Z-twist vessels have been associated

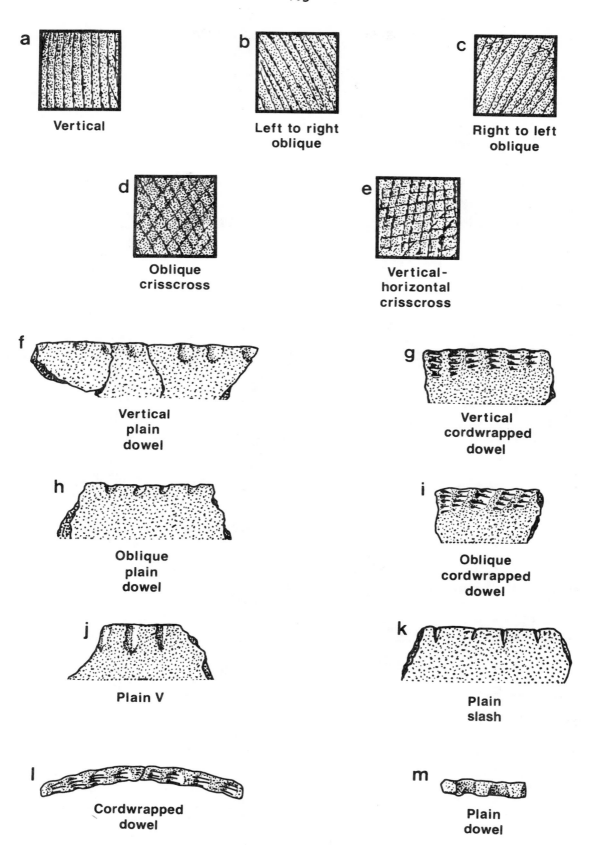

Figure 36. Key to Rim Cordmark Orientations and Lip Impressions: a-e, cordmark orientations; f-k, interior lip impressions; l-m, superior lip impressions

104

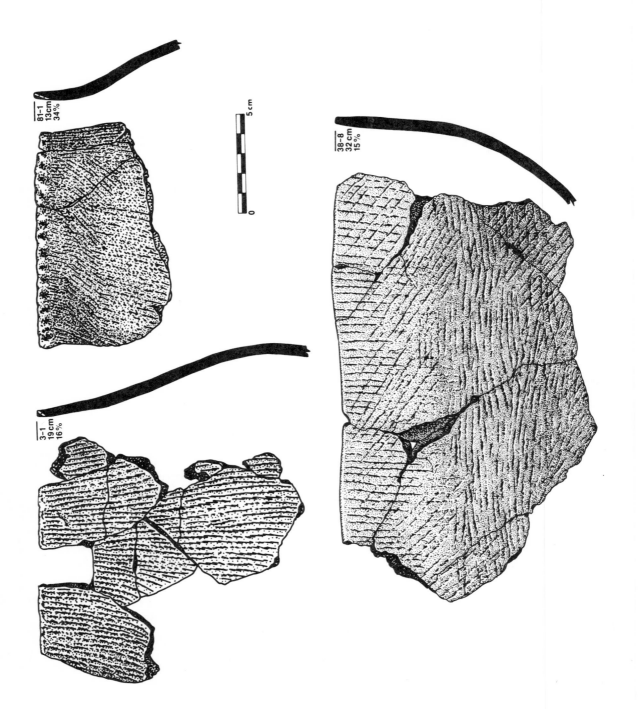

81-1
13cm
34%

5 cm

0

38-8
32 cm
15%

3-1
19 cm
16%

Figure 37. Examples of Exterior Surface Treatments

Table 14. Rim Cordmark Orientation and Cordmark Twist

Vessel Category	Rim Cordmark Orientation								Cordmark Twist				
	Vertical	L-R Oblique	R-L Oblique	Oblique Crisscross	Vert.-Hor. Crisscross	Ind.	Plain	Total	S-twist	Z-twist	Ind.	Plain	Total
Jars	70	19	14	1	1	3	-	108	20	10	78	-	108
Bowls	12	8	5	-	-	-	-	25	9	4	12	-	25
Miniature Vessels	-	1	1	-	-	-	7	9	1	-	1	7	9
Jar/Bowl Ind.	2	3	1	-	-	3	-	9	2	-	7	-	9
Total	84	31	21	1	1	6	7	151	32	14	98	7	151

Ind. -Indeterminate

Table 15. Lip Form by Vessel Category

Vessel Category/ Rim Category	Rounded	Squared Interior	Flattened Interior	Squared Vertical	Flattened Exterior	Squared Exterior	Ind.	Total
Jars								
Inslanting	1	6	36	2	-	-	-	45
Vertical	5	-	4	52	1	-	-	62
Flaring	-	-	-	-	-	1	-	1
Bowls								
Vertical	-	-	2	14	4	-	-	20
Outslanting	-	-	-	-	2	3	-	5
Miniature Vessels	7	1	-	1	-	-	-	9
Jar/Bowl Ind.	-	-	-	-	-	-	9	9
Total	13	7	42	69	7	4	9	151

Ind. - Indeterminate

with the Emergent Mississippian (Late Bluff) period (Munson 1971). Within these two periods, however, cordmark twist categories cannot be used to relate assemblages to specific phases. Other ceramic attributes, particularly lip impressions and lip appendages, were used in this analysis to situate the Fish Lake assemblage within a specific Late Woodland phase.

The Fish Lake assemblage followed the Late Woodland pattern in that there were more S-twist vessels than Z-twist vessels. A total of 32 vessels (22%) exhibited S-twist cordmarking, while 14 vessels (10%) had Z-twist cordmarking. However, the cord twist direction on the great majority of Fish Lake vessels (68%) could not be determined. This is because cordmarking in the Fish Lake assemblage was less distinct than it was in Late Woodland Mund phase components.

No discernible pattern was present in the distribution of the S-twist and Z-twist vessels across the site. The two cord twist varieties appeared to be distributed uniformly throughout the four occupation areas.

Applique Nodes

Applique nodes were present on a single grog-tempered, cordmarked body sherd recovered from Feature 121 in Occupation Area 3. Based on the sherd's slight curvature and relative thinness, it was apparently from the shoulder of a vessel, probably a jar. Two nodes were located on the exterior surface (Figure 38). Evidently, they had been added to the vessel surface prior to firing.

Punctates

One grog-tempered, cordmarked jar (138-1) had eight punctates on its exterior surface at 0.5 cm to 1.0 cm below the lip (Figure 38). They were arranged in a discontinuous linear pattern roughly parallel to the lip. They were ca. 1.0 mm to 1.5 mm in diameter and ca. 1.0 mm deep, and were considerably smaller than punctates known from earlier Late Woodland phases. This mode of decoration occurred infrequently during the Patrick phase in the American Bottom.

Shell Slip

One jar (36-2) in the Fish Lake assemblage had a possible shell slip over an exterior cordmarked surface. The small size of the rim sherd precluded positive identification of the slip, which was composed of small shell fragments in a clay base. Due to the tentative nature of this identification, it was not included in the exterior surface treatment tables. Patrick phase vessels with shell slips over cordmarked surfaces have been reported from the Stolle Quarry (Hall 1980) and Range (Steven J. Ozuk, personal communication) sites.

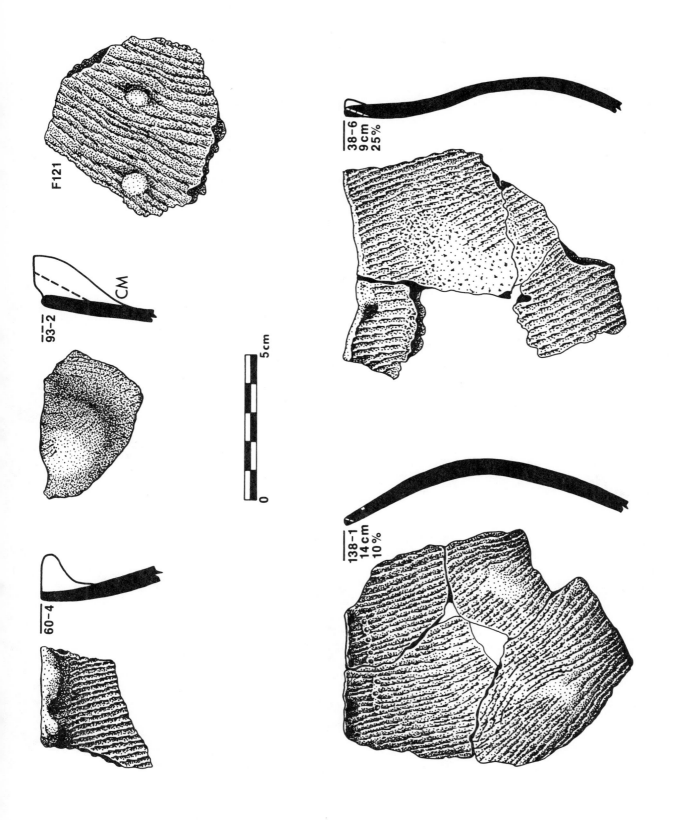

F121

93-2

CM

60-4

5 cm

0

38-6
9 cm
25%

138-1
14 cm
10%

Figure 38. Miscellaneous Vessel Body and Lip Treatments

Interior Surface Treatment

The interior surfaces of Fish Lake vessels were plain, with one exception, a miniature vessel (138-2) with a tan interior slip over a plain surface. Many vessel interiors showed evidence of hand molding in the form of slight finger impressions and fingerprints, which had produced wavy, uneven surfaces. The finger impressions were from the inside of an open hand, which had apparently been held inside the vessel while the exterior was beaten with a cordwrapped paddle. Most interior surfaces had been smoothed by hand, as evidenced by wavy surfaces. The interiors of several jar bases had numerous small scrape marks, indicating the use of a tool to smooth the interior. Only in bowls was there any evidence of interior burnishing with hand-held objects.

Lip Attributes

Lip Forms

Patrick phase vessel lips were, for the most part, simply unmodified termini of vessel walls. In profile, these lips were flattened, squared, or rounded. Six lip form categories were used in this analysis (Figure 26). Flattened and squared lips had angular edges that separated the superior surface from the exterior and interior surfaces. These types contrasted with rounded lips, which exhibited a continuous curving surface, without angular intersections, from the vessel exterior to the interior.

Flattened and squared lips (91%) dominated the Fish Lake vessel assemblage, mirroring a general Late Woodland trend in the American Bottom. Variation among flattened and squared lips fell into five categories. These categories were distinguished by the configurations of the superior lip surfaces and by their orientations. Although the lip form categories were defined separately from the rim form categories, certain lip forms and rim forms were associated (Table 15). For example, squared interior lips and flattened interior lips were often found on vessels with inslanting rims; squared vertical lips were often found on vessels with vertical rims.

Squared interior lips (N=7; 4.6%) exhibited a squared configuration that slanted to the interior and a superior surface that was oriented ca. 30 degrees from horizontal. Squared interior lips are known from other Late Woodland sites in the American Bottom and were common during the preceding Mund phase. This lip form was invariably associated with inslanting rims.

Flattened interior lips (27.8%) comprised the second largest lip form category. The superior lip had a horizontal orientation, and the exterior and interior edges were slanted to the vessel interior. Most specimens with this lip form had inslanting rims. Typical examples of flat interior lips included Vessels 138-1 and 37-1 (Figure 29). This was a common Late Woodland lip form in the American Bottom.

The most frequently occurring lip form (45.7%) in the Fish Lake assemblage was squared vertical (Table 15). In profile, these lips had squared configurations and were oriented vertically. Squared vertical lips occurred throughout the Late Woodland period and persisted into the subsequent Emergent Mississippian period in the American Bottom. They were typically found on jars with vertical rims.

A flattened exterior lip was found on only one jar in the Fish Lake assemblage, but six of the outslanting bowls (4.6%) exhibited this lip form. In profile, the flattened exterior form had the superior lip surface positioned horizontally while the exterior and interior lip surfaces were slanted to the vessel exterior.

The squared exterior lip form also occurred infrequently on jars (2.6%). This lip form had a squared configuration that was slanted to the exterior. The superior lip surface was oriented ca. 150 degrees from the horizontal. Examples of this form in the Fish Lake assemblage occurred on three outslanting bowls. The orientation of this lip form virtually restricted its occurrence to bowls with outslanting rims.

Rounded lips comprised 8.6% of all vessel lips. They were found on seven miniature vessels but on only six jars. Rounded lips were present on 78% of the miniature vessels. In contrast, the flattened and squared lip categories accounted for 95% of the jars and bowls. This indicates that efforts were made by potters to flatten the superior lip surfaces of large vessels, but not of miniature vessels.

Several jars with interior lip impressions exhibited "rippled" lips. These resulted from the application of lip impressions to interior lip surfaces, which pushed relatively equal amounts of clay outward. The ripples generally extended 1 mm to 3 mm outward.

Lip Thickness

Vessel lip thicknesses were recorded to the nearest 0.5 mm. Several specimens exhibited a several millimeter variation in the thickness of their walls. The figure recorded for each vessel, therefore, represents an average lip thickness. In the Fish Lake assemblage, lip thicknesses for all vessels ranged from 2.5 mm to 9.0 mm. The range for jars was 2.5 mm to 6.0 mm (Figure 39). Figure 39 includes 150 of the 151 Fish Lake vessels; the lip thickness of only one vessel could not be determined.

The mean lip thickness for all vessels was 3.96 mm (s=1.02). Approximately two-thirds of the jars had lip thicknesses of 3.0 mm to 4.0 mm, with nearly all the vessels falling between 2.5 mm and 5.0 mm. The mean jar lip thickness was 3.79 mm (s=0.77). The bowl

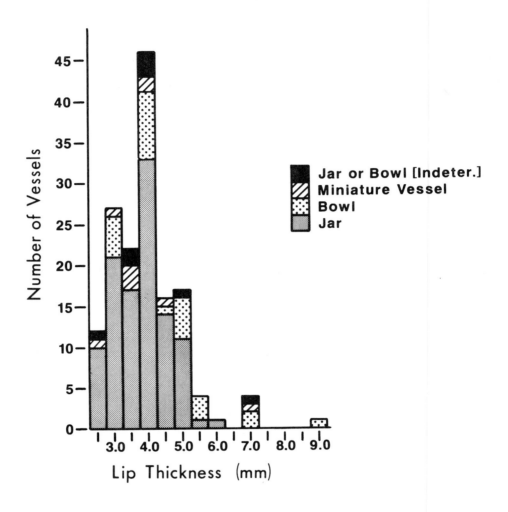

	JARS	ALL VESSELS
N	108	150
Mean	3.79 mm	3.96 mm
s	0.77 mm	1.02 mm

Figure 39. Frequency Distribution of Vessel Lip Thickness

(mean=4.64 mm) and miniature vessel (mean=3.94 mm) lips were, on the average, somewhat thicker than the jars.

In contrast to the preceding Mund phase, jar lip thicknesses for the Patrick phase were apparently not affected by the addition of lip impressions. This was probably because Patrick phase lip impressions were applied to the interior lip surface; the Mund phase lip impressions were applied to the superior lip surface, which sometimes flattened the lip (Fortier et al. 1982).

Lip Treatments

Interior lip impressions included plain dowel, cordwrapped dowel, plain V-shape, and plain slash. Superior lip treatments included plain dowel and cordwrapped dowel. Examples of these lip impression types are illustrated in Figure 36.

The interior and superior lip treatments were described separately since lip treatment location, as a general trend, had chronological significance within the Late Woodland period (Fortier et al. 1982). In the Patrick phase, a basic dichotomy occurred between vessels with lip treatments and vessels with plain lips. Approximately 55% of the Fish Lake vessels exhibited various lip impressions while the remaining 45% had plain lips (Table 16). These percentages varied greatly among the different vessel forms. Jars frequently had lip impressions; lip impressions occurred infrequently on bowls and miniature vessels. This observation is paralleled in Patrick phase vessel assemblages from the nearby Dohack (Ann Stahl, personal communication) and Schlemmer (Szuter 1979) sites.

Interior Lip Impressions

Plain dowel impressions occurred on the interior lip surfaces of slightly over one-quarter of the Fish Lake vessels (Figure 40; Table 16). Plain dowel impressions were recorded on jars (N=37), miniature vessels (N=2), and on jar/bowls (N=1). Two lip impression variants, one oriented vertically and the other obliquely (from the upper right to lower left) were recognized in the Fish Lake assemblage. Vessels with vertically oriented plain dowel lip impressions (N=26; 65%) outnumbered those with oblique impressions (N=14; 35%). Further variation occurred in the amount of spacing between impressions. Although this spacing varied from one vessel to another, the spacing on each vessel was consistent. No examples of discontinuous sequences of impressions were present. Plain dowel impressions occurred on between 14% and 29% of the vessels within each occupation area at the Fish Lake site. A higher percentage, 42% of the vessels, was found in features of nonoccupational affiliation.

The earliest known occurrence of plain dowel lip impressions in the

Table 16. Lip Treatments by Vessel Category

| Vessel Category | Interior Lip Impressions | | | | | | Superior Lip Impressions | | | Total |
| | Plain Dowel | | Cordwrapped Dowel | | | | | | | |
	Vertical	Oblique	Vertical	Oblique	Plain V	Plain Slash	Plain Dowel	CW Dowel	Plain	
Jars	23	12	21	8	4	2	1	2	35	108
Bowls	-	-	1	-	-	1	-	-	23	25
Miniature Vessels	2	-	-	-	-	-	-	-	7	9
Jar/Bowl Ind.	1	2	-	2	-	-	-	-	4	9
Total	26	14	22	10	4	3	1	2	69	151

Ind. - Indeterminate

Table 17. Lip Appendages by Vessel Category

| Vessel Category | None | Lug | Spout | Effigy | | | Total |
				Zoomor.	Pumpkin	Ind.	
Jar	101	3	2	1	-	1	108
Bowl	22	-	1	-	2	-	25
Miniature Vessels	7	-	2	-	-	-	9
Jar/Bowl Ind.	7	-	1	-	1	-	9
Total	137	3	6	1	3	1	151

Ind. -Indeterminate
Zoomor.-Zoomorphic

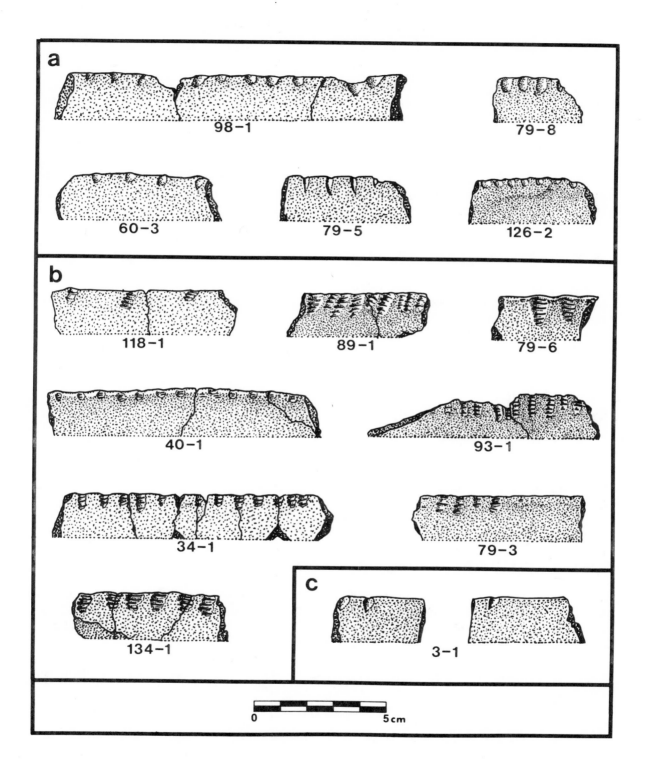

Figure 40. Interior Lip Impression Variation: a, plain dowel;
b, cordwrapped dowel; c, plain V-shaped

Late Woodland period is in the Patrick phase. Plain dowel interior lip impressions, usually in association with limestone-tempered cordmarked jars, persist through the subsequent Emergent Mississippian Dohack and Range phases.

Vertical plain dowel impressions occur in even greater frequencies during the subsequent Dohack and Range phases than during the Patrick phase. The oblique orientation variant, albeit in association with cordwrapped dowel impressions, was predominant in the preceding Mund phase assemblage (Fortier et al. 1982).

Cordwrapped dowel impressions on the interior lip occurred on one-fifth of the Fish Lake vessels (Table 16). Thirty-one of 32 vessels with cordwrapped dowel lip impressions were jars; the other specimen was a bowl. As with the plain dowel impressions, vertical and oblique (upper right to lower left) orientation variants were found. Two vessels (79-3 and 79-6) with discontinuous sequences of lip impressions were present (Figure 40). The lengths of the lip sections lacking impressions could not be determined for either vessel since the rim segments were both small. The total number of vessels with a discontinuous series of lip impressions is not known; however, these vessels are believed to comprise only a small percentage of the assemblage.

The impressions on most vessels with cordwrapped dowel lips were spaced 0.5 cm to 1.0 cm apart. One specimen (118-1) however, had intervals of 2.5 cm between impressions (Figure 40).

Vessels with vertically oriented cordwrapped dowel lip impressions (N=22) outnumbered those with oblique cordwrapped dowel impressions (N=10). The predominance of the vertically oriented lip impressions mirrored the trend among the plain dowel impressions.

The distribution of vessels with cordwrapped dowel lip impressions in different occupation areas ranged from 14% to 32%. Only 12% of the vessels from features of nonoccupational affiliation had cordwrapped dowel impressions.

Cordwrapped dowel impressions are found throughout the Late Woodland period, and extend back to the Middle Woodland Cement Hollow phase (Fortier et al. 1982). Following the Late Woodland Patrick phase, cordwrapped dowel impressions are rarely found. Apparently, the Patrick phase marked a transition from cordwrapped dowel impressions to plain dowel impressions. Both lip impression types occurred in Patrick phase assemblages at the Fish Lake, Dohack (Ann Stahl, personal communication), and Schlemmer (Szuter 1979) sites.

Four jars in the assemblage exhibited plain lip impressions that had a V-shape (Figure 40). All of the plain V-shape lip impressions had a vertical orientation. The V-shape (wedge shape) distinguished these impressions from U-shaped plain dowel impressions. A distinction between V-shaped and U-shaped impressions was made previously in the analysis of the Patrick phase assemblage at the Dohack site (Ann Stahl, personal communication).

All four Fish Lake jars with V-shaped lip impressions were recovered from Occupation Area 1. One jar (3-1) had a discontinuous series of plain V-shaped lip impressions (Figure 40). The interval between the series of lip impressions was ca. 4 cm.

Three vessels (two jars and one bowl) had plain slash lip impressions (Figure 40). All of the plain slash lip impressions had a vertical orientation. The jars were from a feature in Occupation Area 4 and from a feature of nonoccupational affiliation; the bowl was from Occupation Area 2.

In defining the lip impression types for this study, it was noted that plain dowel impressions and plain slash impressions could form the ends of a size continuum. Yet it seemed that the widths and depths of the impressions resulted in two distinct size classes. Plain slash impressions were narrow and U-shaped; they were ca. 2 mm wide and 1 mm to 2 mm deep. Plain slash impressions, therefore, were distinctly smaller than plain dowel impressions. Plain slash lip impressions are also known from Patrick phase assemblages at the Dohack (Ann Stahl, personal communication) and Schlemmer (Thomas Berres, personal communication) sites.

Superior Lip Impressions

Only three jars in the Fish Lake assemblage had lip impressions located on the superior lip surface. Superior lip impressions are common in Mund phase assemblages and are found infrequently in subsequent Patrick and Dohack phase assemblages.

One jar (143-3), from a feature of nonoccupational affiliation, had lip impressions placed directly on top of the lip. These impressions were the plain dowel type; however, they were similar to fingernail scraping marks. Examples of superior lip plain dowel impressions are unknown, or unreported, in other Patrick phase assemblages.

Two Fish Lake site jars had cordwrapped dowel impressions on the superior lip surface. These vessels were from Occupation Area 3 (58-1) and from a feature of nonoccupational affiliation (79-2). The impressions on both vessels were closely spaced (0.5 cm). No other reference for lip impressions being located on the superior lip surface is available for Patrick phase assemblages.

Lip Appendages

Thirteen Fish Lake vessels (9%) had alterations or additions on their lip surfaces that could not appropriately be described as lip impressions. These appendages were classified as lugs, spouts, a zoomorphic effigy, and a split pumpkin effigy (Table 17).

Lugs

Lugs occurred on the exterior lip surfaces of three jars. The jars were found in Occupation Areas 1 and 2 and in a feature of nonoccupational affiliation. Two types of lugs were identified in the assemblage: simple lugs and multiple lugs. Simple lugs were roughly triangular-shaped clay additions to the exterior lip surface. These were similar to many lugs from the subsequent Emergent Mississippian period. The Patrick phase lugs from the Fish Lake site represent the earliest known occurrence of such lugs in the Late Woodland period. One example of a multiple lug was present in the Fish Lake assemblage. It consisted of two simple lugs placed side-by-side. Similar lugs occur in Patrick phase ceramic assemblages from the Range site (Steven J. Ozuk, personal communication).

Spouts

Six Fish Lake vessels, including two jars, one bowl, two miniature vessels, and one jar/bowl, had spouts on their exterior lip surfaces. Spouts represent the outward pinching of a small portion of the lip. The sizes of the spouts suggested that fingers or sticks had been used to alter the vessel lip. Vessel 93-2 had a comparatively large, pronounced spout; the spout on vessel 38-6 was comparatively small (Figure 38). The vessel 93-2 spout was 3.5 cm long, and it projected outward from the rim for ca. 1.5 cm. By contrast, the spout from vessel 38-6 was ca. 1.0 cm long and projected outward from the rim only 0.5 cm. Spouts are also reported for Patrick phase Range site vessels (Steven J. Ozuk, personal communication).

Zoomorphic Effigy

Vessel 123-1, a jar from Occupation Area 3, had a lug on the superior and exterior lip surface that represented a zoomorphic effigy (Figure 41). The animal depicted is unknown. One of its limbs had been broken off.

Split Pumpkin Effigy

Three Fish Lake vessels had split pumpkin effigies. The term split pumpkin effigy, in reference to inward pinched rims, was borrowed from

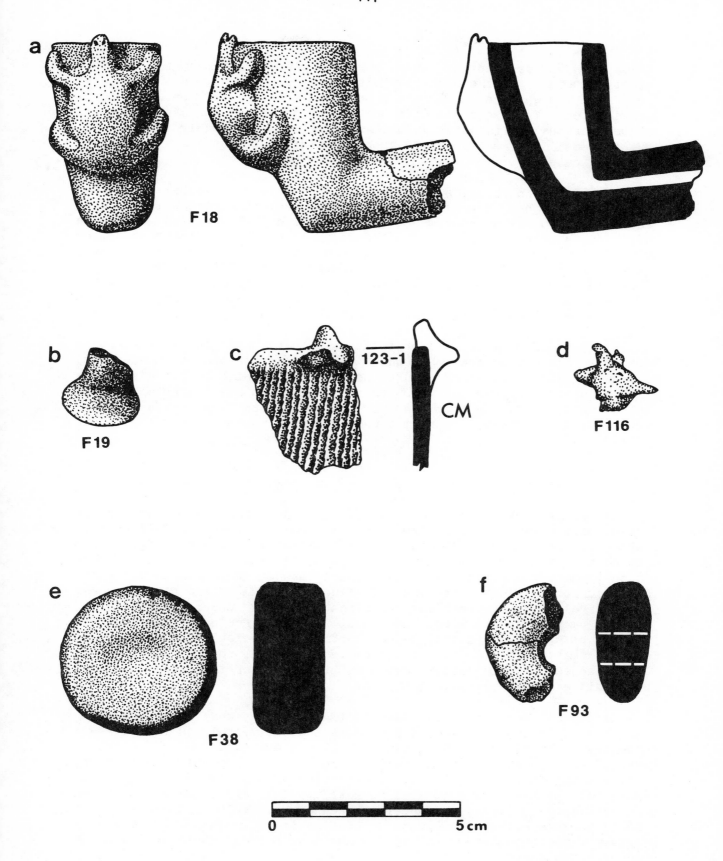

Figure 41. Miscellaneous Ceramic Items

Kelly's (1980) description, where such effigies were said to resemble split pumpkins. At the Fish Lake site, they were found on two bowls, one from Occupation Area 2 and one from a feature of nonoccupational affiliation. They were also found on a jar/bowl in a feature of nonoccupational affiliation. The last specimen is probably also a bowl, but the small size of the rim segment prohibited positive assignment to the bowl category.

Split pumpkin effigies represent small sections of vessel lips that had been pinched toward the vessels' centers. Unfortunately, none of the three Fish Lake specimens were complete. The sizes of these effigies appeared similar to those of lip spouts. The distinction between them is that lip spouts projected outward from the rim, whereas split pumpkin effigies projected inward. Two split pumpkin effigies (Vessels 18-3 and 82-2) are illustrated among the rim profiles (Figures 32 and 33). In addition, Vessels 143-2 and 82-2, with split pumpkin effigies, also had interior lip impressions.

Examples of pinched lips or split pumpkin effigies in Patrick phase contexts are known from the Dohack (Ann Stahl, personal communication) and Range sites (Steven J. Ozuk, personal communication). This lip appendage type is also known from the Emergent Mississippian Merrell phase (Kelly 1980) and from the Mississippian Stirling phase (Milner with Williams 1981b). It is unknown from assemblages prior to the Patrick phase.

Vessel Paste and Temper

Macroscopic examination of the vessels indicated the presence of three distinctively colored pastes. The color categories were gray to dark gray, reddish orange, and tan. The tan-colored paste category was restricted to the miniature vessels. The remaining two pastes were found in jars and bowls. The distinction between gray and red pastes is believed to reflect the use of floodplain and upland clay sources, respectively. It has been suggested that the gray color results from organic materials in floodplain clays, while the red color results from the use of upland clays that do not contain appreciable quantities of organic materials. While this remains unproven, the use of different clay sources probably better explains these color distinctions than would differential firing conditions.

Ninety-one percent of the vessels (N=137) had gray to dark gray pastes. This included all of the bowls and the vessels in the jar/bowl category, as well as all but five jars. There was great variation within the gray paste category, which was probably related to differential firing conditions. The reddish-orange (N=5; 3%) and tan (N=9; 6%) pastes occurred infrequently. The reddish-orange pastes occurred only in jars. One specimen each came from Occupation Areas 1 and 4; three specimens came from Occupation Area 2. These jars may have derived from the uplands east of the American Bottom. Miniature vessels had only tan pastes.

Vessel tempers included grog, grog/limestone, limestone, and grit/grog. All temper identifications were made by macroscopic examination. Grog temper consisted of angular or subangular crushed sherds, which were usually black, gray, or tan; occasionally, the grog was red or a black to blue hue. The temper of the grog fragments themselves was unknown, but in many cases, the grog was likely derived from previously broken grog-tempered sherds. Limestone was recognizable as rounded or subangular white fragments in the vessel paste. Much of the limestone had been leached out, leaving only casts of temper fragments. Grit temper included crushed rock fragments, except limestone. Grit fragments in the Fish Lake vessels were characteristically angular. The temper identifications listed as grog/limestone and grit/grog represent combinations of distinct temper categories. Table 18 summarizes the Fish Lake assemblage recovered from Patrick phase features by temper and exterior surface treatment.

An examination of Table 18 reveals that most vessels (94%) and sherds were grog tempered, as is typical of Patrick phase occupations located far from the bluff edge. It has been suggested that Patrick phase sites in the uplands had predominantly grit-tempered assemblages, while floodplain Patrick phase sites had grog-tempered assemblages. Grog/limestone (N=5; 3%) and limestone (N=3; 2%) tempered vessels were only infrequently represented in the Patrick phase in Fish Lake site assemblages (Kelly 1980; 1981c). During subsequent Emergent Mississippian phases in the American Bottom, limestone-tempered vessels predominate; grog, grit/grog, and grit-tempered vessels become rare in Emergent Mississippian phases, except as trade wares.

Miscellaneous Nonvessel Ceramics

Nonvessel ceramic items included discs, miscellaneous objects, effigies and effigy fragments, pipes and pipe fragments, potters' clay, daub, and burned clay (Tables 19, 20, and 21).

Discs

Six intentionally worked or ground body sherds that had been shaped into discs were identified in the Fish Lake assemblage. They ranged in diameter from 2.5 cm to 5.5 cm by 6.0 cm; in weight they ranged from 4.7 g to 37.3 g. All specimens had cordmarked exterior surfaces and plain interior surfaces and were grog tempered. They were distributed among Occupation Areas 1 (Features 6, 26, and 166), 2 (Features 82 and 88), and 3 (Feature 105).

Ceramic Objects

Miscellaneous ceramic objects included a discoidal and a perforated disc. The ceramic discoidal was recovered from Feature 38 in Occupation

Table 18. Ceramic Assemblage by Exterior Surface Treatment and Temper
Listed by Feature

Feature	Cordmarking										Plain						Indeterminate				Total	
	Grog		Grog/LS		Grit		LS		G/G		Grog		None		LS		LS		Grit			
	N	Wt(g)	N	Wt(g)	N	Wt(g)	N	Wt(g)	N	Wt(g)	N	Wt(g)	N	Wt(g)	N	Wt(g)	N	Wt(g)	N	Wt(g)	N	Wt(g)
2	2	5.0	-	-	-	-	-	-	-	-	-	-	-	-	-	-	-	-	-	-	2	5.0
3	236	1042.3	-	-	-	-	-	-	-	-	1	1.0	-	-	-	-	-	-	-	-	237	1043.3
4	41	61.1	-	-	-	-	4	4.2	-	-	-	-	-	-	-	-	-	-	-	-	45	65.3
5	10	35.6	-	-	-	-	-	-	-	-	-	-	-	-	-	-	-	-	-	-	10	35.6
6	78	366.0	-	-	-	-	-	-	-	-	1	0.7	-	-	-	-	-	-	-	-	79	366.7
9	222	892.3	-	-	-	-	1	0.2	-	-	-	-	-	-	-	-	-	-	-	-	223	892.5
11	76	481.0	-	-	-	-	-	-	-	-	-	-	-	-	-	-	-	-	-	-	76	481.0
13	2	7.0	-	-	-	-	-	-	-	-	-	-	-	-	-	-	-	-	-	-	2	7.0
18	172	764.8	-	-	-	-	1	3.2	-	-	2	4.2	-	-	-	-	-	-	-	-	175	772.2
19	14	24.4	-	-	-	-	-	-	-	-	-	-	-	-	-	-	-	-	-	-	14	24.4
20	1	0.1	-	-	-	-	-	-	-	-	-	-	-	-	-	-	-	-	-	-	1	0.1
21	8	18.1	-	-	-	-	-	-	-	-	1	2.1	-	-	-	-	-	-	-	-	9	20.2
22	12	30.8	-	-	-	-	-	-	-	-	-	-	-	-	-	-	-	-	-	-	12	30.8
23	17	38.6	-	-	-	-	-	-	-	-	1	1.3	-	-	-	-	-	-	-	-	18	39.9
25	1	0.5	-	-	-	-	-	-	-	-	-	-	-	-	-	-	-	-	-	-	1	0.5
26	122	739.1	-	-	-	-	-	-	-	-	-	-	-	-	-	-	-	-	-	-	122	739.1
27	97	586.3	-	-	-	-	97	103.2	-	-	3	4.6	-	-	-	-	-	-	-	-	197	694.1
28	30	132.1	-	-	-	-	-	-	-	-	-	-	-	-	-	-	-	-	-	-	30	132.1
30	-	-	-	-	-	-	-	-	-	-	-	-	-	-	-	-	7	8.3	-	-	7	8.3
31	1	1.0	-	-	-	-	-	-	-	-	-	-	-	-	-	-	-	-	-	-	1	1.0
32	122	576.1	-	-	-	-	-	-	-	-	-	-	-	-	-	-	-	-	-	-	122	576.1
33	61	69.2	-	-	-	-	-	-	-	-	-	-	-	-	-	-	-	-	-	-	61	69.2
34	203	433.2	-	-	-	-	-	-	-	-	-	-	-	-	-	-	-	-	-	-	203	433.2
35	8	56.8	-	-	-	-	-	-	-	-	2	3.4	-	-	-	-	-	-	-	-	10	60.2
36	163	1467.0	-	-	-	-	1	2.4	-	-	-	-	-	-	2	4.1	-	-	-	-	166	1473.5
37	90	493.2	-	-	-	-	2	3.7	-	-	1	0.6	-	-	-	-	-	-	-	-	93	497.5
38	303	2167.9	-	-	-	-	17	50.0	-	-	-	-	-	-	-	-	-	-	-	-	320	2217.9
39	9	40.4	-	-	-	-	-	-	-	-	-	-	-	-	-	-	-	-	-	-	9	40.4
40	50	295.2	-	-	-	-	1	3.1	-	-	-	-	-	-	-	-	-	-	-	-	51	298.3
41	20	207.0	-	-	-	-	-	-	-	-	-	-	-	-	-	-	-	-	-	-	20	207.0
42	8	27.7	-	-	-	-	-	-	-	-	-	-	-	-	-	-	-	-	-	-	8	27.7
43	128	594.6	-	-	-	-	2	6.5	-	-	-	-	-	-	-	-	-	-	-	-	130	601.1
44	31	177.4	-	-	-	-	-	-	-	-	1	4.0	-	-	-	-	-	-	-	-	32	181.4
48	37	144.4	-	-	-	-	-	-	-	-	-	-	-	-	-	-	-	-	-	-	37	144.4
52	3	4.0	-	-	-	-	-	-	-	-	-	-	-	-	-	-	-	-	-	-	3	4.0
56	8	16.5	3	15.9	-	-	-	-	-	-	-	-	-	-	-	-	-	-	-	-	11	32.4
57	15	83.3	-	-	-	-	-	-	-	-	-	-	-	-	-	-	-	-	-	-	15	83.3
58	164	904.7	-	-	-	-	-	-	-	-	1	1.0	-	-	-	-	-	-	-	-	165	905.7
60	256	941.7	-	-	-	-	-	-	-	-	-	-	-	-	-	-	-	-	-	-	256	941.7
61	1	3.8	-	-	-	-	-	-	-	-	-	-	-	-	-	-	-	-	-	-	1	3.8
66	7	25.6	-	-	-	-	-	-	-	-	-	-	-	-	-	-	-	-	-	-	7	25.6
70	50	241.1	-	-	-	-	-	-	-	-	-	-	-	-	-	-	-	-	-	-	50	241.1
71	4	2.6	-	-	-	-	-	-	-	-	-	-	-	-	-	-	-	-	-	-	4	2.6
72	103	817.7	-	-	-	-	-	-	-	-	-	-	-	-	4	32.0	-	-	-	-	107	849.7
74	9	58.8	-	-	-	-	-	-	-	-	-	-	-	-	-	-	-	-	-	-	9	58.8
76	2	16.2	-	-	-	-	-	-	-	-	1	0.7	-	-	-	-	-	-	-	-	3	16.9
79	362	2539.9	9	139.9	-	-	-	-	-	-	-	-	-	-	-	-	-	-	-	-	371	2679.8
80	69	415.7	-	-	-	-	-	-	-	-	-	-	-	-	-	-	-	-	-	-	69	415.7
81	512	2115.7	-	-	-	-	5	50.0	-	-	-	-	-	-	3	38.9	-	-	-	-	520	2204.6
82	135	530.9	-	-	-	-	-	-	-	-	-	-	-	-	-	-	-	-	-	-	135	530.9
85	2	13.5	-	-	-	-	-	-	-	-	-	-	-	-	-	-	-	-	-	-	2	13.5
86	16	87.9	-	-	-	-	-	-	-	-	-	-	-	-	-	-	-	-	-	-	16	87.9
87	9	13.4	-	-	-	-	-	-	-	-	2	4.7	-	-	-	-	-	-	-	-	11	18.1
88	136	852.8	-	-	-	-	-	-	-	-	-	-	-	-	-	-	-	-	-	-	136	852.8
89	72	143.8	-	-	-	-	-	-	6	47.9	1	4.1	-	-	-	-	-	-	-	-	79	195.8
90	16	54.3	-	-	1	5.7	-	-	-	-	-	-	-	-	-	-	-	-	-	-	17	60.0
91	2	20.8	-	-	-	-	-	-	-	-	-	-	-	-	-	-	-	-	-	-	2	20.8
92	15	64.8	-	-	-	-	-	-	-	-	-	-	-	-	-	-	-	-	-	-	15	64.8
93	402	1605.9	-	-	-	-	-	-	5	32.5	1	10.9	-	-	-	-	-	-	-	-	408	1649.3
94	23	186.2	-	-	-	-	-	-	-	-	-	-	-	-	-	-	-	-	-	-	23	186.2
95	48	133.1	-	-	-	-	-	-	-	-	-	-	-	-	-	-	-	-	-	-	48	133.1
96	1	3.7	-	-	-	-	1	1.2	-	-	-	-	-	-	-	-	-	-	-	-	2	4.9
97	38	55.1	-	-	-	-	-	-	-	-	-	-	-	-	-	-	-	-	-	-	38	55.1
98	87	1592.1	-	-	-	-	-	-	-	-	1	4.5	-	-	-	-	-	-	-	-	88	1596.6

Table 18. Continued

Feature	Cordmarking Grog N	Wt(g)	Grog/LS N	Wt(g)	Grit N	Wt(g)	LS N	Wt(g)	G/G N	Wt(g)	Plain Grog N	Wt(g)	None N	Wt(g)	LS N	Wt(g)	Indeterminate LS N	Wt(g)	Grit N	Wt(g)	Total N	Wt(g)
99	3	1.3	-	-	-	-	-	-	-	-	-	-	-	-	-	-	-	-	-	-	3	1.3
100	27	59.0	-	-	-	-	-	-	-	-	-	-	-	-	-	-	-	-	-	-	27	59.0
101	4	35.8	-	-	-	-	-	-	-	-	-	-	-	-	-	-	-	-	-	-	4	35.8
102	1	11.6	-	-	-	-	-	-	-	-	-	-	-	-	-	-	-	-	-	-	1	11.6
104	29	78.9	-	-	-	-	-	-	-	-	-	-	-	-	-	-	-	-	-	-	29	78.9
105	66	426.1	-	-	-	-	1	1.1	-	-	-	-	-	-	-	-	-	-	-	-	67	427.2
106	103	642.0	-	-	-	-	-	-	-	-	1	11.8	-	-	-	-	-	-	-	-	104	653.8
116	220	785.8	-	-	-	-	-	-	-	-	4	8.5	-	-	-	-	-	-	-	-	224	794.3
117	50	225.7	-	-	-	-	-	-	-	-	-	-	-	-	-	-	-	-	-	-	50	225.7
118	43	278.3	-	-	-	-	-	-	-	-	-	-	-	-	-	-	-	-	-	-	43	278.3
119	3	11.3	-	-	-	-	-	-	-	-	-	-	-	-	-	-	-	-	-	-	3	11.3
120	47	267.4	8	41.9	-	-	-	-	-	-	-	-	-	-	-	-	-	-	-	-	55	309.3
121	5	44.5	-	-	-	-	-	-	-	-	-	-	-	-	-	-	-	-	-	-	5	44.5
122	4	10.3	-	-	-	-	-	-	-	-	-	-	-	-	-	-	-	-	-	-	4	10.3
123	104	443.2	-	-	-	-	-	-	-	-	-	-	-	-	-	-	-	-	-	-	104	443.2
124	13	120.9	-	-	-	-	-	-	-	-	-	-	-	-	-	-	-	-	-	-	13	120.9
125	3	10.2	-	-	-	-	-	-	-	-	-	-	-	-	-	-	-	-	-	-	3	10.2
126	52	505.6	-	-	-	-	-	-	-	-	-	-	-	-	-	-	-	-	-	-	52	505.6
127	7	30.3	-	-	-	-	-	-	-	-	-	-	-	-	-	-	-	-	-	-	7	30.3
128	3	23.5	-	-	-	-	-	-	-	-	-	-	1	3.3	-	-	-	-	-	-	4	26.8
129	3	9.4	-	-	-	-	-	-	-	-	-	-	-	-	-	-	-	-	-	-	3	9.4
130	28	244.6	-	-	-	-	-	-	-	-	-	-	-	-	-	-	-	-	-	-	28	244.6
131	10	63.4	-	-	-	-	-	-	-	-	-	-	-	-	-	-	-	-	-	-	10	63.4
132	162	495.1	27	159.3	-	-	-	-	-	-	1	2.0	-	-	-	-	-	-	-	-	190	656.4
134	201	1124.7	-	-	-	-	-	-	-	-	2	5.6	-	-	-	-	-	-	-	-	203	1130.3
137	67	425.2	-	-	-	-	-	-	-	-	6	78.0	-	-	-	-	-	-	-	-	73	503.2
138	89	491.2	-	-	-	-	-	-	-	-	2	64.9	-	-	-	-	-	-	-	-	91	556.1
139	115	765.5	-	-	-	-	-	-	-	-	-	-	-	-	-	-	-	-	-	-	115	765.5
141	49	307.5	2	2.7	1	2.3	-	-	-	-	-	-	-	-	-	-	-	-	-	-	52	312.5
142	17	149.3	-	-	-	-	1	2.0	-	-	1	3.5	-	-	-	-	-	-	-	-	19	154.8
143	74	446.3	-	-	-	-	-	-	-	-	-	-	-	-	-	-	-	-	-	-	74	446.3
144	7	8.4	-	-	-	-	-	-	-	-	-	-	-	-	-	-	-	-	-	-	7	8.4
146	35	197.1	-	-	-	-	-	-	-	-	-	-	-	-	-	-	-	-	-	-	35	197.1
147	14	35.9	-	-	-	-	-	-	-	-	-	-	-	-	-	-	-	-	-	-	14	35.9
148	30	132.3	-	-	-	-	1	6.6	-	-	-	-	-	-	-	-	-	-	-	-	31	138.9
149	58	296.3	1	7.5	-	-	4	15.9	-	-	-	-	-	-	-	-	-	-	-	-	63	319.7
151	29	260.0	-	-	-	-	-	-	-	-	-	-	-	-	-	-	-	-	-	-	29	260.0
152	24	85.0	-	-	-	-	-	-	-	-	-	-	-	-	-	-	-	-	-	-	24	85.0
153	9	37.4	-	-	-	-	-	-	-	-	-	-	-	-	-	-	-	-	-	-	9	37.4
154	2	15.5	-	-	-	-	-	-	-	-	-	-	-	-	-	-	-	-	-	-	2	15.5
155	12	57.3	-	-	-	-	-	-	-	-	-	-	-	-	-	-	-	-	-	-	12	57.3
156	18	102.9	-	-	-	-	-	-	-	-	-	-	-	-	-	-	-	-	-	-	18	102.9
157	15	75.3	-	-	-	-	-	-	-	-	-	-	-	-	-	-	-	-	-	-	15	75.3
159	2	5.8	-	-	-	-	-	-	-	-	-	-	-	-	-	-	-	-	1	2.1	3	7.9
160	43	334.1	-	-	-	-	-	-	-	-	-	-	-	-	-	-	-	-	-	-	43	334.1
161	28	152.8	-	-	-	-	-	-	-	-	-	-	-	-	-	-	-	-	-	-	28	152.8
162	4	17.4	-	-	-	-	-	-	-	-	-	-	-	-	-	-	-	-	-	-	4	17.4
163	7	28.5	-	-	-	-	-	-	-	-	-	-	-	-	-	-	-	-	-	-	7	28.5
164	56	549.7	-	-	-	-	-	-	-	-	-	-	-	-	-	-	-	-	-	-	56	549.7
165	55	267.3	-	-	-	-	-	-	-	-	3	3.9	-	-	-	-	-	-	-	-	49	271.2
166	122	747.4	-	-	-	-	-	-	-	-	6	33.1	-	-	-	-	-	-	-	-	128	780.5
167	7	14.8	-	-	-	-	-	-	-	-	-	-	-	-	-	-	-	-	-	-	7	14.8
168	48	302.5	-	-	6	45.0	-	-	-	-	-	-	-	-	-	-	-	-	-	-	54	347.5
169	197	1655.3	-	-	-	-	-	-	-	-	-	-	-	-	-	-	-	-	-	-	197	1655.3

Key
LS –Limestone
G/G–Grit/Grog

Table 19. Ceramic Tools and Unidentified Objects

Feature	N	Wt(g)	Temper/Ext.	Description
38	1	38.1	grog/plain	discoidal
93	1	6.8	grog/plain	perforated disc
126	2	8.4	grog/plain	unidentified
138	1	3.4	grog/plain	unidentified
Total	5	56.7		

Table 20. Pipe Fragments

Feature	N	Wt(g)	Temper/Ext.	Description
18	1	58.2	grog/plain	turtle effigy on bowl frag.
19	1	7.2	grog/plain	handle frag.
81	1	5.5	grog/plain	bowl frag.
82	1	3.6	grog/plain	bowl frag.
121	5	6.0	grog/plain	bowl frag.
160	1	1.2	grog/plain	stem frag.
166	1	4.2	grog/plain	handle frag.(?)
Total	11	85.9		

Table 21. Effigies and Possible Effigies

Feature	N	Wt(g)	Temper/Ext.	Comments
38	1	0.5	grog/plain	
58	1	10.8	grog/plain	
80	1	2.3	grog/plain	
92	1	5.5	none/plain	burned silt?
116	4	8.5	grog/plain	
117	4	5.6	grog/plain	
137	1	7.5	grog/plain	
138	1	1.5	grog/plain	
Total	14	42.2		

Area 3. It was ca. 4.1 cm in diameter, 1.9 cm thick, and weighed 38.1 g. It had a plain surface, and was grog tempered (Figure 41e). The plain surface had no alterations beyond slight depressions in the center of each face. Ceramic discoidals have been reported from other Patrick phase assemblages, and their first occurrence in the American Bottom was during the Patrick phase.

A ceramic artifact from Feature 93 in Occupation Area 2 was classified as a perforated ceramic disc (Figure 41f). Its estimated diameter was 3.4 cm and it was ca. 1.5 cm thick. It had a plain exterior surface and appeared to be grog tempered.

Effigies and Effigy Fragments

Fourteen complete and fragmentary effigies were found (Table 21). They did not appear to have been manufactured from the same pastes as the jars and bowls, but rather from pastes similar to those of the grog-tempered miniature vessels. An effigy from Feature 116 apparently depicted a dog's head (Figure 41d); the effigy had a snout, one eye, and ears. It was ca. 2.4 cm long, 1.4 cm wide, and 1.8 cm high. It appeared to be grog tempered.

Pipes and Pipe Fragments

Ceramic pipes were represented by four bowl fragments, one stem fragment, and two handle fragments (Table 20). Two distinct styles, referred to as Category 1 and Category 2, were apparent among the pipe fragments. The Category 1 specimens included pipe bowl fragments from Features 81 (Occupation Area 1), 82 (Occupation Area 2), and 121 (Occupation Area 3). There were at least three Category 1 pipes. They were comparatively small, and the pipe bowls perhaps had been molded around potters' thumbs. A stem fragment from Feature 160 (Occupation Area 4), was also a Category 1 specimen. It had a maximum exterior diameter of 12 mm and a minimum hole diameter of 1 mm. All of these fragments were grog tempered and had plain exteriors. Overall, the Category 1 pipes shared certain characteristics with the miniature vessels, in particular, similar light yellow or tan pastes and uneven exterior surface contours. The Category 1 specimens were cruder and smaller than the Category 2 pipes.

Three fragments were placed in Category 2, representing minimally two discrete pipes. Category 2 pipe fragments were large, had plain, smoothed surfaces; and had effigies and handles. The only Category 2 pipe bowl fragment was from Feature 18, a feature of nonoccupational affiliation. It was larger in size than Category 1 bowl fragments, particularly in terms of bowl height. The Category 2 bowl fragment was grog tempered and had a turtle effigy located on its exterior surface (Figure 41a). The turtle's limbs and head extended from the shell. It was positioned on the distal end of the pipe bowl; the head barely appeared over the bowl lip. The effigy also had eyes and an open mouth. This pipe was reminiscent of effigy pipes reported by Titterington (1935) as being associated with the so-called Bluff culture. The exact temporal placement of the effigy pipes described by Titterington (1935) is uncertain; they may date to a slightly later time period than the Fish Lake site pipes, perhaps to the Emergent Mississippian period (Plate 9).

Titterington (1935) has noted the widespread occurrence of handles on pipes and refers to them as handled pipes. While no handle was found on the Fish Lake site turtle effigy pipe, two other Category 2 pipe fragments were recovered that are believed to represent handles. Both handle fragments came from pits (Features 19 and 166) located within 4 m of the western excavation limits. These pits were 23 m apart. The Feature 19 specimen was a distal portion of a handle; it had a round stem, and its distal end was bulb-shaped (Figure 41b). The Feature 166 specimen was the medial portion of a handle. Both handle fragments were grog tempered and had plain, smoothed exterior surfaces. Patrick phase handled pipes are known from the Schlemmer site, where two complete specimens were recovered (Thomas Berres, personal communication).

Potters' Clay

Potters' clay consisted of pieces of nonfired gray clay that appeared to be tempered with grog. All of the potters' clay consisted of gray clay lumps that were clearly distinct from subsoil zones in the field. There were 13 potters' clay lumps, weighing a total of 214.7 g. Two of three features that yielded potters' clay were located in Occupation Area 4; the third feature was in Occupation Area 2.

Daub

Daub consisted of oxidized soil that had a rounded or amorphous shape. It was characterized by various types of cordage, thatch or stick impressions on the exterior surface. There were 73 daub fragments that collectively weighed 233.9 g. Daub fragments were found in 14% of the Fish Lake site features. Their distribution, however, did not include features in Occupation Area 4, and more than 50% of the daub fragments were found in Occupation Area 1. Daub fragments were found in pits, pits internal to the Feature 52 post structure, and in one keyhole structure.

Burned Clay

A total of 2852 items that collectively weighed 5877.0 g were placed in a burned clay category. These items represent both oxidized clay and oxidized silts. Burned clay was characterized as oxidized soil that had either a rounded or amorphous shape, but lacked the impressions on the

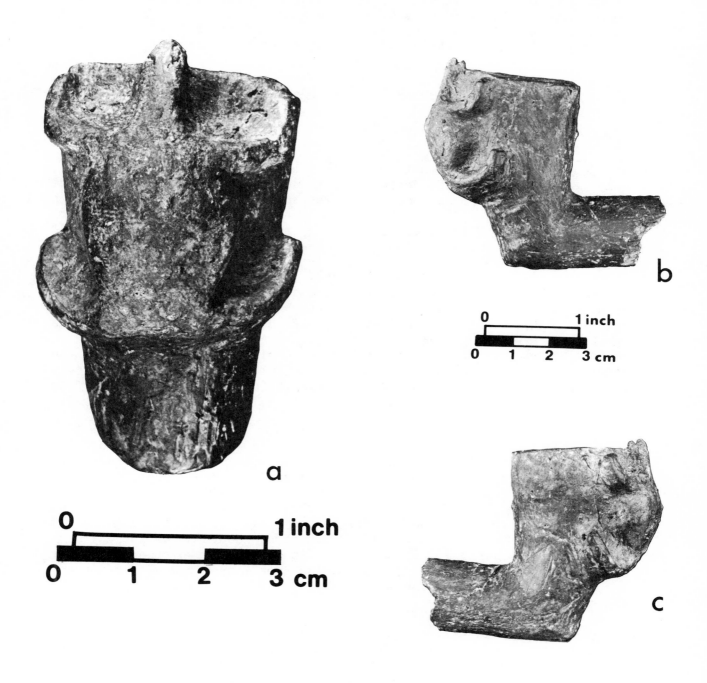

Plate 9. Turtle Effigy Pipe: a, front view; b-c, side views

exterior surface that typified the daub category. The burned clay fragments may have originated from cooking or heating fires. Due to their small size (mean=2.06 g), these items were not systematically recovered during feature excavations, although they were recovered from 59% of the features distributed throughout the Fish Lake site.

Distribution of Fish Lake Ceramics

Vessel Distribution

The 151 Fish Lake vessels were distributed in 59 features. However, only 25 of the Fish Lake features contained more than 2 vessels. These features were concentrated along the western edges of Occupation Areas 1, 2, and 3 (Figure 42). The total number of vessels in each occupation area ranged from 62 in Occupation Area 1 to 7 in Occupation Area 4 (Table 22). Twenty-six Fish Lake vessels were recovered from features of nonoccupational affiliation. They were primarily derived from Features 18, 60, 79, 143, and 168. Overall, 85% of the vessels recovered from features came from pits and the remaining 15% from the keyhole structures. Interestingly, the keyhole structures comprised only 4% of the Patrick phase features, but they contained 15% of the vessels. This may indicate either that more vessels were used in keyhole structures than in pits, or more likely, it simply reflects the comparatively larger keyhole structure volumes. Among the keyhole structures there was a considerable range in the number of vessels, from zero in Feature 117 to eight in Feature 81.

Jars and bowls each comprised fairly consistent percentages of the various occupation area assemblages. Jars accounted for between 68% (Occupation Area 3) and 75% (Occupation Area 2) of the occupation area assemblages. Bowls accounted for from 13% (Occupation Area 1) to 25% (Occupation Area 3). The percentages of jars and bowls recovered from features of nonoccupational affiliation fell within the ranges given above. The distribution of miniature vessels, however, was not uniform. Occupation Area 1 had 78% of the miniature vessels. Two other miniature vessels were from a feature in Occupation Area 2 and from a feature of nonoccupational affiliation. Two-thirds of the miniature vessels and all of the jar/bowls came from pits.

Only rarely did multiple bowls or miniature vessels occur in a single pit (Figure 43). The 25 bowls and 9 miniature vessels were distributed in 22 and 8 features, respectively. By contrast, the 108 jars were found in 52 features. In 28 of those features, jars were the only type of vessel recovered.

Bowls and miniature vessels tended to be found with, and were perhaps used with, jars. Bowls and miniature vesssels were associated with jars in 18 and 6 features, respectively. Only two features had all three vessel forms. In another feature (Feature 165) only the bowl and miniature vessel categories occurred.

Known or suspected ceramic fits between two or more features are summarized in Figure 44. Ceramic fits occurred among features within Occupation Areas 1, 2, and 3. They involved adjacent or superimposed features and features separated by less than 4 m. Ceramics from three features in different occupation areas also fit together (Features 94 and 98 in Occupation Area 2 and Feature 121 in Occupation Area 3). This ceramic fit linked features nearly 9 m apart. A second ceramic fit between occupation areas involved Feature 101 in Occupation Area 2 and Feature 151 in Occupation Area 3; these features were located ca. 11 m apart.

Assemblage Distribution

The preceding sections concentrated on Fish Lake site rim sherds. Several aspects of the overall ceramic assemblage distribution, however, provide insights unavailable from a study of vessels alone. The distribution of the entire ceramic assemblage (by weight) among occupation areas is compared with the distribution of vessels in Table 23. There was a close correspondence between the weight of the ceramic assemblage and the numbers of vessels recovered from the occupation areas and from features of nonoccupational affiliation. This suggests that the Fish Lake site vessels are representative of the ceramic assemblage as a whole.

For comparative purposes a figure here referred to as the ceramic recovery estimate, has been calculated for the Fish Lake assemblage. A ceramic recovery estimate of 268.5 g per vessel was calculated by dividing the weight of the entire ceramic assemblage recovered from feature contexts (40,536.4 g) by the number of vessels (N=151). The recovery estimate for complete vessels, of course, would have been much higher. For example, several complete Mund phase vessels were found at the Mund site; their recovery estimate was 1983.4 g (Fortier et al. 1982). The Fish Lake site ceramic recovery estimate of 268.5 g represents only 13.5% of the Mund site figure for complete vessels. This percentage figure was comparable to that of the entire Mund phase assemblage at the Mund (Fortier et al. 1982) and George Reeves sites (Table 24). Apparently, significant portions of the vessels were not abandoned in Late Woodland period features. At least some of the Fish Lake sherds were probably used to provide grog temper for new vessels. Some may have been purposely removed from the site area.

Lip Impression Distribution

Vessels with plain dowel and cordwrapped dowel lip impressions were distributed throughout the occupation areas. The vertical and oblique varieties of these lip impression types were also uniformly distributed.

128

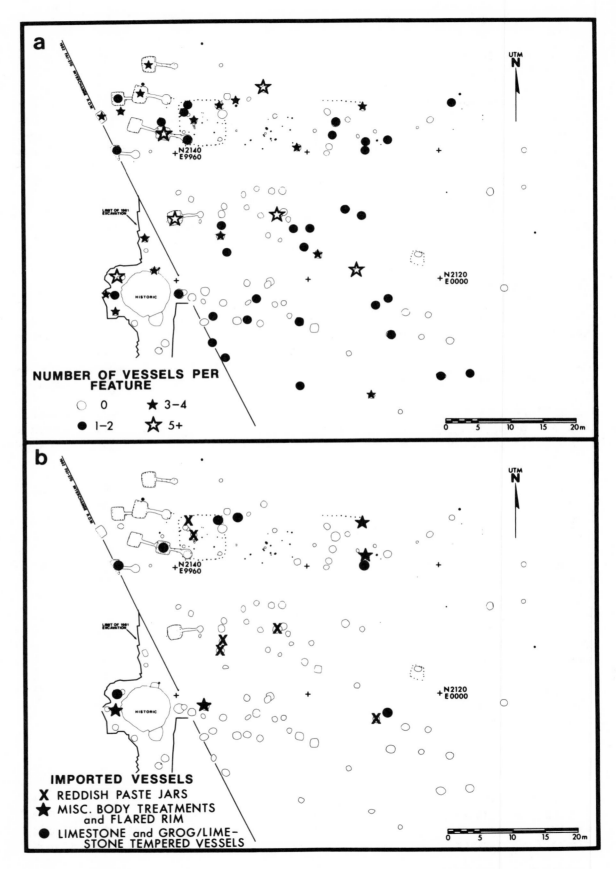

Figure 42. Distribution of Vessels: a, number of vessels per feature; b, possible imported vessels

129

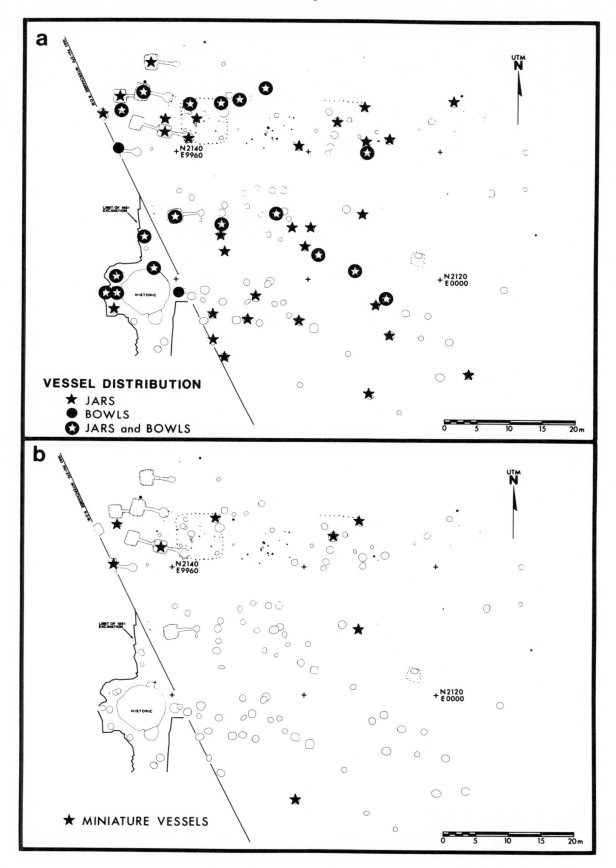

Figure 43. Distribution of Vessels

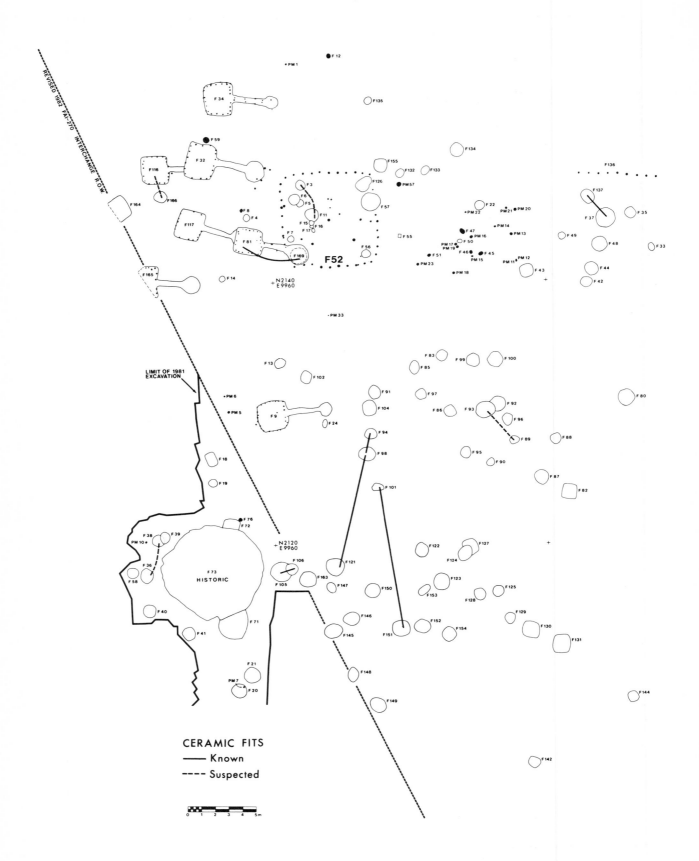

Figure 44. Vessel Fits

Table 22. Comparisons of Assemblage and Vessel
Percentages by Occupation Area

Occupation Area	Assemblage Wt(g)	%	Vessel N	%	Mean Wt(g) Per Vessel
1	17,003.4	41.9	62	41.1	274.2
2	7,030.4	17.3	28	18.5	251.1
3	9,234.9	22.8	28	18.5	329.8
4	1,286.7	3.2	7	4.7	183.8
N/A	5,981.0	14.8	26	17.2	230.0
Total	40,536.4		151		268.5

N/A - Nonoccupational affiliation

Table 23. Ceramic Density by Occupation Area

Occupation Area	Mean	Ceramic Density* Low	High
1	0.6	0.1 (Feas. 23, 28, 57, 155)	4.0 (Fea. 132)
2	0.9	0.1 (Feas. 13, 96, 99, 102)	2.7 (Feas. 89, 90)
3	1.5	0.1 (Fea. 20)	5.7 (Fea. 38)
4	0.6	0.1 (Feas. 119, 159, 167)	2.0 (Fea. 160)
N/A	1.9	0.1 (Fea. 66)	8.9 (Fea. 79)
Total Mean	0.9		

* Ceramic density = ceramic assemblage weight (g) per dm3
  of feature fill

N/A - Nonoccupational affiliation

Table 24. Ceramic Recovery Estimate for Late Woodland Vessels

Site	Ceramic Assemblage (g)	Vessels (N)	Vessel Mean Wt(g)	Ceramic Recovery Estimate# (%)
Mund (11-S-435)##	71,210.5	323	220.5	11.1
George Reeves (11-S-650)###	14,502.8	45	322.3	16.2
Fish Lake (11-Mo-608)####	40,536.4	151	268.5	13.5

Mean weight (1983.4 g) for complete Late Woodland vessels is based on three Mund phase vessels from the Mund site. The ceramic recovery estimate (%) represents the ratio between the mean vessel weight for each assemblage and the mean weight for the known complete Late Woodland vessels.

Fortier et al. (1982)

McElrath and Finney (report in progress)

Includes bowls; the other assemblages do not include bowls

The vessels with plain V-shaped and plain slash impressions, however, were not uniformly distributed. Vessels with plain V-shaped lip impressions were restricted to Occupation Area 1 (Figure 45b). Vessels with plain slash lip impressions were found in Occupation Areas 2 and 4 as well as in one feature of nonoccupational affiliation, which is not shown in Figure 45. Vessels with impressions on their superior lip surfaces were restricted to Occupation Area 3 and to two features of nonoccupational affiliation (Figures 45b and 46).

The distributions of vessels with plain V-shaped and plain slashed lip impressions indicate the presence of at least two potters in the Fish Lake community. Although these lip impression types could have been produced by a single potter in a prehistoric community, their differential distribution would seem to imply otherwise.

The mutually exclusive distributions of vessels with plain V-shaped and plain slashed lip impressions is unusual. Analyses of intrasite vessel distributions are not available for Patrick phase sites, although plain V-shaped and plain slashed lip impressions are known from American Bottom sites. One such study, however, is available for a Mund phase site (Fortier et al. 1982). At the Mund site, 70% to 80% of vessels with a single type of lip impression were restricted to two occupation areas, and 70% to 80% of vessels with a different form of lip impression were restricted to two other occupation areas. The best explanation for these data is the probable presence of two potters.

Nonlocal Vessels

Identifying nonlocal vessels at the Fish Lake site was difficult because of the ubiquitous occurrence of cordmarking and lip modification on vessels. Local vessels are referred to here as vessels manufactured at or near (within 1 km) of the Fish Lake site. Nonlocal vessels were grouped in two categories. One category included all vessels from other portions of the American Bottom; the other category referred to nonlocal trade wares derived from portions of the Midwest outside the American Bottom. The second category of vessels was not represented in the Fish Lake assemblage.

Six jars exhibited a distinctive red paste, which clearly stood out in the Fish Lake assemblage. It has been suggested that such red pastes were derived from upland clays. Floodplain sources for red pastes are unknown (Porter 1964). The position of the Fish Lake site far out on the floodplain indicated that the six red paste jars were obtained as finished products. These jars were found in three of the four occupation areas (Figure 42).

A number of infrequently occurring body treatments and one rim form suggested nonlocal origins for several vessels. None of these vessels were typical of the Fish Lake site assemblage. These specimens included a slipped miniature vessel (138-2), a jar with punctations (138-1), a

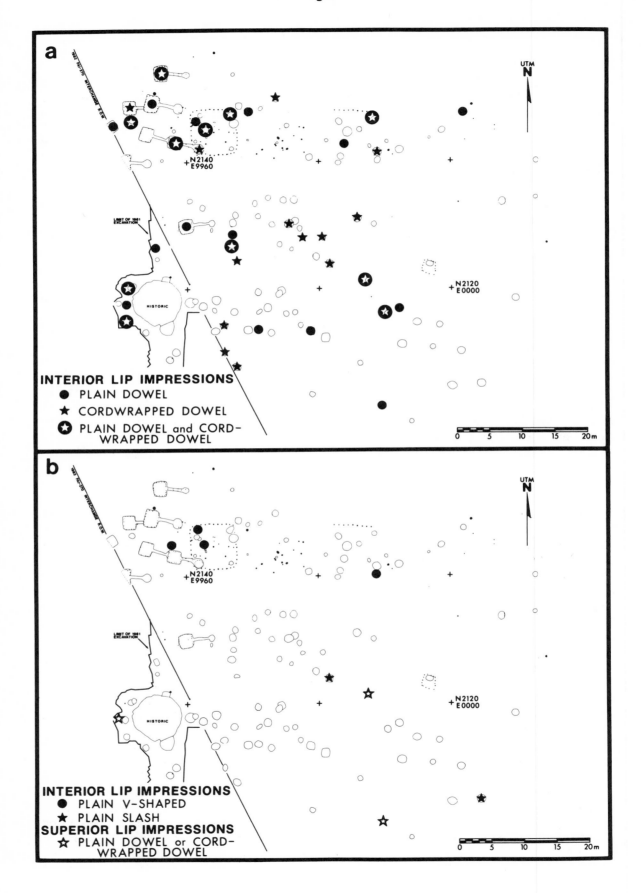

Figure 45. Distribution of Interior and Superior Lip Impressions

135

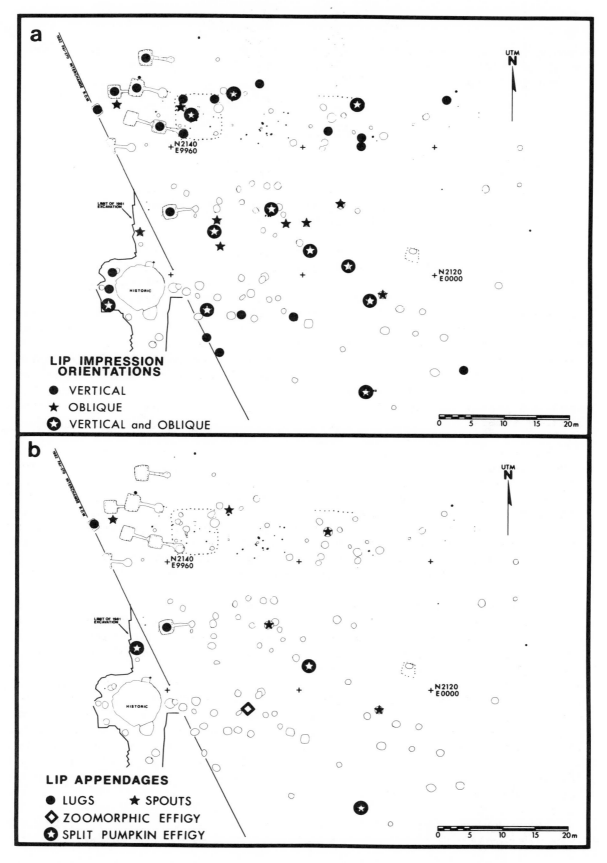

Figure 46. Distribution of Lip Impression Orientations and Lip Appendages

vessel with applique nodes (Feature 121), a shell-slipped jar (36-2), and a jar with a flared rim (28-1). These five specimens occurred in Occupation Areas 1 and 3 (Figure 42).

Vessel Usage and Manufacture

Only general statements can be made about the use of jars, bowls, and miniature vessels as portable containers in the Fish Lake community. Specific functions could not be assigned to specific vessels, particularly since many vessel forms have ethnographically been documented as having multifunctional uses.

Jars are usually considered as multipurpose cooking, storage, and water-hauling vessels. There are two lines of evidence at the Fish Lake site for their use in cooking. First, a sizeable portion of jar rim sherds exhibited an encrusted, charred organic residue. This is interpreted as having been caused by cooking. Specimens from the Fish Lake site had this organic residue on both interior and exterior surfaces, often in the lip area. There was a greater incidence of residue occurrence on the exterior surfaces, probably because residues would have more easily become entrapped between the cordmarked impressions. Charred organic residues are fairly common on Late Woodland jars from the Fish Lake, Mund, George Reeves, and Carbon Dioxide sites.

Bowls contrasted with jars in their nonconstricting shape. They were viewed as serving containers as well as cooking vessels. Charred organic residues were found on some of the Fish Lake bowls, but such residues occurred less often on bowls than on jars. Of great significance in the Fish Lake assemblage was the very presence of bowls; they did not occur in the preceding Late Woodland Rosewood and Mund phases. It is assumed that the addition of bowls to the Late Woodland ceramic assemblage during the Patrick phase signifies the introduction of as yet unspecified activities or methods of preparing food.

Miniature vessels are common in Late Woodland assemblages from the American Bottom. They are often viewed as paint pots, childrens' toys, or vessels produced by apprentice potters. These interpretations are influenced by the aesthetically crude appearance of miniature vessels. The suggestion that they were manufactured by persons other than the usual village potters, however, may be accurate. Other suggested functions for these vessels include use as drinking cups and grain scoops (Fortier et al. 1982). Another possibility is suggested in the ethnographic accounts of Hopi pottery manufacturing: "Finally in firing the large water jar, a toy water jar of similar shape to the large one, is cast into the fire to propitiate the spirits. By this act the potter ensures that her large jar will come from the fire uncracked and evenly burnt" (Beaglehole 1937:57).

Vessels were shaped by the paddle and anvil technique. This was

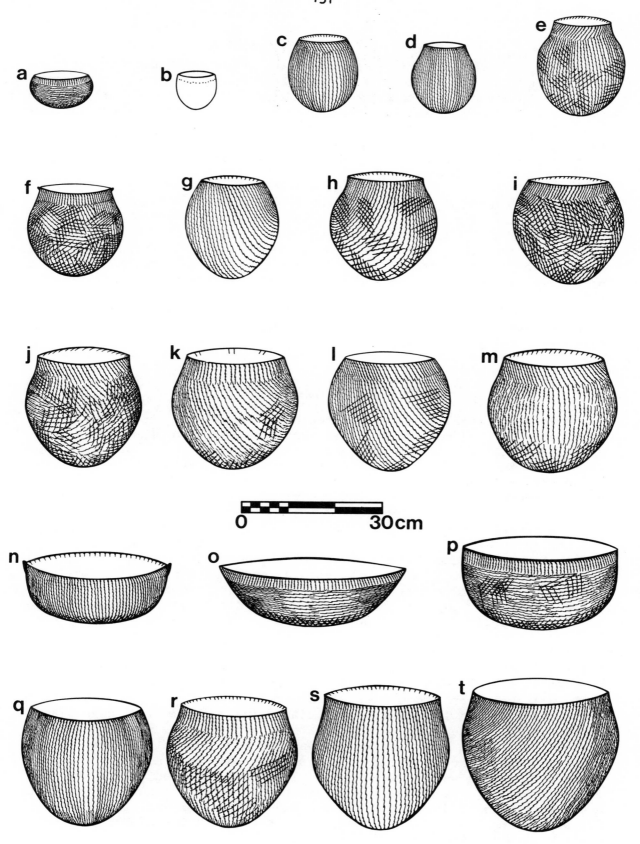

Figure 47. Patrick Phase Ceramic Vessels from the Fish Lake site

inferred from the plain interior surfaces, which exhibited fingerprints and fingerlobe impressions, and from the cordmarked exterior surfaces, with random cordmarking patterns that implied the use of cordwrapped paddles. Cordmarking on the uppermost 5 cm to 10 cm of the exterior rim would have been applied by rolling a cordwrapped dowel across that portion of the vessel, as indicated by the consistent cordmark orientations. Lip impressions, when present, would have been the last item added to the vessel.

The most notable aspect of vessel breakage was the tendency for jars to be broken along their shoulders. At the Fish Lake site, the lack of large rim sherds was notable when compared to the Late Woodland components at the Mund and George Reeves sites. Large rim sherds included those that were 10 cm by 10 cm or greater in size. This lack of large rim sherds may be a reflection of vessel recycling at the Fish Lake site. The Fish Lake ceramic assemblage was more than 95% grog tempered. It is very likely that this temper was available through the cannibalization of broken vessels. Sherds were also occasionally reworked into rounded discs.

Summary of Fish Lake Ceramics

This ceramic analysis has focused on the stylistic and technological attributes of 151 Patrick phase vessels from the Fish Lake site. Three vessel forms, i.e., jars (72%), bowls (16%), and miniature vessels (6%) comprised the vessel assemblage (Figure 47). A few other vessels (6%) could not be separated into jar and bowl forms. A small quantity of ceramic nonvessel items were also recovered.

The vessel assemblage was remarkably uniform in terms of technique of manufacture and style. The variation that was present can be attributed to the manufacture of vessels by more than one potter and the introduction to the site of vessels made elsewhere in the American Bottom. The Fish Lake site vessels were probably used in many different activities, but cooking activities were directly indicated by the presence of charred residues on many jars and a few bowls.

Patrick phase ceramic assemblages are traditionally viewed as being rather bland and lacking in variation. Such changes in ceramic form and decoration that do exist are often interpreted as a consequence of time rather than internal variation. This analysis has shown, however, that considerable variation did occur within a single community assemblage, particularly in the areas of lip treatment and cordmark patterning. The mutually exclusive distributions of various lip impression types across the occupation areas of this site indicate that analyses of previously ignored micro-traits may be very useful for future studies of Patrick phase assemblage variation. It may be possible to eventually discern specific styles of decoration for certain localities in the American Bottom during the Patrick phase or an American Bottom Patrick phase style within the Midwest.

LITHIC ASSEMBLAGE

by Richard B. Lacampagne

A great variety of lithic material was recovered from the Patrick phase occupation at the Fish Lake site. Most of the material was obtained from features and postmolds (Table 25), but a small amount was found in the plowzone (Table 26). Additional material was recovered during surface surveys of the Fish Lake site; of the survey-derived material, only tools are described in this volume.

The entire lithic assemblage consisted of materials that had been discarded by the site's inhabitants. No intentionally cached lithic items were found. The lithic materials, with the exception of limestone, were rather scant, considering the size of the occupation area. This is most likely a function of the distance of lithic sources from the site.

Lithic materials were separated into two general categories: debitage and tools. Lithic items utilized as tools were separated into chert and nonchert categories. All lithic items from feature contexts were categorized, counted, weighed, and examined for evidence of use. Appendix 1 lists the recovered materials for each feature.

Raw Materials

The lithic raw materials included chert, hematite, igneous rock, limestone, limonite, Missouri River clinker, quartz, quartzite, sandstone, silicified sediment, siltstone, water-worn pebbles, unidentified rough rock, and historical materials. Most of this material would have been transported to the site from bluff outcroppings to the east and from stream beds that wash out from the bluffs. Some material may have come from the Missouri side of the Mississippi River or, possibly, from sources outside the immediate area. There are no lithic resources available in the immediate vicinity of the Fish Lake site.

The inhabitants of the Fish Lake site made efficient use of the materials they brought to the site. For example, over 25% of the chert, by weight, was modified to form tools (Figure 48). Tools from the site were fashioned out of chert, igneous rock, sandstone, silicified sediment, quartzite, and limestone. Limestone, and possibly sandstone and other rocks, were often used to line hearths and for secondary heating in earth-ovens and perhaps keyhole structures. Very few of the recovered lithic items could be considered nonfunctional.

Table 25. Materials from Feature Context

Material Type	N	Wt(g)	Wt %
Burned clay	2852	5877.0	3.0
Ceramics (vessel)	7638	40536.4	20.9
Ceramics (nonvessel)	43	399.5	0.2
Daub	73	233.9	0.1
Nonlithic subtotal	10606	47046.8	24.3
Chert (debitage)	2704	11725.7	6.0
Chert tools	62	1999.7	1.0
Hematite	3	4.7	0.1
Historic materials	3	85.7	0.1
Igneous rock	12	1491.7	0.8
Limestone	5977	115905.5	59.8
Missouri River clinker	6	59.6	0.1
Nonchert tools	55	6273.8	3.2
Quartz	1	1.2	0.1
Quartzite	9	1188.1	0.6
Retouched flakes	292	2032.0	1.0
Rough rock	33	1191.1	0.6
Sandstone	291	4629.2	2.4
Silicified sediment	3	75.5	0.1
Siltstone	10	51.5	0.1
Waterworn pebbles	38	160.8	0.1
Lithic subtotal	9499	146875.8	75.7
Total	20105	193922.6	

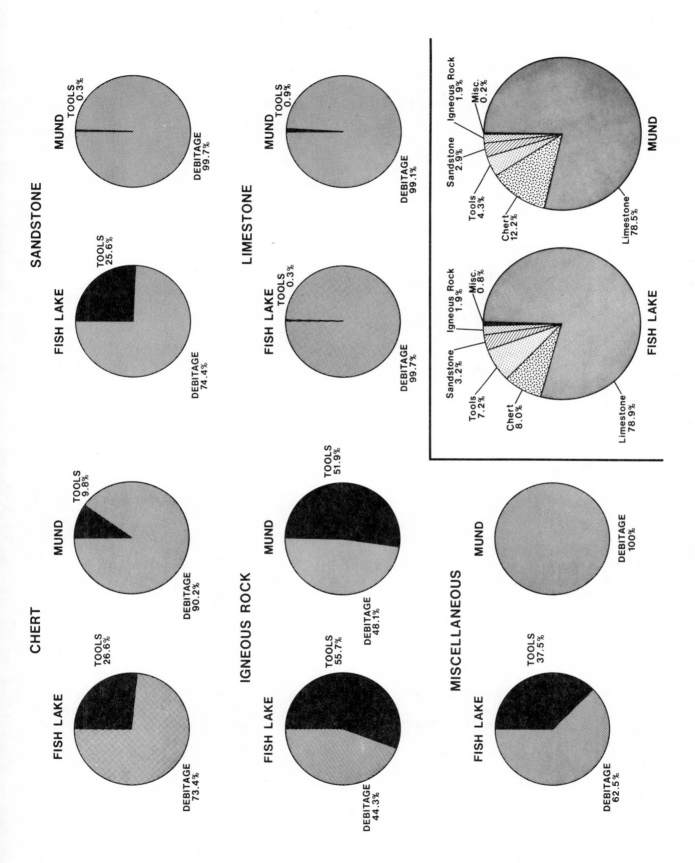

Figure 48. Lithic Raw Materials (by weight) from the Fish Lake and Mund Sites

Table 26. Materials from Plowzone

Material Type	N	Wt(g)
Burned clay	2	11.2
Ceramics	141	732.8
Chert	102	1052.8
Cinder	1	4.0
Limestone	13	906.5
Road gravel	1	28.0
Sandstone	3	62.0
Silicified sediment	1	5.6
Tools	31	284.1
Total	295	3087.0

Tool Type	N	Wt(g)
Flake point	1	1.9
Flake point	1	1.1
Flake point	1	0.5
Reworked core	1	24.2
Retouched flakes	26	190.9
Celt fragment	1	65.5

Surface and Plowzone Materials

A great deal of lithic debris was recovered during surface surveys of the Fish Lake site (Wittry 1981). Most of this material was located on the ridge directly south of the excavated portion of the site. Only the tools recovered from the surface are described below. The tools represented several different components; they are listed in Table 27 and illustrated in Figure 49.

Table 27. Tools from Surface Contexts

Description	Figure	Blade Length (cm)	Stem Length (cm)	Maximum Length (cm)	Shoulder Width (cm)	Neck Width (cm)	Base Width (cm)	Maximum Thickness (cm)	Wt(g)	Chert Type
Expanding stem point	49a	-	0.8	1.5	1.0	0.7	1.0	0.3	0.4	Burlington
Expanding stem point	49b	1.7	0.7	2.4	0.9	0.6	0.8	0.3	0.5	Burlington
Expanding stem point	49c	1.3	0.6	1.9	0.8	0.6	0.8	0.3	0.4	Burlington
Expanding stem point	49d	-	1.6	5.5	-	2.1	2.6	1.2	16.3	Burlington
Contracting stem point	49i	5.6	-	6.5	3.1	2.1	-	0.9	20.3	Dongola
Contracting stem point	49j	4.7	2.2	6.9	2.6	-	0.9	1.1	18.1	Indeterminate
Point base	-	-	-	-	-	0.9	1.3	0.2	0.5	Burlington
Point base	-	-	-	-	-	-	2.5	0.5	1.6	Burlington
Hoe fragment	49e	-	-	-	-	-	-	-	18.7	Burlington
Hoe/scraper fragment	49f	-	-	-	-	-	-	-	44.7	Indeterminate
Hoe fragment	49k	-	-	-	-	-	-	-	99.9	Mill Creek
Flake scraper	49g	-	-	-	-	-	-	-	5.2	Burlington
End scraper	49h	-	-	-	-	-	-	-	4.0	Salem Creamy
Celt fragment	-	-	-	-	-	-	-	-	232.5	Nonchert

Six projectile points and two point bases were recovered from surface contexts. Three of these points (Figure 49a-c) and a base were small bifacial points. They were similar to points recovered from Patrick phase features at the site. The other points apparently were not associated with the Patrick phase assemblage. One, an expanding stemmed point that had been reworked, may date to any time along the Archaic to Late Woodland continuum. Two contracting stemmed points were identified. One had been fashioned from Dongola chert, and resembled an Early to Middle Woodland Waubesa type (Perino 1971a:98-99) [Figure 49j]. The other point (Figure 49i) had been reworked and exhibited a snapped base, which could have been either broken or created intentionally. This point resembled those of the Archaic through Middle Woodland periods. The remaining point base was possibly from an expanding stemmed point; it was too large to be a Patrick phase point.

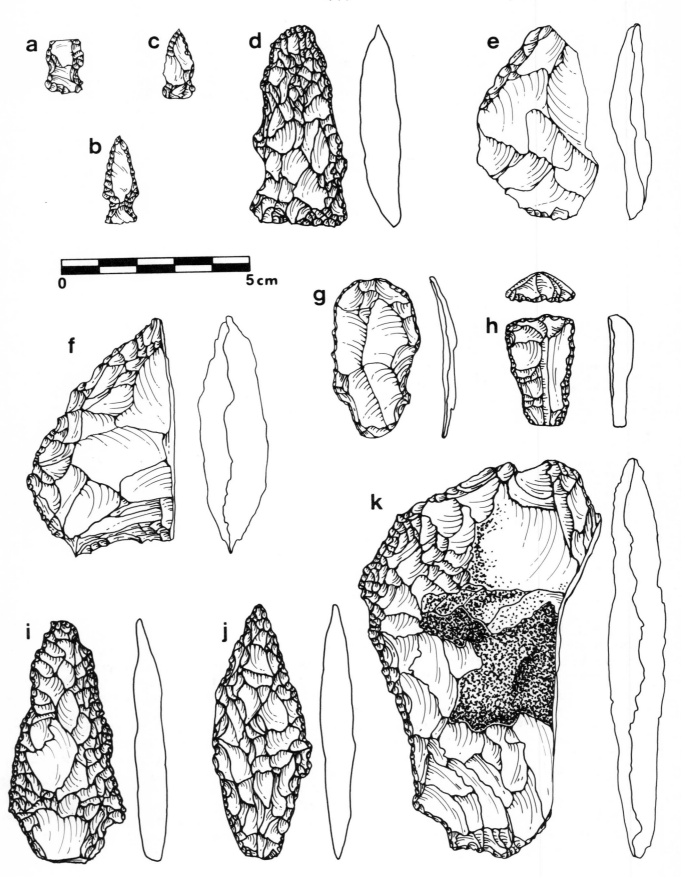

Figure 49.   Chert Tools from Surface Contexts

Three hoe fragments were also recovered. All exhibited some silica gloss near their utilized edges. The largest specimen (Figure 49k) had been made from Mill Creek chert. Chert hoes are common in the Emergent Mississippian and Mississippian periods; rarely are they encountered in earlier assemblages.

A flake scraper (Figure 49g) and an end scraper (Figure 49h) also were found on the surface. The end scraper was triangular in profile and had steep retouching along its edges. This tool resembled thumb scrapers often found in later Mississippian and Oneota sites (Griffin 1952).

The only nonchert tool recovered from the surface was a fragmentary celt. The bit end of this tool was missing; the butt end was battered.

A small amount of cultural material was recovered during machine stripping of the plowzone, during shovel-scraping for pit definition, and from feature backdirt. It is surprising that so little material was found in the plowzone of so heavily occupied a site.

The small plowzone assemblage represents materials dislodged from features truncated by plowing and materials once distributed on the occupational surface of the site. The low debris density may be because of soil build-up on the site surface postdating the Late Woodland occupation. If this occurred, pit features were probably only minimally disturbed by plowing. The 3,087 g of cultural material recovered from the Fish Lake plowzone contrasted with the large amount of plowzone materials recovered from other sites. The Mund site excavations produced over 100,000 g of material from plowzone contexts above the Late Woodland occupational area at that site. The features at the Fish Lake site also contained a lower density of materials than features at the Mund site. These results suggest that the overall intensity of occupation at the Fish Lake site was less than that at the Mund site. This suggests that the amount of surface materials recovered from a site may be a useful indicator of subsurface feature density.

A total of 31 lithic items were recovered from the plowzone, including 26 retouched flakes. Three small bifacial points were also recovered in the plowzone, including corner-notched, triangular, and serrated blade points. A reworked core and a celt fragment were also found in the plowzone.

Feature Materials

Chert Debitage

Chert represents the second most common lithic material, after limestone, at the Fish Lake site. Chert types from local Burlington, Ste. Genevieve, Salem, and St. Louis limestone formations were represented in the assemblage.

Chert tools were separated from debitage and are dealt with in a later section. All nonutilized (nontool) chert was categorized by chert type and by flake type. The debitage included cores and core fragments, block fractures, primary decortication flakes, secondary decortication flakes, and reduction flakes. Blades were not found in the assemblage.

A small percentage of the chert debitage exhibited thermal alteration. Heat treatment of chert results in changes in color and texture; the chert often turns shiny or waxy. These changes vary depending on the type of chert, and they are as yet not well documented. It has been suggested that the heating of chert increases its flaking qualities, making the production of chert tools easier (Crabtree and Butler 1964). Heat treatment was evident on many of the small retouch flakes in the Fish Lake assemblage, but it was virtually absent on large flakes and block fractures. This suggests that some chert tools were heated just prior to the final fine retouching stage of manufacture.

A full range of chert manufacturing stages was represented by items in the Fish Lake assemblage (Table 28). Very few large cores were recovered at the site; over 77% of the debitage pieces consisted of reduction flakes that lacked cortex. This indicates that, for the most part, only prepared cores and large flakes were brought to the site where they were then subjected to further modification. In general, chert knapping at the Fish Lake site may be characterized as relating primarily to tool maintenance activities.

The distributions of cherts and of flake types across the site were surprisingly uniform. The amount of chert recovered per feature did not seem to reflect either its morphological type or source. Chert debitage recovered from pits was dispersed throughout the fills; very few concentrations of lithic material were found. This indicates that the chert found in pit fills resulted from debris disposal. Therefore, the Fish Lake site pits functioned, at least partially, as receptacles for discarded chert rather than as pits associated with chert tool manufacture. Chert tool manufacturing areas may have been located between pits, and the unused chert could have been swept into open pits.

Cores

Cores are defined as sizable pieces of chert that exhibit evidence of purposeful flake removal. All cores were multidirectionally flaked; no prismatic (blade) cores were observed. About half of the cores had some cortex present on their surfaces. Core fragments are defined as broken pieces of cores or expended cores. Sixty-three cores and core fragments were recovered; the mean weight of these items was 47.3 g. However, the mean weight of the cores is somewhat misleading because of the inclusion of a single large core (ca. 800 g) recovered from Feature 72. The majority of cores had been made from Salem and unidentified chert types; only a few Burlington and Ste. Genevieve cores were present in the assemblage. Several types of tools had been made from cores, including chert hammerstones, reworked cores, and gouges or wedges.

Table 28. Cores, Block Fractures and Flakes
from Feature Contexts

Manufacturing Stages	N	N %	Wt(g)	Wt %	Mean Wt(g) per Item
Cores	63	2.3	2980.4	25.4	47.3
Block fractures	247	9.1	3280.0	28.0	13.3
Primary decortication flakes	52	1.9	828.8	7.1	15.9
Secondary decortication flakes	258	9.5	1372.7	11.7	5.3
Reduction flakes	2084	77.1	3263.8	27.8	1.6
Total	2704		11725.7		4.3

Table 29. Debitage Chert Types from Feature Contexts

Chert Type	N	N %	Wt(g)	Wt %	Mean Wt(g) per Item
Burlington	596	22.0	1313.1	11.2	2.2
Ste. Genevieve	158	5.8	1123.3	9.6	7.1
Tan Speckled	344	12.7	1763.9	15.0	5.1
Salem Creamy	288	10.6	1408.9	12.0	4.9
Appaloosa	6	0.2	114.2	1.0	19.0
Gray Oolitic	299	11.0	836.9	7.1	2.8
Old Blue	1	<0.1	4.4	<0.1	4.4
Indeterminate	1012	37.4	5161.0	44.0	5.1
Total	2704		11725.7		4.3

Block Fractures

Block fractures are angular pieces of chert that do not exhibit flake scars or flake characteristics. They result from the preparation of large chert pieces or nodules. The unwanted cortex or low grade chert rinds are removed before flakes are driven from the core. Many small block fractures were recovered from the Fish Lake site that did not exhibit cortex; these could represent shatter that resulted from striking cores during flake removal. Many large pieces were also recovered that had cortex present, and most of these were of unidentified chert types. Burning or scorching was observed on several block fractures. This may indicate the heating of chert nodules for core preparation, or the burning of discarded block fractures in cooking and trash pits. The mean weight of block fractures was 13.3 g.

Flakes

Primary decortication flakes are large chert pieces that have cortex present on their dorsal surface and fresh ventral surfaces. These flakes are produced during the initial stage of chert core or nodule reduction. Most of the primary decortication flakes recovered from the Fish Lake site were of unidentified and Salem cherts. The mean weight of these flakes was 15.9 g.

Secondary decortication flakes are flakes that have cortex present on portions of their dorsal surfaces. Primary and secondary decortication flakes are removed from cores in a similar manner. Some flakes in the Fish Lake assemblage that had been made from secondary decortication flakes showed evidence of having been later retouched. The sizes of decortication flakes varied greatly; their mean weight was 5.3 g.

Reduction flakes include all chert pieces that have no cortex but exhibit flake characteristics, including a bulb of percussion, ventral and dorsal surfaces, and the like. There was a great diversity in reduction flake size and shape, and their mean weight was 1.6 g. Many large, heavy flakes had been made from Tan Speckled chert; most of the smaller flakes had been made from Burlington or Salem Creamy cherts. Smaller, so-called shatter flakes were also included in this category. Many of these flakes were recovered from flotation samples. Shatter flakes result from percussive action during chert knapping and often do not exhibit true flake characteristics. Over 77% of the chert items recovered from the site were reduction flakes (Table 28). In addition, almost all the tools recovered from the site had been fashioned from these smaller flakes.

Blades

Although blades were not found at the Fish Lake site, they were previously used during Middle Woodland times. A small number of blades and retouched blades were found in the preceding Mund phase occupations at the Mund (Fortier et al. 1982) and Columbia Quarry (Finney and Bentz 1983) sites. This suggests that a blade technology continued into the earlier phases of the Late Woodland period, but it subsequently disappeared in the Patrick phase.

Debitage Chert Types

All chert debitage and tools recovered from feature contexts were categorized by chert type (Table 29). Almost all of the chert recovered from the site would have been available from limestone formations in the American Bottom. Only Burlington chert, which has sources on the western side of the Mississippi River as well as in the American Bottom, and Dongola chert (represented by a single flake point) may have been imported to the site from outside the immediate vicinity. Eight distinct chert types were identified: Burlington, Ste. Genevieve, Tan Speckled, Old Blue, Salem Creamy, Appaloosa, Gray Oolitic, and Dongola. The Tan Speckled, Old Blue, and Salem Creamy types were probably derived from local Salem limestone formations. Appaloosa and Gray Oolitic may have been obtained from the Salem or St. Louis limestone formations. All chert that did not fit into these categories was included in an unidentified category.

Burlington chert was represented at Fish Lake by two different types. A glossy variety was white, homogeneous, and fine grained, with a medium glossy texture, which would have been easily flaked. It was used extensively by prehistoric people in the American Bottom from Archaic through Mississippian periods. The other type of Burlington chert had a chalky, fossiliferous texture and was white or light gray. This chert type was medium grained with many small fossil impurities. When heated, Burlington chert turns red, pink, purple, or gray-black. This chert type was represented mostly by medium to small reduction flakes. Over 45% of the chert tools at the Fish Lake site had been made from Burlington chert, including 13 of a total of 22 projectile points (Table 30). The source for this chert was the Keokuk-Burlington limestone formations that outcrop near Valmeyer, Illinois, and possibly other places in the American Bottom. This chert also outcrops on the Missouri side of the Mississippi River.

Ste. Genevieve chert would have been available in the Ste. Genevieve limestone outcrops in St. Clair and Monroe counties in the American Bottom area. Three varieties of this chert (purple speckled, orange speckled, and red) were represented in the Fish Lake assemblage and have been described elsewhere (Fortier 1981a; Fortier et al. 1982). Only a few pieces of the purple and orange speckled varieties were present in the Fish Lake debitage. The red variety, however, was common. The red

Table 30. Chert Types for Tool Categories

Tool Type	Burlington	Ste. Genevieve	Tan Speckled	Salem Creamy	Appaloosa	Gray Oolitic	Old Blue	Dongola	Indet.	Total	% of Total
Retouched flakes	146	9	37	32	1	12	1	-	54	292	81.6
Projectile Points	13	-	-	1	-	1	-	1	6	22	6.1
Perforators	3	-	1	3	-	1	-	-	-	8	2.2
Biface fragments	2	-	1	4	-	-	-	-	3	10	2.8
Chert hammerstones	-	-	-	5	-	-	-	-	3	8	2.2
Flake scrapers	-	-	1	4	-	1	-	-	2	8	2.2
Gouge/wedges	-	-	-	1	-	1	-	-	1	3	0.8
Knives	-	-	-	2	-	-	-	-	1	3	0.8
Denticulates	-	-	-	-	-	-	-	-	1	1	0.3
Reworked cores	-	1	2	-	-	-	-	-	1	3	0.8
Total	164	9	42	52	1	16	1	1	72	358	
% of Total	45.8	2.5	11.7	14.5	0.3	4.5	0.3	0.3	20.1		

variety was pale brown to dark reddish brown and was fine grained. Several core fragments and primary decortication flakes had been made from this type of chert, although most of the Ste. Genevieve chert was represented in the form of reduction flakes. Nine retouched flakes were the only tools made from this chert.

Tan Speckled chert is believed to have been obtained from the locally occurring Salem limestone formations. This chert varied in color from tan to brown, was medium to fine grained, and had many small, white, fossil inclusions. When heated, this chert becomes gray-purple in color. The cortex was chalky and white, resembling that of Salem Creamy chert. Thirty-seven retouched flakes had been made from this type of chert, as well as a perforator, biface fragment, flake scraper, and two reworked cores. Most of the Tan Speckled debitage was composed of large secondary decortication and reduction flakes.

Salem Creamy, from the Salem limestone formations, was a fine to medium grained, glossy chert. Its color ranged from light gray to pale brown. Banding was occasionally observed in this chert. The cortex was white, with a chalky, limestone-like texture. Several large cores were made of this chert, as well as primary and secondary decortication flakes and numerous reduction flakes. Salem Creamy had been used to make a number of tools, including 32 retouched flakes, 5 chert hammerstones, 4 biface fragments, 4 flake scrapers, 3 perforators, 2 knives, a gouge or wedge, and a projectile point.

A distinctive white and gray mottled chert that is only occasionally found at American Bottom sites is referred to here as Appaloosa chert. The source for this type is unknown: it may have come from either the St. Louis or Salem formations. This chert was medium grained. Its white matrix exhibited numerous dark gray mottles and occasional tan mottles. White portions of this chert turn pink when heated. Several block fractures and one large retouched flake had been fashioned from Appaloosa chert. It is possible that Apppaloosa chert is not, in fact, a distinct chert type, but rather it represents discolored chert found immediately below the cortex of various other chert types.

Gray Oolitic was a medium to coarse grained chert that probably was obtained from Salem limestone formations in the Hill Lake Creek locality (Fortier 1981a). It exhibited a dull, light gray color with occasional dark gray bands. Many Gray Oolitic block fractures, mostly without cortex, were present in the debitage. Several tools had been made from this chert type, including 12 retouched flakes.

A retouched and an unretouched flake made of Old Blue chert were present in the Fish Lake assemblage. Old Blue was a fine-grained, light gray-blue chert with a glossy texture. This type is thought to have been obtained from the Salem limestone formation, and it has been found in Sparrow Creek in St. Clair County, Illinois (John Kelly, personal communication).

The remainder of the chert was categorized as unidentified. Most, or all, of this chert was probably obtained from local sources. No known exotic (nonlocal) cherts were placed in this category. The majority of this chert was medium to coarse grained. Pieces of chert cortex and water-worn chert pebbles were also included in the unidentified category. Many block fractures were included, as were 54 retouched flakes, and 18 other chert tools. The unidentified category probably also included many specimens of other chert types that, because they were coarse grained or burned, or consisted of pieces of cortex, were difficult to properly identify.

Nonchert Debitage

Most of the debitage at the site consisted of nonchert materials, including limestone, sandstone, igneous and rough rock, miscellaneous lithics, and various historical materials. Limestone, sandstone, and igneous cobbles were used as raw materials for tools. Historical materials were also recovered as adventitious inclusions in prehistoric pits. A small historical component was present at the Fish Lake site; it is described in a later section of this volume.

Limestone

Limestone accounted for 78.9% by weight of the recovered lithic materials from the site. This material would have been locally available in the bluff outcrops located ca. 3 km east of the site. Most of the limestone at the site exhibited evidence of burning. The burning of limestone, as well as its decomposition through weathering or leaching, indicates that there may have been much more limestone at the site prehistorically than was recovered.

The limestone had several possible functions. It was probably used to line hearths and to heat or boil food in earth oven pits. Limestone was often scattered throughout the fills of the pit; this is in contrast with the distinct layers of oxidized clay and soil found in the Mund site earth ovens. This indicates that the Fish Lake pits, and the limestone within them, had been reused many times.

Several limestone tools were identified, including a hoe, a pick, and two smoothing tools. Other limestone tools may have been present in the collection, but could not be identified due to the decomposed state of much of the limestone. In addition to its use for tools, limestone was also employed as a tempering agent in the pastes of several vessels.

A total of 5979 pieces of limestone, weighing 115,905.5 g, were recovered from Fish Lake site features. The amount of limestone recovered from each feature ranged from none to 8505.7 g. The mean weight of limestone per pit was 800.1 g.

Sandstone

Sandstone was recovered in moderate amounts from pit features. Prehistoric sources for sandstone were in bluff outcrops and glacial till. Sandstone was used as an abrasive material for grinding food as well as for forming and sharpening tools. Twenty-two sandstone tools were recovered, including both flat and slot abraders. Additionally, sandstone may have been used like limestone for the secondary heating of food in earth ovens, since many pieces were burned.

A total of 4623.6 g of sandstone were recovered from pit features; the amount per pit ranged from none to 404.2 g. In addition, four features contained silicified sediment (4 pieces; 81.1 g) and four features had siltstone (10 pieces; 51.1 g). Sandstone, silicified sediment, and siltstone accounted for 2.5% by weight of the recovered lithic materials.

Igneous and Rough Rock

Eighty-three pieces of igneous and rough rock, weighing 2843.6 g, were recovered from pit features. These materials were probably acquired from local glacial tills or from bluff outcrops. Most of the pieces were small and blocky, although several larger cobbles were also present. Some specimens exhibited burning; these may have been used in hearths or earth ovens. Most of the large igneous cobbles had been utilized as either hammerstones or grinding stones.

Miscellaneous Lithics

Six pieces of Missouri River clinker and 38 water-worn pebbles were recovered. Clinker and water-worn pebbles were available in the local streams and rivers, and may have been incidentally washed into the site area. Clinker was used prehistorically as an abrasive, although none of the pieces from the site appeared to have been utilized. The water-worn pebbles tended to be small, smooth igneous rocks, which may have been used as small smoothers or, possibly, as gaming pieces, ornaments, or in rattles. None of the pebbles appeared to have been intentionally modified.

Three small pieces of hematite were recovered, none of which appeared to have been rubbed or ground. Hematite was used prehistorically as a red pigment. Additional items included a single piece of quartz, eight small pieces of quartzite, and one large, nonutilized quartzite cobble. A few tools were also made of quartzite.

Historical Materials

Several historical items were recovered from Late Woodland features. These included glass, ceramics, and metal objects. The presence of six historical features at the site, as well as disturbance by modern plowing and building, explain the occurrence of historical materials in prehistoric pits.

Chert Tools

Sixty-six chert tools and 318 retouched flakes were recovered from the Fish Lake site. Sixty-two of the tools and 292 of the retouched flakes were from feature contexts, while the remainder were from the plowzone. A prehistoric knife was recovered from the area around Feature 73, a historical disturbance, and it was included in the count of tools recovered from features. It is presumed that this item, and a sandstone slot abrader also found in Feature 73, had been displaced from prehistoric features superimposed by this historical feature. The number of chert tools, with the exception of retouched flakes, was rather small considering the number of features in the Patrick phase occupation. Tool types included projectile points, perforators, knives, flake scrapers, biface fragments, chert hammerstones, gouge/wedges, retouched cores, retouched flakes, and a denticulate. At least seventeen of the projectile points were small bifacial points typical of Patrick phase assemblages (Plate 10).

The full range of chert types present in the debitage was also represented in the chert tool assemblage, although the percentages of occurrence differed. For example, Burlington chert, which accounted for only 22.0% by number of the chert debitage, was represented by 45.8% by number of the chert tools. In general, the finer grained Burlington, Ste. Genevieve, and Salem cherts were used for the small, finely retouched tools. Coarse-grained, low grade cherts, which made up a large portion of the chert debitage, rarely were used for the production of tools. The only piece of Dongola chert from the site was represented by a projectile point. This item may have been made elsewhere and brought to the site. Ten chert tools exhibited evidence of heat alteration; another five had been burned or scorched.

The use of the term "tool" may not necessarily denote the function of a chert artifact. For example, tools categorized as projectile points may not have been used to tip arrows. The functions of some tool types are unknown, and many tools may have had several functions. Unmodified flakes in the debitage could have been used for various cutting activities. Conversely, some retouched flakes may never have been used.

155

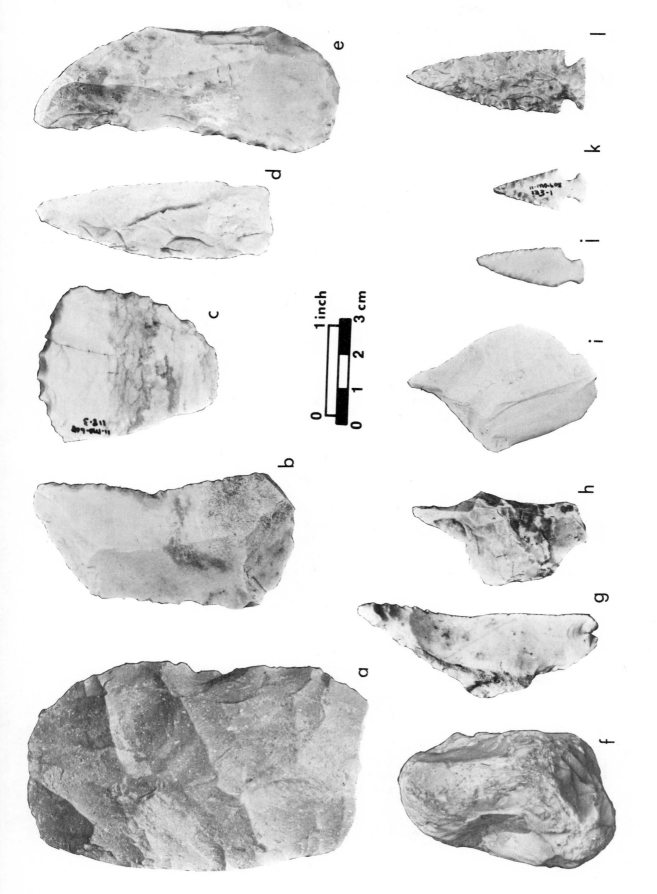

Plate 10. Selected Chert Tool Types: a, gouge/wedge; b-c, flake scrapers; d-e, knives; f, hammerstone; g-i, perforators; j-l, projectile points

Projectile Points

Twenty-two projectile points were recovered from the Fish Lake excavations; 19 were from feature contexts (Table 31). Seventeen points were assigned to the Patrick phase component, since they represent typical examples of Patrick phase type points. The other five points may belong to earlier or later cultural periods (Figure 50).

The 17 diagnostic Patrick phase points, as well as three similar points recovered from surface surveys, represent a fairly uniform type collection. They were small (mean length=2.9 cm) and had been made from thin chert flakes. Thirteen of the points exhibited bifacial retouch along the blade edges, with the dorsal surface showing greater amounts of working. Several points were flaked across the entire ventral and dorsal surfaces. Most of the points had expanding stems, created by either corner notching or side notching. The shoulders were usually distinct, and there were several barbed examples. The bases often exhibited steep flaking on their dorsal surfaces. Three points apparently were never finished. They were large and exhibited only preliminary unifacial retouch. In addition, a unifacially retouched blade from a broken point was found in Feature 93. None of the flake points had been reworked or used as knives or scrapers.

These tools were typically made from fine-grained varieties of chert. Nine points had been made from Burlington chert, one from Dongola, one from Salem, and six from unidentified chert types. Two points had been burned, and three others had been fashioned from heat-treated flakes.

Several points resembled Schild Spike points found at the Late Woodland and Mississippian Schild burial site near Eldred, Illinois (Perino 1971b). The best example of a Schild Spike type was recovered from Feature 60 (Figure 50g). It exhibited a long, slender blade, had weak shoulders and had an eared base. The largest of these points, from Feature 38 (Figure 50e), was the only point made from a nonlocal chert, Dongola. It exhibited fine bifacial retouch across its entire surface. Although larger than the other points in the assemblage, it generally resembled them. This point may have been imported from outside the immediate area. The remaining flake points resembled types often referred to as Koster, Klunk (Perino 1971a:100-101), Wanda, or Roxana (Harn 1971:74-75).

Small, so-called dart points first appeared in the Patrick phase and continued to be manufactured through Mississippian times. These points contrasted with Middle Woodland points, which were larger. Patrick phase points were produced from small reduction flakes. The worked areas were often restricted to lateral edges, with the medial portions of the ventral and, sometimes, dorsal surfaces exhibiting little or no retouch. Middle Woodland points were made from prepared bifacial pieces and were extensively flaked over all their surfaces.

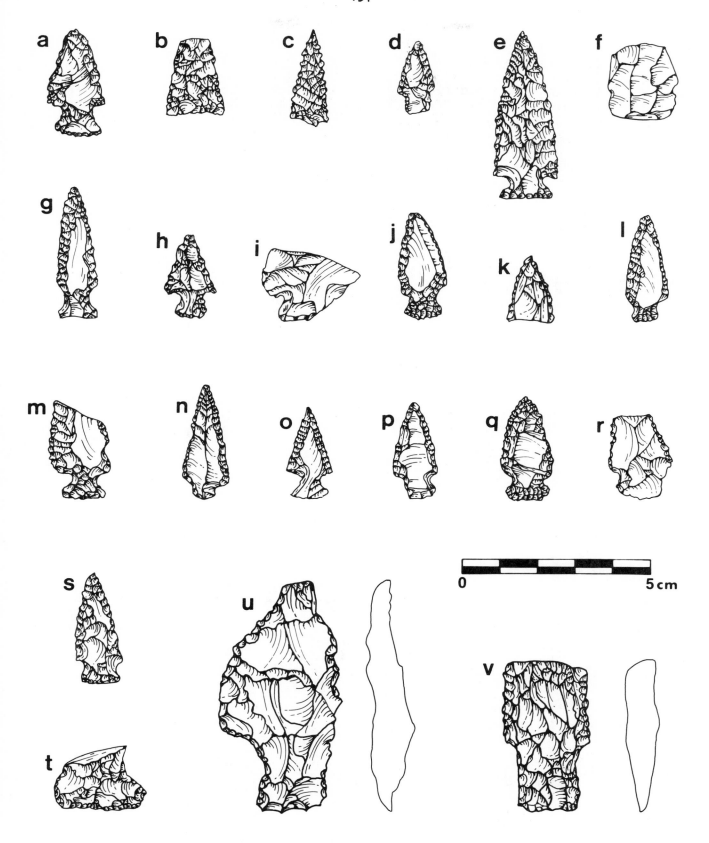

Figure 50.   Projectile Points: a-c, from plowzone; d-v, from features

Table 31. Metric Attributes for Projectile Points

Feature	Figure	Blade Length (cm)	Stem Length (cm)	Maximum Length (cm)	Shoulder Width (cm)	Neck Width (cm)	Base Width (cm)	Maximum Thickness (cm)	Wt(g)	TA*	Chert	Comments
PZ	50a	2.2	0.7	2.9	1.5	0.8	1.2	0.5	1.9	B	Indet	Corner notched
38	50d	1.5	0.4	1.9	1.0	0.6	0.7	0.3	0.7	U	Burl	Expanding stem
38	50e	4.0	0.6	4.6	1.7	0.9	1.4	0.4	2.8	U	Dong	Corner notched
60	50h	1.7	0.6	2.3	1.3	0.6	0.8	0.4	1.2	H	Burl	Expanding stem
60	50g	2.7	0.9	3.6	1.1	0.7	1.0	0.4	1.7	U	Burl	Corner notched
80	50j	2.2	0.7	2.9	1.3	0.7	1.0	0.4	1.3	U	Gray	Expanding stem
93	50l	2.3	0.6	2.9	1.1	0.6	0.7	0.2	1.5	U	Burl	Expanding stem
117	50n	2.9	-	3.2	1.2	0.6	-	0.3	1.0	H	Burl	Base broken?
123	50o	1.9	0.6	2.5	1.2	0.5	0.9	0.3	0.7	H	Burl	Corner notched
125	50p	2.0	0.6	2.6	1.2	0.7	-	0.3	0.8	U	Burl	Expanding stem
134	50q	2.3	0.6	2.9	1.4	0.8	1.2	0.4	1.2	H	Burl	Side notched
149	50r	-	0.8	2.3	1.7	1.1	-	0.4	1.5	B	Indet	Tip missing
164	50s	2.4	0.6	3.0	1.2	0.8	1.0	0.3	1.6	U	Indet	Expanding stem
40	50f	-	0.8	2.0	1.8	1.6	1.7	0.4	1.7	U	Salem	Unfinished, unifacial
74	50i	-	0.7	2.6	-	1.2	1.4	0.7	2.6	H	Indet	Unfinished ?
93	50k	-	-	1.9	1.2	-	-	0.2	0.7	U	Burl	Base missing
116	50m	-	0.6	2.8	1.5	0.6	1.0	0.4	1.8	U	Burl	Corner notched
PZ	50b	-	-	2.1	-	-	1.5	0.2	1.1	U	Burl	Triangular flake pt
PZ	50c	2.5	-	2.6	1.0	-	-	0.3	0.5	U	Burl	Serrated blade
89	50t	-	1.3	1.7	-	1.7	2.5	0.8	3.2	H	Burl	Point base
130	50u	-	2.0	6.1	-	1.6	1.7	1.3	20.1	B	Indet	Archaic point
168	50v	-	1.9	4.1	2.3	1.6	1.6	0.9	10.1	U	Indet	Kramer point

*TA - Thermal alteration (B - burned, H - heated, U - unaltered)

Generally, the points of the Late Woodland Rosewood and Mund phases showed a reduction in size and complexity from earlier Middle Woodland points. One of the most obvious differences was in the ratio between blade length and blade width. Manker (ratio=1.07) and Snyder (ratio=0.97) points have very wide blades (White 1968:68). Mund points exhibited a much narrower (ratio=1.95) blade. The Patrick phase points at the Fish Lake site had a ratio of 1.77. Some of the stylistic characteristics of the Mund phase points (i.e., fishtailed shapes and long slender blades) were evident in the Patrick phase projectile point assemblage. This demonstrates a stylistic continuity within the Late Woodland period. A rather dramatic shift in point technology, however, was apparent in the introduction of small dart points. This change in projectile point manufacture may be related to a transition from spear and atlatl to bow and arrow weaponry (Wray and MacNeish 1961:67).

The previously described points are presumed to be from the Patrick phase component, but it should be noted that similar point types are present in Emergent Mississippian and Mississippian periods. Points from later periods tend to be unifacially flaked or bifacially flaked only on their lateral edges (Milner with Williams 1981a:89). Two Fish Lake site points recovered from the plowzone may belong to either the Late Woodland or Mississippian periods. The first example was a triangular point with a missing tip (Figure 50b). It had been bifacially worked from a small, unheat-treated Burlington flake; it resembled the Madison point type. The second example was found near Feature 142, and may, in fact, have come from the fill of that feature (Figure 50c). It was made from heat-treated Burlington chert and was missing its base. Its blade exhibited a serrated edge that had apparently been made by very fine pressure flaking. Triangular points and flake points with serrated blades are probably more typical of Mississippian lithic assemblages than of Late Woodland assemblages. The presence of later material in the site area was indicated by a Mill Creek hoe fragment and possible Emergent Mississippian ceramics in the surface collection.

A burned and broken point was recovered from Feature 130 (Figure 50u). It had been crudely fashioned from an unidentified chert type, and one side had been reworked and may have been reused as a knife or scraper. This point resembled types from either Late Archaic or, possibly, Middle Woodland tool assemblages. A broken Early Woodland Kramer point was recovered from Feature 168 (Figure 50v). It exhibited a long, straight stem, a flat base, and weak shoulders. These attributes were similar to those of Kramer points described by Munson (1971:6-7). This point had been made from an indeterminate chert type, and part of its midsection and tip were missing. A point base made from heat-treated Burlington chert was found in Feature 89 (Figure 50t). It was fairly thick and seemed to be from an expanding stemmed point. This fragment possibly represents a Late Woodland Mund phase or Middle Woodland Manker point type.

The presence of points from earlier components is common at American

Bottom archaeological sites. The prehistoric inhabitants seem to have collected and reused tools left behind by previous peoples. Conversely, points from later components are often found on the surface or in the plowzone of earlier sites.

Knives

Three bifacially worked knives were recovered from feature contexts (Table 32). Feature 43 contained a flake knife with bifacial retouch around its entire circumference, except for its snapped base (Figure 51a). Feature 73 produced a finely flaked, asymmetrical knife made from Salem Creamy chert (Figure 51b). This tool may have been hafted. The last specimen, from Feature 80, had been burned (Figure 51c). Its surface exhibited evidence of heat spalling, and its tip and base were missing. These tools were probably used as weapons or to cut and scrape food, hide, and wood.

Gouge/Wedges

Three gouge/wedges were recovered: two from Feature 104 and one from Feature 98. These two pits were located about 3 m apart, directly east of a keyhole structure (Feature 9). A biface fragment that appeared to be from a broken gouge was also found in Feature 9. All of these tools had been made from large cores. They exhibited bifacial flaking over their entire surface. The bit edges showed the most intense retouch, and the opposite butt ends were battered. One item had been burned and broken on both ends and on one side (Figure 52b). The tool found in Feature 98 had been crudely fashioned, and some of the chert cortex was still present (Figure 52a). This specimen may represent an unfinished gouge. The battering present on the butt end suggests that it was used as a wedge or, possibly, as a chert maul. The only complete specimen (Figure 52c) recovered was also the only gouge that exhibited a silica gloss around its bit edge.

These tools were probably used for woodworking and, possibly, for hide scraping, excavating feature basins, and butchering. The occurrence of these four items in such close proximity to one another may be significant. Perhaps the area around Feature 9 was a center of woodworking activities.

Biface Fragments

Ten biface fragments were recovered from feature contexts. Any bifacially worked tool fragment that did not definitely fit in any of the other tool categories was classified as a biface fragment. These fragments consisted of tips, bases, and midsections of knives, projectile points, and other bifacially worked tools. One large, thick, crudely flaked piece may have been part of a gouge.

Table 32. Metric Attributes for Chert Tools

Tool Type	Feature	Length (cm)	Width (cm)	Thickness (cm)	Wt(g)	TA*	Chert	Comments
Hammerstone	3	-	-	-	33.9	U	Indet	Glacial cobble
Hammerstone	19	-	-	-	58.4	U	Salem	
Hammerstone	94	-	-	-	113.8	U	Indet	Glacial cobble
Hammerstone	106	-	-	-	59.3	U	Salem	
Hammerstone	122	-	-	-	220.8	U	Indet	Glacial cobble
Hammerstone	130	-	-	-	512.7	U	Salem	
Hammerstone	134	-	-	-	48.1	U	Salem	
Hammerstone	169	-	-	-	30.9	U	Salem	Fragment
Perforator	18	6.4	2.3	1.0	10.3	U	Salem	Bifacially worked tip
Perforator	19	5.8	2.7	1.1	8.4	U	Salem	2 worked edges
Perforator	32	4.9	3.6	1.3	14.1	U	Salem	Bifacially worked tip
Perforator	34	3.7	3.2	1.2	9.2	U	Gray	
Perforator	81	4.4	3.3	0.6	7.1	U	Tan Sp	
Perforator	94	3.5	3.3	0.9	8.4	U	Burl	
Perforator	131	3.5	2.2	0.5	3.0	B	Burl	Reworked point
Perforator	137	4.7	2.6	0.5	5.9	H	Burl	
Denticulate	11	3.0	2.2	0.6	3.1	H	Burl	
Biface fragment	9	5.3	3.6	1.9	42.3	U	Indet	Gouge fragment
Biface fragment	26	2.1	2.0	0.7	2.1	U	Salem	Tip
Biface fragment	32	3.7	2.9	1.4	15.3	U	Indet	Midsection
Biface fragment	34	3.1	2.9	0.8	5.5	U	Salem	Tip
Biface fragment	40	3.5	2.4	0.9	8.5	U	Salem	Knife/point base
Biface fragment	43	3.3	3.2	1.5	14.6	U	Burl	Tip
Biface fragment	60	3.5	2.0	0.7	4.5	U	Tan Sp	Base
Biface fragment	134	3.6	3.0	0.5	6.0	H	Indet	Knife fragment
Biface fragment	137	5.0	2.7	1.2	11.1	U	Salem	Knife tip
Biface fragment	149	3.1	2.4	0.7	4.6	U	Burl	
Flake scraper	2	7.2	3.7	1.4	28.8	U	Salem	
Flake scraper	79	5.5	2.0	1.0	10.3	U	Salem	Bifacially worked
Flake scraper	79	4.8	3.8	0.5	7.3	U	Gray	
Flake scraper	81	3.2	3.1	0.6	6.0	H	Indet	Circular
Flake scraper	82	6.5	6.2	1.5	70.5	U	Tan Sp	Unfinished ?
Flake scraper	93	6.6	3.9	1.3	27.8	U	Indet	
Flake scraper	117	4.4	3.6	1.3	19.5	U	Salem	
Flake scraper	118	4.7	4.2	0.9	17.9	U	Salem	
Gouge/wedge	98	0.1	5.5	3.8	210.8	U	Indet	Gouge preform
Gouge/wedge	104	8.5	5.3	2.1	98.4	U	Salem	
Gouge/wedge	104	8.3	4.7	1.6	57.7	U	Gray	Broken
Knife	43	8.0	3.3	0.9	25.9	U	Salem	Flake knife
Knife	73	6.3	2.2	0.8	11.6	U	Salem	Finely flaked
Knife	80	6.0	2.3	0.8	9.6	B	Salem	Fire cracked

*TA - Thermally altered (B - burned, H - heated, U - unaltered)

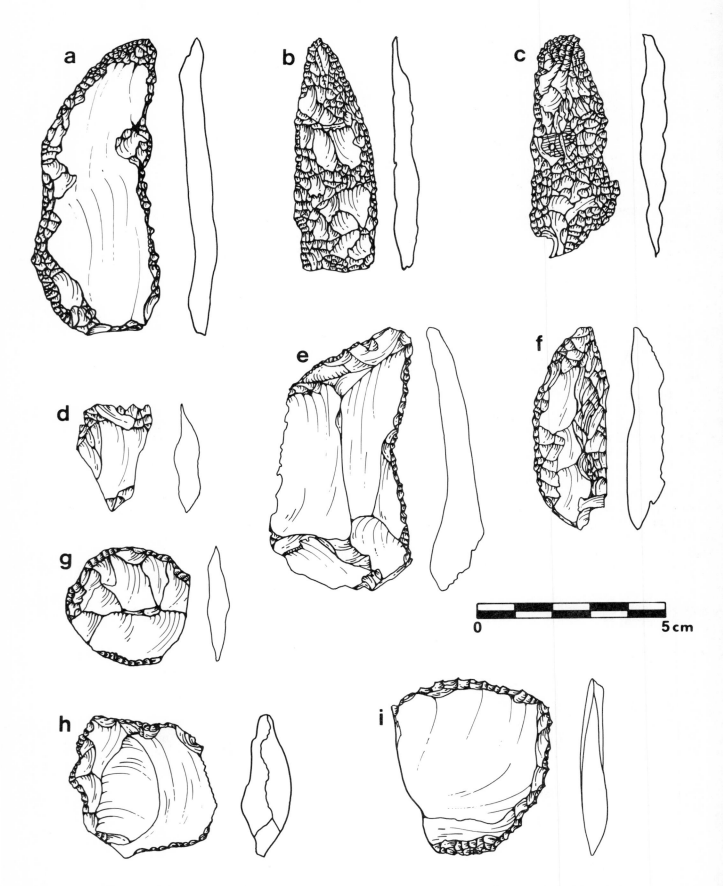

Figure 51. Chert Tools: a–c, knives; d, denticulate; e–i, scrapers

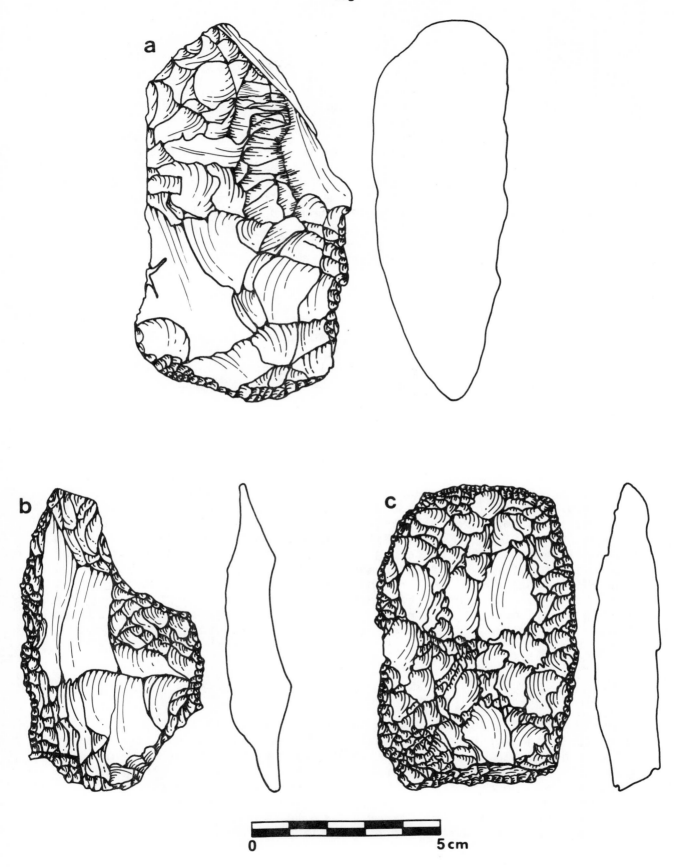

Figure 52. Gouge/Wedges

Flake Scrapers

Eight flake scrapers were recovered from feature contexts. Their dorsal surfaces were always retouched, and one scraper showed evidence of some bifacial retouch. The flakes had been retouched at a steep angle (ca. 45 degrees) along 25% to 75% of their circumferences. Most were classified as side scrapers; none of these tools exhibited evidence of hafting. One scraper (Figure 51i) had a serrated edge; it was classified as a denticulate scraper. Flake scrapers were differentiated from retouched flakes by their regular pattern of retouch and the steepness of their utilized edges. Retouched flakes typically exhibited irregular flaking on a single surface or, occasionally, on multiple surfaces. Flake scrapers were probably held with the thumb and first two fingers when cutting and scraping hides, wood, and plant materials.

Denticulate

A single denticulate was found in Feature 11 (Figure 51d). It had been made from a small Burlington flake and exhibited a serrated edge, with retouch evident within the serration grooves. Denticulates were presumably used for shredding plant material or animal flesh.

Hammerstones

One broken and seven complete chert hammerstones were recovered, all from feature contexts. These tools usually exhibited fine crushing and pitting on multiple surfaces; only two items had single utilized surfaces. Three specimens had been made from water-worn chert cobbles (Figure 53a), four from Salem chert cores (Figure 53b), and one from a large nodule of Salem chert (Figure 53c). Several other chert cores in the debitage exhibited battering associated with the preparation of striking platforms for flake removal. These items were not included in the chert hammerstone category, however, because they did not display the large crushed areas that repeated use creates. Chert hammerstones were probably used, like igneous hammerstones, to manufacture lithic tools, to process nuts and seeds, and to perform other percussive type activities.

Perforators

Eight perforating tools were recovered, all from feature contexts. The criterion for placing a tool in this category included the presence of a modified tip or point suitable for perforating, incising, or fine cutting. Such utilized chert items are generally categorized as perforators, reamers, spurs, or gravers; no microperforators or microdrills were present. The perforators from the Fish Lake site had been fashioned from flakes or small core fragments. A single tool had been reworked from a possible projectile point that had been previously

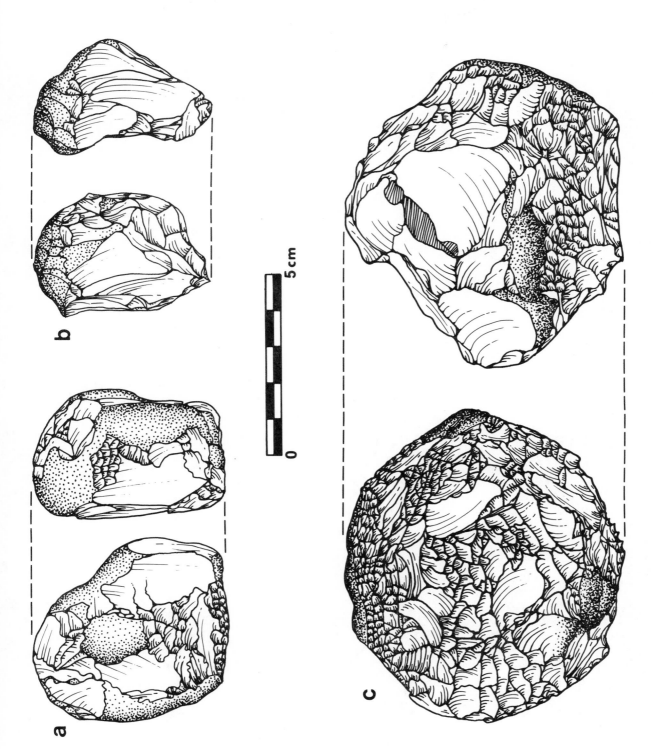

Figure 53. Chert Hammerstones

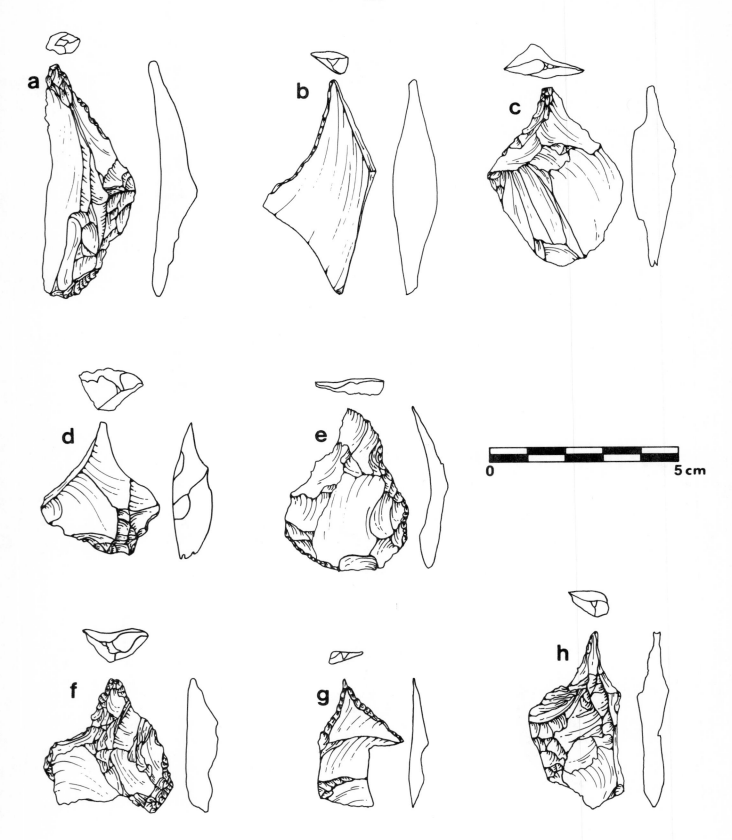

Figure 54. Perforators

broken and burned (Figure 54g). Five specimens exhibited unifacial flaking on their utilized tips, while the other three items were bifacially worked. One perforator exhibited two utilized tips.

Seven of the tools had small slender tips, which would have been suitable for the type of twisting motions used in drilling holes through leather, wood, and bone. The eighth tool had a wide flat tip that would have served better in cutting and graving activities (Figure 54e). All of the tools were small enough to have been held between the thumb and fingers for fine manipulative tasks; none appeared to have been hafted. These tools could have been used for perforating, cutting, engraving, and drilling soft materials. In addition, some unmodified flakes in the lithic assemblage exhibited sharp protrusions that could have been used for the same purposes as perforators.

Retouched Flakes

A total of 292 retouched flakes were recovered from feature contexts and an additional 26 from the plowzone. The retouched flake category included all flakes that exhibited retouch to form thin, sharp cutting edges. Retouch was often limited to small areas or occasionally, to several edges in an irregular pattern. A variety of chert types were represented in this tool category. Burlington chert accounted for half of the retouched flakes (N=146; 50.0%), followed by unidentified chert (N=54; 18.5%), Tan Speckled (N=37; 12.7%), Salem Creamy (N=32; 11.0%), Gray Oolitic (N=12; 4.1%), Ste. Genevieve (N=9; 3.1%), Appaloosa (N=1; 0.3%), and Old Blue (N=1; 0.3%). The sizes and shapes of the flakes varied greatly, ranging in weight from less than a gram to over 75 grams (mean=6.9 g).

Several features contained disproportionately large numbers of retouched flakes: Feature 81 (N=18), Feature 134 (N=18), Feature 32 (N=17), and Feature 38 (N=16). Two (Features 32 and 81) were keyhole structures. The seven keyhole structures contained a total of 59 retouched flakes, an average of 8.4 items per structure. In contrast, the 134 pit features contained only 232 retouched flakes, an average of 1.7 items per feature. Although the house basin volumes were much greater than pit volumes, the larger number of retouched flakes found in the keyhole structures may instead reflect differential patterning of activities within the Fish Lake community.

Retouched flakes would have been easily produced, even by unskilled flint knappers, and they seem to be present at almost all American Bottom archaeological sites. They were probably used for cutting, scraping, and puncturing hide, bone, wood, and food. Some of these items may represent unfinished points or other chert tools.

Three reworked or modified cores were also recovered, two from feature contexts. These items exhibited retouch on the edges of the flake scars that covered their surfaces. These cores may have been preforms for other tools or crude cutting and chopping devices.

Nonchert Tools

Fifty-six nonchert lithic tools were recovered from the Fish Lake site, all but one from feature contexts (Table 33). Tool types included celt fragments, hammerstones, grinding stones, sandstone abraders, limestone tools, and utilized cobble fragments. The raw materials utilized for these tools included igneous and metamorphic cobbles, quartzite, sandstone, silicified sediment, and limestone. Items were classified according to shape and nature of alteration, both of which indicate the possible functions of these tools. Some tools may have functioned in many different ways, but they were categorized by what is thought to have been their primary function.

Although the number of nonchert tools was relatively small, the fact that many of these tools had multiple functions indicates a larger effective tool kit. It is also important to note that most of the large pieces of sandstone, quartzite, and igneous rock had been utilized as tools. The exception was limestone. Although many large pieces of limestone were recovered, only four limestone tools were found.

Hammerstones

Nine nonchert hammerstones and three hammerstone fragments were recovered from feature contexts (Figure 55a,b,e). Each of these tools exhibited one or more areas of battering or crushing. Hammerstones ranged in size from 21.1 g to 376.3 g. The small specimens probably were utilized as pecking stones for fine chert flaking; battering and crushing on these specimens were restricted to one or two small areas. These items tended to be made from small quartzite and water-worn pebbles. The large specimens probably were used as mauls for breaking large chert cobbles, crushing food, and for other activities. These tools were generally palm sized and had been fashioned from medium to large igneous cobbles. The large hammerstone/mauls exhibited battering over several surfaces. Portions of several items had broken off. Grinding and pitting were present on several items, indicating multiple use.

Grinding Stones

Four igneous grinding stones were recovered from feature contexts. Two were pitted and two were unpitted (Figure 56). The pitted specimens exhibited flattened surfaces with very shallow depressed areas. These pitted areas were discolored and resembled pitted grinding stones recovered from the Mund site (Fortier et al. 1982). An item from Feature 70 had one pitted surface; a specimen from Feature 143 had two opposed pitted surfaces. The depressed areas appear to have resulted from use. An apparent lack of evidence for crushing activities suggests that these tools were primarily used for grinding food substances. The discolorations may have resulted from grinding oily plant substances, such as nuts.

Table 33. Metric Attributes for Nonchert Tools

Tool Type	Feature	Wt(g)	Comments
Celt fragment	PZ	65.5	Midsection
Celt fragment	6	10.7	Midsection
Celt fragment	43	7.6	Bit
Celt fragment	82	207.3	Butt end
Celt fragment	134	127.0	Midsection
Celt fragment	147	2.9	Midsection
Sandstone slot abrader	18	37.6	2 slots
Sandstone slot abrader	27	12.3	1 slot
Sandstone slot abrader	38	45.1	1 slot and grinding
Sandstone slot abrader	60	34.5	3 slots
Sandstone slot abrader	73	47.1	4 slots
Sandstone slot abrader	82	58.7	1 slot
Sandstone slot abrader	102	15.4	1 slot
Sandstone slot abrader	134	26.4	4 slots
Sandstone slot abrader	149	78.4	1 slot
Limestone tool	72	69.7	Pick
Limestone tool	72	10.0	Pottery smoother ?
Limestone tool	165	4.2	Pottery smoother ?
Limestone tool	168	291.8	Hoe, maul ?
Sandstone abrader	18	22.9	2 ground surfaces
Sandstone abrader	27	15.8	1 ground surface
Sandstone abrader	57	118.3	1 ground surface, burned
Sandstone abrader	60	35.1	1 ground surface
Sandstone abrader	60	206.5	1 ground surface, burned
Sandstone abrader	72	159.9	1 ground surface
Sandstone abrader	79	14.2	1 ground surface
Sandstone abrader	98	253.7	1 ground surface
Sandstone abrader	98	203.7	Pitted and burned
Sandstone abrader	105	6.8	1 ground surface
Sandstone abrader	116	8.5	1 ground surface, broken
Sandstone abrader	116	84.5	1 ground surface, broken
Sandstone abrader	117	19.8	1 ground surface
Grinding stone	6	746.6	2 opposing ground surfaces
Grinding stone	70	494.9	Pitted surface, some battering
Grinding stone	82	290.3	2 opposing ground surfaces, broken
Grinding stone	143	301.1	2 pitted surfaces, burned
Hammerstone	11	113.8	2 opposing pitted surfaces
Hammerstone	28	126.7	2 pecked surfaces
Hammerstone	52	21.1	Quartzite, small pecking stone
Hammerstone/maul	70	256.1	Quartzite, battered and broken
Hammerstone	81	53.4	Waterworn pebble
Hammerstone/maul	82	376.3	Quartzite, battered and broken
Hammerstone	88	29.4	Waterworn pebble, pecked
Hammerstone	93	352.6	Burned, 1 pitted surface
Hammerstone	98	211.8	2 pecked surfaces
Utilized cobble frag.	9	2.7	Quartzite pecking stone
Utilized cobble frag.	11	88.7	Grinding stone?
Utilized cobble frag.	13	38.5	Silicified sediment grinding stone?
Utilized cobble frag.	18	45.9	Hammerstone?
Utilized cobble frag.	27	96.4	Grinding stone?
Utilized cobble frag.	36	20.4	Hammerstone?
Utilized cobble frag.	37	30.8	Grinding stone?
Utilized cobble frag.	38	93.4	Silicified sediment grinding stone?
Utilized cobble frag.	48	40.1	Grinding stone?
Utilized cobble frag.	49	97.1	Quartzite grinding stone?
Utilized cobble frag.	100	109.3	Grinding stone?

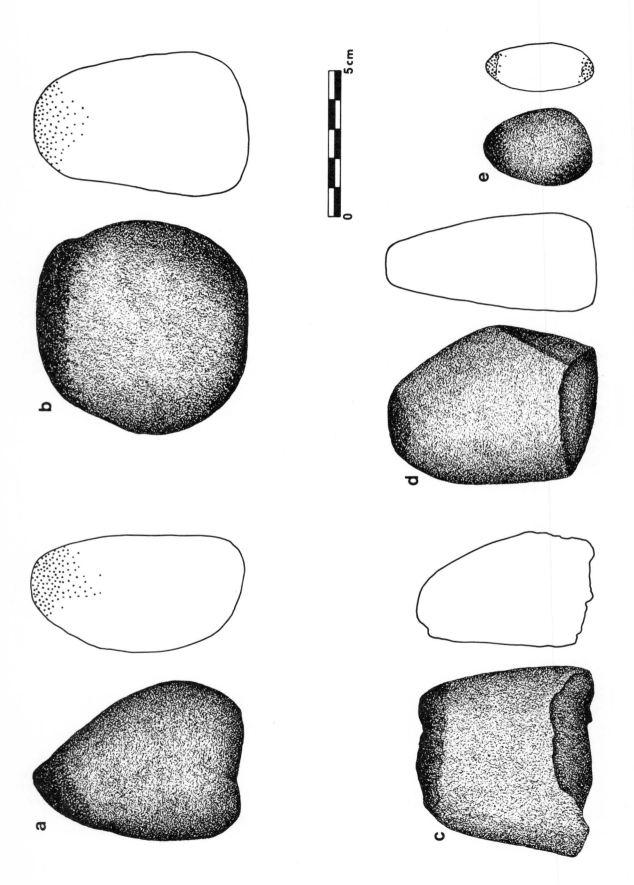

Figure 55. Nonchert Tools: a-b,e, hammerstones; c-d, celt fragments

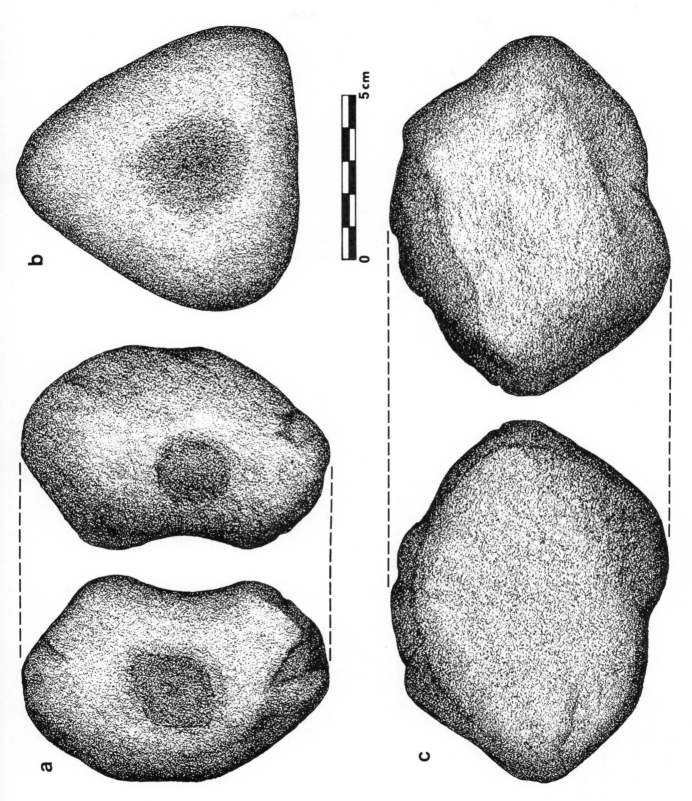

Figure 56. Grinding Stones: a-b, pitted; c, nonpitted

The two unpitted grinding stones exhibited two opposed, flat ground surfaces. No depressed areas were present, although one of these tools exhibited a discolored area in the middle of one ground surface. These tools were probably used in a similar manner as the pitted grinding stones, although some battering and crushing was observed on these specimens. This may indicate both crushing and grinding functions.

Celt Fragments

Six celt fragments were recovered, five from feature contexts (Figure 55c,d). The other fragment was found during the original surface survey of the site. These celts were made of fine-grained, dark gray igneous (basalt) rock and had been ground to a smooth, almost polished, surface. The fragments included one small bit fragment, one large butt end, and four midsections. Several fragments could have come from a single complete tool. Celts were probably hafted and used as woodworking tools and weapons.

Utilized Cobble Fragments

Eleven utilized cobble fragments were recovered from feature contexts. Seven were pieces of grinding stones, one was a rectangular ground stone tool fragment that may have been a grinding stone, two were hammerstone fragments, and one was a small quartzite pebble fragment probably used as a peckingstone.

Limestone Tools

Four limestone tools were recovered from feature contexts. Feature 72 contained a small limestone disc that had been ground flat on two sides. It measured about 3.5 cm in diameter and was 0.6 cm thick. Several small pits were evident on its surface, but it is not known whether these represent natural or man-made depressions. Feature 165 produced a small piece of limestone that had been ground on three surfaces. These two items may have been used as pottery smoothers, as ornaments, or as gaming pieces.

Feature 72 also contained a limestone pick. It was 10.8 cm in length and 2.6 cm in width at its base; it tapered toward the tip, which was missing. This tool presumably was used as a digging implement. Feature 168 produced a large, ground limestone slab. It was triangular in cross section, and one end was battered. It is not known whether this item was a complete or an unfinished tool. This object was similar in shape to limestone hoes found at other Late Woodland sites. The presence of battering suggested an additional use as a maul or pestle.

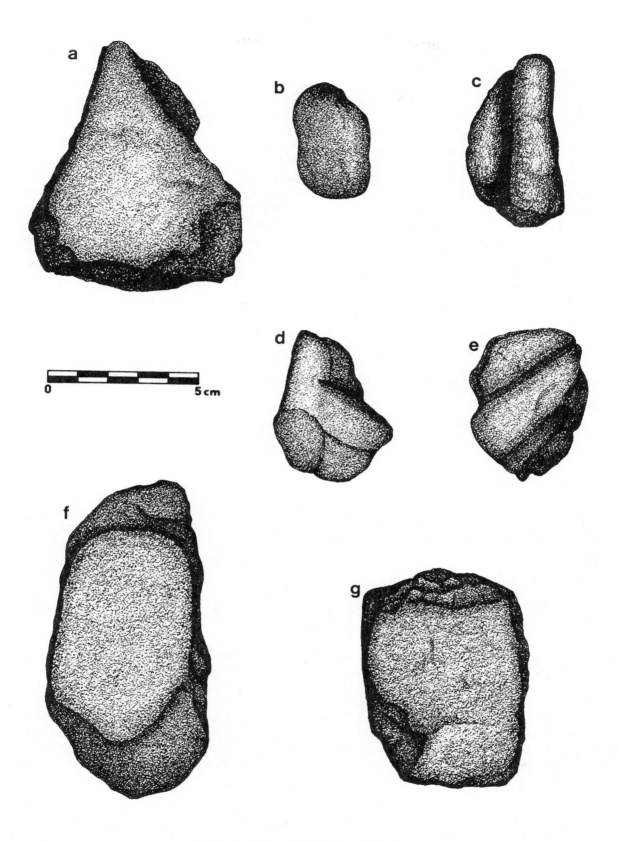

Figure 57. Sandstone Tools

Sandstone Tools

Twenty-two sandstone tools were recovered from feature contexts, including 9 slot abraders (Figure 57c,d,e) and 13 flat abraders (Figure 57b,f,g). The slot abraders were characterized by V-shaped or U-shaped grooves on one or more surfaces. The grooves ranged in width from 0.1 cm to 0.5 cm, and in depth from 0.1 cm to 0.8 cm. These tools usually had been made on small pieces of sandstone (mean weight=39.5 g). Their small size may be a function of repeated use rather than of selection for small pieces of raw material. Several examples showed additional grinding that was not associated with the slots. Slot abraders presumably were used to sharpen wood and bone tools, to shape arrow shafts, and possibly to prepare core surfaces prior to flake removal. The thirteen flat sandstone abraders exhibited grinding on one or more surfaces. These tools were generally larger than the slot abraders (mean weight=88.4 g), with several specimens weighing more than 200 g. One of the larger items, from Feature 60, may have been a fragment of a sandstone metate (Figure 57a). Three items had been burned and one exhibited a shallow depressed area in the center of a ground surface. Pitting was evident on a few specimens; this may have been caused by drilling and percussion during use, by natural causes, or by fire popping. The flat abraders were probably used for multipurpose grinding and abrading of wood, bone, plant materials, and stone.

Site Activities

Functional Categories

The 440 tools from the Fish Lake site were divided into functional categories to identify the spatial distribution of activities performed by the site inhabitants (Table 34). These categories represent an expanded version of Winters' (1969) system, and included cutting/piercing tools, manufacturing/maintenance tools, plant processing tools, woodworking tools, scraping tools, and digging tools. Obviously, some tools could have been used for several different activities. For our purposes, however, tools were categorized by what was believed to have been their primary function.

Cutting/piercing tools, totalling 363 items, made up 82.5% of all tools recovered from the site. Cutting/piercing tool types included retouched flakes, projectile points, biface fragments, perforators, knives, and reworked cores. The number of tools in this category was greatly inflated by the inclusion of 318 retouched flakes, which accounted for over 72% of all chert and nonchert tools. The retouched flakes and knives would have been used for a number of cutting activities. These two tool types, along with reworked cores, may have been primarily associated with the butchering of animals. The perforating tools were probably utilized to work wood, bone, and hides. Small projectile points were most likely hafted and used for hunting and

Table 34. Functional Tool Categories

	N	% of Total	% of Total w/o Ret. Flakes
Cutting/piercing tools	363	82.5	36.9
Retouched flakes	318		
Projectile points	22		
Biface fragments	9		
Perforators	8		
Knives	3		
Reworked cores	3		
Manufacture/maintenance tools	44	10.0	36.1
Sandstone abraders	13		
Sandstone slot abraders	9		
Igneous hammerstones	9		
Chert hammerstones	8		
Hammerstone fragments	3		
Limestone smoothers	2		
Plant processing tools	12	2.7	9.8
Grinding stones	4		
Grinding stone fragments	8		
Woodworking tools	10	2.3	8.2
Celt fragments	6		
Gouge/wedges	3		
Gouge fragment	1		
Scraping Tools	9	2.0	7.4
Scrapers	8		
Denticulates	1		
Digging tools	2	0.4	1.6
Limestone hoe	1		
Limestone pick	1		
Total	440		

as weapons. The biface fragments presumably represent broken portions of points, knives, and other bifacially worked cutting tools.

Manufacture/maintenance tools, including sandstone abraders, hammerstones, and limestone smoothers, were used to produce, modify, and sharpen other tools. Sandstone abraders would have been used to grind (shape) and sharpen ground stone, bone, wood, and chert tools. Hammerstones were utilized in chert tool manufacturing as well as in other types of percussive activities. Two limestone smoothers may have been utilized to form and smooth ceramic vessels.

Plant processing tools (grinding stones) were used to grind and crush seeds, nuts, and other plant substances. Only four complete grinding stones and eight fragments were recovered. Given the large amount of floral materials recovered from the site, it was expected that more tools of this type would have been found. Perhaps sandstone abraders were also used in plant processing.

Woodworking tools, including celts and gouge/wedges, presumably were utilized for a number of activities, including producing wood tools as well as felling trees and modifying wood when building structures. Of the six celts and three gouge/wedges recovered, only one item was complete. This indicates intensive use of these items. A relatively large amount of wood charcoal recovered from pits indicates widespread use of wood as a fuel for heating and cooking.

Scraping tools (flake scrapers and denticulates) were presumably used to modify hides. Animal skins probably were used as clothing, containers, and shelter. Flake scrapers would have been used to separate meat from hides, and denticulates would have been used to shred meat and cut hides.

The two limestone digging implements, a pick and a hoe, could have been used to excavate feature basins or to cultivate fields. Wooden digging implements may have been used for the same purpose, but such implements were not preserved. In addition to these tools, two chert hoe fragments were recovered from the surface, although these flakes may not have been associated with the Patrick phase occupation.

Spatial Distribution

The distribution of tools and raw materials was fairly uniform across the site (Figure 58; Table 35). No discrete areas, where specialized activities could have been performed, were found. Only one tool type, the gouge/wedge, appeared to be restricted to a specific area. However, since these tools were represented by only three specimens, their apparent concentration in a single area of the site may be merely a reflection of small sample size.

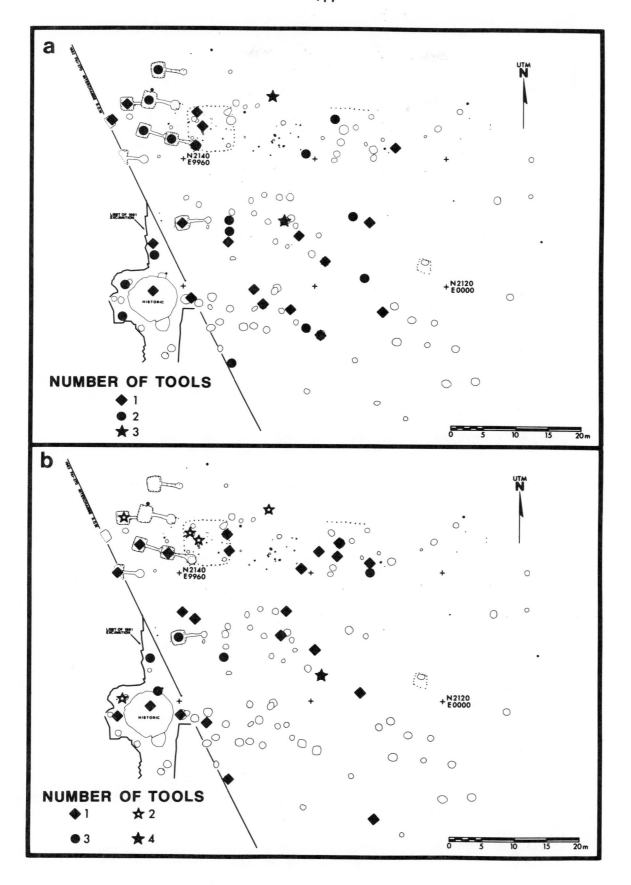

Figure 58. Tool Distribution: a, chert; b, nonchert

Table 35. Tool Types by Occupation Area

Tool Type	1	2	3	4	N/A*	PZ	Total
	Occupation Area						
Chert hammerstones	3	1	3	-	1	-	8
Perforators	4	1	1	-	2	-	8
Denticulates	1	-	-	-	-	-	1
Biface fragments	6	1	2	-	1	-	10
Flake scrapers	2	2	-	1	3	-	8
Gouge/wedge	-	3	-	-	-	-	3
Knives	2	1	-	-	-	-	3
Projectile points	4	5	7	-	3	3	22
Reworked cores	2	-	-	-	-	1	3
Retouched flakes	143	54	58	1	36	26	318
Chert Subtotal	167	68	71	2	46	30	384
Celt fragments	3	1	1	-	-	1	6
Sandstone tools	8	4	4	-	6	-	22
Limestone tools	1	-	2	-	1	-	4
Grinding stones	1	1	-	-	2	-	4
Hammerstones	4	4	-	-	1	-	9
Utilized cobble frags	5	3	2	-	1	-	11
Nonchert subtotal	22	13	9	0	11	1	56
Total	189	81	80	2	57	31	440

*N/A - Nonoccupational affiliation

Occupation Area 1

The northernmost area (Occupation Area 1), in which were found 7 structures and 39 pits, contained 32.6%, by weight, of the raw materials at the site (Figure 59).   The largest amounts of every lithic raw material type, except limestone, were recovered from this area. Occupation Area 1 contained 43.5%, by number, of the chert tools and 39.3% of the nonchert tools. The material density per feature, however, was the lowest of all occupation areas. This was a reflection of the high number of large deep pits located in Occupation Area 1. The average weight per item was also smaller in Occupation Area 1 for almost all material types. Only one high density pit (> 10.0 g/dm3), Feature 166, was located in this area.

Occupation Area 2

The central occupation area (Occupation Area 2), which consisted of a single keyhole structure and 25 pits, contained 20.7% by weight of the raw materials. Three of the high density pits (Features 82, 93, and 98) were located in this area. Occupation Area 2 had only 18.4% of the total number of lithic tools; however, this tool assemblage was the heaviest (31.3% by weight) of any occupation area at the site. Several large, heavy tools accounted for the great weight of this tool assemblage. As previously noted, the only gouge/wedges recovered from the site came from features near the keyhole structure (Feature 9) in Occupation Area 2. This may indicate that woodworking at the site was centralized in this vicinity.

Occupation Area 3

The southwestern occupation area (Occupation Area 3) contained 33 prehistoric pits and a large historical pit. The pits in this area had about twice the average pit density for the site. Thirteen of the 19 high density pits found at the site were located in this area. The high density of materials in these pits was mainly due to the large amounts of limestone recovered in Occupation Area 3; also, pit volumes were relatively low. These pits averaged 1557.4 g of limestone, almost twice the average amount per pit for the site. The average weight per item of all materials was also the highest at the site. Seven projectile points were recovered from Occupation Area 3.

The pits surrounding historical Feature 73 tended to be larger and contained more material than features to the east in Occupation Area 3. The 10 features encircling Feature 73 (Features 36, 38, 39, 40, 41, 58, 71, 72, 105, and 106) contained a great amount of limestone (mean=3305.3 g). Chert was also recovered in larger than usual quantities, but sandstone occurred only infrequently in these pits. These ten features also produced twelve tools and 38 retouched flakes. Due to right-of-way restrictions, the limits of this area could not be

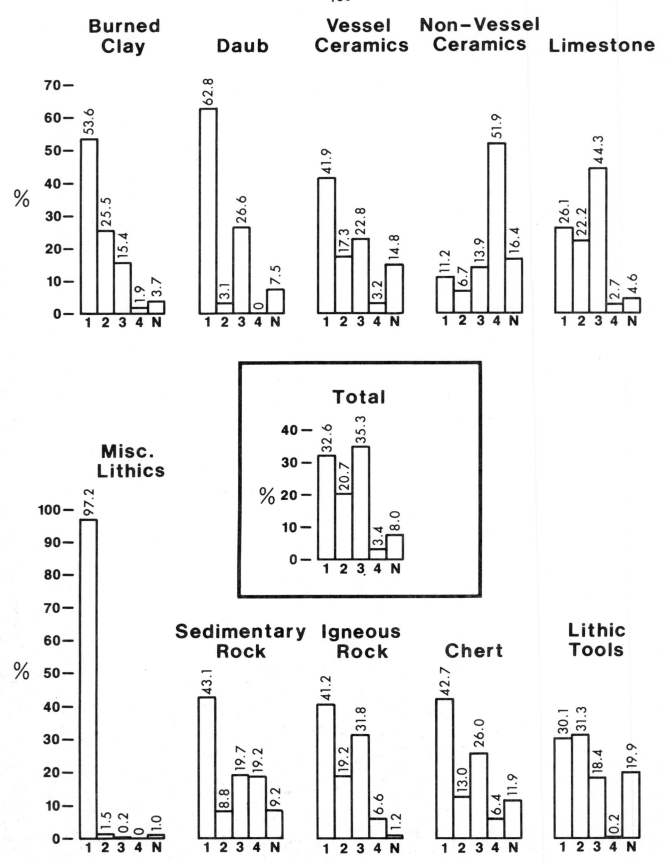

Figure 59. Percentile Distribution of Material Types (by weight) among Occupation Areas 1-4 and Nonaligned Features (N)

delineated. Additional pits and structures probably occurred in this area, but outside of the excavation limits.

Occupation Area 4

The southeastern area (Occupation Area 4) included 10 pit features and a post structure. Little material was recovered from these features. A single flake scraper and one retouched flake were the only chert tools recovered in Occupation Area 4; nonchert tools were absent. The presence of a specialized structure (Feature 77) in this area may be related to the scarcity of materials. Whether the pits in this area were related to the structure is not known. There was no evidence for any major lithic processing activities in Occupation Area 4.

Features of Nonoccupational Affiliation

Twenty-seven pit features could not be directly associated with the four occupation areas. Most of these pits were small and contained fewer materials than the site average. Two high density pits (Features 79 and 143) were located between occupation areas. These two pits may represent special processing areas, intentionally separated from the centers of other feature clusters. Feature 79 contained 3 tools and 12 retouched flakes, as well as various other materials.

Two other features of nonoccupational affiliation contained numerous tools. Feature 18, located between Occupation Areas 2 and 3, contained 4 tools and 8 retouched flakes. Feature 60, located in the extreme eastern portion of the site, contained six tools and seven retouched flakes. These two features may also represent specialized and/or purposefully isolated pits. Feature 60 is of interest particularly because of its distance from the main occupation area.

Materials from Structures

The 7 keyhole structures produced 10 chert tools, 59 retouched flakes, and 6 nonchert tools. They contained an average of 1743.6 g of material per structure. None of these materials were associated with structure floors. Tool density was relatively low (0.90 g/dm3). The only artifacts recovered in significant numbers were retouched flakes. Since much of the debris in these structures was presumably washed in after abandonment, it was not possible to definitely associate different lithic activities with the houses. However, the relatively small sizes of the structures and the lack of materials within them indicate that these features served primarily for sleeping.

The two post structures probably had different functions than the keyhole structures. Feature 77 did not contain material in its post molds, nor was any material recovered from its shallow internal hearth

(Feature 78). The large post structure, Feature 52, produced several items in its post molds, including a hammerstone and a retouched flake. The pits within this structure, which were probably associated with it, contained 3 chert tools, 28 retouched flakes, and 6 nonchert tools. The size of this structure and the materials recovered within it suggest that some processing and production activities were performed within this structure.

Summary

Several aspects of the Patrick phase lithic assemblage are significant for inferring activities undertaken by the prehistoric inhabitants of the Fish Lake site. The generally small amounts of material recovered from both plowzone and feature contexts may reflect an overall low level of activity at the site. The relatively uniform distribution of materials and tools across the site is indicative of an unspecialized activity orientation.

When compared to the occupations at the Late Woodland Mund (Mund phase), and Range (Patrick phase) sites, the Fish Lake occupation was similar in terms of the size and complexity of its feature distribution. The lithic assemblage from Fish Lake, however, was significantly smaller and less complex than those of the other two sites (Figure 60). A primary factor affecting the Fish Lake site assemblage may have been the distance of this site from sources of raw materials. Both Mund and Range were located within several hundred meters of bluff outcrops and stream bed washes. Fish Lake, situated on the floodplain, was about 3 km from such lithic sources. The amount of effort and time required to transport materials from their sources to the site would have been much greater for the inhabitants of the Fish Lake site.

Table 36 compares feature and material data from several Late Woodland sites excavated by the FAI-270 Project. Included are both habitation and resource procurement sites located in both floodplain and upland environments and dating to three phases of the Late Woodland period. There were great discrepancies among these occupations in terms of the material densities of the features and the degrees to which debitage was utilized. The material densities of the Fish Lake site features closely resembled those of small extractive camps, including the Cramer #2 (11-S-699) [Lacampagne and Bentz 1982] and Steinberg (11-S-653) [Lacampagne and Bentz 1983] sites located on the bluffs, and the Carbon Dioxide (11-Mo-594) [Finney 1981] site located on the floodplain. The Mund phase occupation at the Mund site had about twice the material density of those four sites, but a lower percentage of the Mund site materials had been worked into tools. The Columbia Quarry (11-S-629) [Finney and Bentz 1983] site, another upland extractive camp, had an extremely high material density, yet a rather low percentage of material utilization.

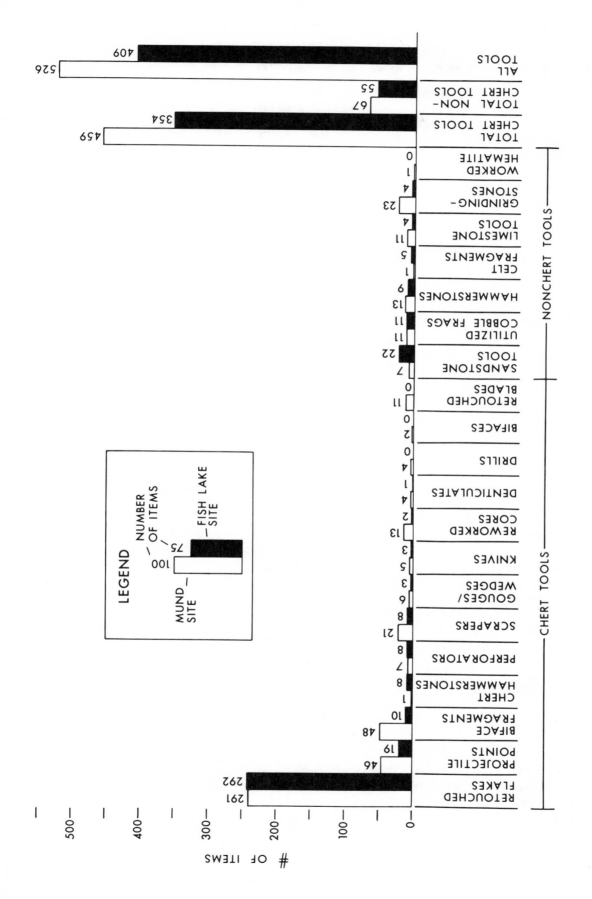

Figure 60. Frequency Distribution of Tool Categories at the Fish Lake and Mund Sites

Table 36. Comparison of Feature and Material Data from Selected
Late Woodland Sites in the American Bottom Area

Site	Phase#	Location	N of Features		Mean Pit Volume (dm3)	Mean Pit Density (g/dm3)	N of Tools		% Util. Chert	% Util. Lithics
			Pits	Str.			Chert	Nonchert		
11-Mo-594	R	Floodplain	23	-	47.4	5.7	28	2	32.8	20.4
11-Mo-608	P	Floodplain	134	9	277.5	5.1	354	55	26.6	7.2
11-S-435	M	Floodplain	161	2	415.5	9.5	459	67	9.8	4.3
11-S-629	M	Upland	31	-	185.5	24.4	160	17	12.5	4.8
11-S-653	R	Upland	24	-	111.6	4.9	22	10	27.9	20.5
11-S-699	P	Upland	20	-	76.4	4.5	11	3	22.7	16.2

#Phase: R - Rosewood, P - Patrick, M - Mund

The fairly uniform distribution of materials and tools across the Fish Lake site may indicate that single or multiple family units were occupying the site area and were performing similar types of activities. There did not appear to be the kind of task-oriented, specialized divisions within the Fish Lake occupation that are evident in later Mississippian period occupations (O'Brien 1978; Prentice 1983).

An overall simplicity in lithic tools and an efficiency in the ways that available raw materials were used were very evident at the Fish Lake site. Most of the lithic items had been altered in some way. Small flake tools could have been easily made from the debitage without a great deal of effort or skill. Few, if any, exotic or nonfunctional (ceremonial or decorative) lithic items were found. A lack of nonlocal raw materials and of imported tools and ceramics suggests that the Fish Lake site represents a small, localized, subsistence-oriented occupation.

Figure 48 illustrates the percentages of utilized tools versus nonutilized debitage for several material types at the Fish Lake and Mund sites. The figure indicates that the prehistoric inhabitants at Fish Lake utilized a much greater proportion of their available raw materials for tools. The work involved in transporting heavy materials from the bluff outcrops was not wasted on carrying heavy igneous or chert cobbles that could not be used. At sites closer to raw material sources, the toolmaker could pick and choose from large amounts of debitage to find the desired piece from which to work. When raw materials are at a premium, however, as at the Fish Lake site, selection would have been limited and may, in fact, have restricted the amounts and types of tools produced. Bone and wood may have been used rather than lithic materials to produce certain types of tools at the Fish Lake site.

In conclusion, the lithic materials recovered from the Fish Lake site indicated a small, perhaps short term, Patrick phase habitation. Raw materials had to be transported from the bluffs to the floodplain, thus accounting for the relatively small amount of material recovered and the low density of materials in pits. Limestone, the most prevalent material recovered, was extensively used for cooking and heating. Most of the tools were not elaborately fashioned and had been made from locally occurring materials. Many tools were utilized or reutilized in multiple activities; both practices would have contributed to the most efficient use of the small tool kit.

WORKED BONE ASSEMBLAGE

by Andrew C. Fortier

A few worked bone artifacts were recovered from the Fish Lake site. These artifacts included 10 utilized deer bone or antler tools, 2 worked mammal bones, 4 worked turtle carapace fragments, and one incised mussel shell fragment. These tools and artifacts were distributed in Occupation Areas 1, 2, and 3, with 64% occurring in Occupation Area 3. Table 37 lists some of the general characteristics of this worked bone assemblage.

Modified Deer Bone and Antler

Of the 17 bone artifacts recovered, 10 had been made from deer bone or antler. Included were two ground antler tines, one ground antler, one deer phalanx fish hook, two deer phalanx cup-and-pin gaming pieces, three awls, and a single piece of grooved metacarpal or metatarsal bone. The antler tines were ground from use and their distal ends were polished. Use striations were apparent along the sides of their distal ends. Such tools may have functioned as flakers or, possibly, as broad awls and punches. The largest antler tool may represent a flaker. Its distal end had been snapped off and it was ground. Its proximal end also exhibited some grinding.

The bone fish hook was unique at the site. It was polished, and it curved sharply at the hook end. No groove or notch for line attachment was apparent, although shallow horizontal striations did occur at the end where such grooves might be expected. The hook measured 3.62 cm in length and was not burned. This hook was recovered from Feature 36, a pit which contained a high quantity of large fish bone. Such hooks may have been utilized exclusively to capture large fish such as channel catfish or drum. Given the relatively high quantity of fish recovered

Table 37. Worked Bone Artifacts from the Fish Lake Site

Feature Number	Occupation Area	Animal Type	Element	N of Pieces	Wt(g)	Burned	Evidence of Utilization	Tool Type
36	3	deer	metatarsal/ metacarpal	1	7.7	no	ground, cut	awl/pin
		deer	phalange?	1	1.0	no	polished	fish hook
		deer	antler	1	75.5	no	ground, cut	flaker
		mammal?	unknown	3	0.4	no	polished, cut	unknown
		turtle	carapace (frag.)	1	5.4	no	cut, incised	dish?
38	3	deer	left ulna	1	19.1	no	polished, cut	awl
		deer?	metacarpal/ metatarsal	1	10.0	no	grooved	stock
43	1	turtle	carapace	8	3.9	yes	ground, cut	unknown
72	3	turtle	carapace	1	19.1	no	cut, ground	dish?
93	2	mammal	unknown	1	0.2	yes	polished	unknown
98	2	deer	phalange	1	4.2	no	polished, drilled	cup and pin game piece
105	3	turtle	carapace	1	5.2	no	ground	unknown
106	3	mussel	shell frag.	1	0.1	yes	incised	unknown
134	1	deer	antler tine	1	0.6	yes	bevelled	flaker
137	1	deer	phalange	1	3.4	no	polished, drilled	cup and pin game piece
149	3	deer?	unknown	1	1.3	no	ground	splinter awl
164	1	deer	antler tine	1	6.0	no	ground	flaker/awl

from this site, it is surprising that only one hook was found. This suggests that other fish capture techniques, such as seining, may have been more popular and efficient (Figure 61b).

Two cup elements of cup-and-pin gaming pieces were recovered at this site. The cups were made from deer phalanges that had been polished and drilled through their centers. The proximal ends of both specimens had been cut. A cup from Feature 98 was also cut at its distal end. Although not a common artifact in archaeological sites, the cup-and-pin game apparently had a wide distribution in the eastern United States, occuring as early as the Archaic period (Culin 1907:527-561; Winters 1969;83-84). In the American Bottom this artifact has not been recovered from archaeological contexts earlier than the Patrick phase.

The three deer bone awls fell into two categories, including those made from complete metatarsals, metacarpals, or ulnae and those made from long bone splinters. All three of these artifacts exhibited heavy polishing over their entire surfaces. Such tools may have functioned as needles or punches for working leather or hides. A single metatarsal or metacarpal midsection exhibited a longitudinal groove along its dorsal side. The groove appears to have resulted from attempts to saw the bone in half, perhaps in an attempt to produce two splinter awls. This midsection portion, therefore, appears to represent a manufacturing by-product rather than a specific tool.

Modified Turtle Shell

Four fragments of modified turtle carapace shell were recovered. These artifacts had intentional cut marks on their interior carapace surfaces and ground edges. The cut marks appeared to be ornamental in nature but definite patterns or designs could not be determined from the fragments recovered. The carapaces were perhaps dishes or fragments resulting from the manufacture of dishes.

Modified Mussel Shell

Very little shell was recovered, although a single fragment of mussel shell was recovered from Feature 106 that exhibited evidence of utilization. This shell fragment was less than a centimeter long but it had four shallow, incised lines along its edge. Its function was problematical but it may have served as a scoop or dish. Another possibility is that it served as a counter or tally for gambling games (Winters 1969:84).

Distribution of Worked Bone

The majority of the worked bone artifacts (64%), as has already been mentioned, occurred in Occupation Area 3. Even more remarkable is the

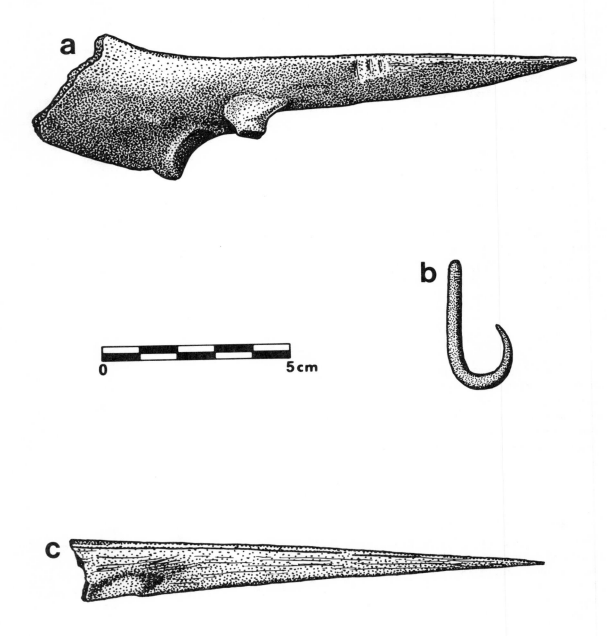

Figure 61. Utilized Bone: a, awl; b, fish hook; c, awl/needle

fact that of the ten artifacts in Occupation Area 3, nine occurred in an areally restricted group of pits (around the Feature 73 historical disturbance). This represents a rather significant distributional pattern, which is indicative of a major focus of bone tool use at this site. It is also significant that this particular area produced the highest amount of animal bone at the site. Fish were found in particularly large numbers in this area, indicating that it was an important animal processing area. Therefore, it is very probable that the bone tool concentration found here was directly related to animal processing activities. Unfortunately, this area lay outside of the 1982 right-of-way limits and could not be further investigated during the second season of work.

PLANT REMAINS

by Sissel Johannessen

Charred plant remains were analyzed from 13 Fish Lake site features, of which three were structures and the remainder were pits. The plant remains and their distributions are described below, and the general pattern is then compared to that of the other Late Woodland sites in the area.

Methods

During excavation of the Fish Lake site, samples of known volume (usually 10 l) for flotation were taken routinely from each zone of every feature excavated. The samples were water floated following the IDOT system (Wagner 1976) using a method of tub flotation with #40 mesh screen (0.42 mm2). Thirteen features were selected by the Site Director for analysis of floral remains. Flotation samples taken from the thirteen features were further separated by zinc chloride flotation (Struever 1968).

The resultant samples of botanical material were sieved through a 2 mm geological screen, and both size fractions (>2 mm and <2 mm) were sorted by hand under low magnification (10X to 30X). It was assumed that uncharred botanical material was modern. All fragments greater than 2 mm in size were sorted into general categories (wood, nutshell, seed, etc.), each category was weighed, and the fragments were counted. The less than 2 mm fraction was scanned carefully and all seeds, seed fragments, and remains of cultivated plants were removed.

An attempt was made to identify all botanical material, with the exception of the wood charcoal, of which the first 20 randomly chosen fragments were identified from each sample. Identifications were made with the aid of standard texts (Martin and Barkley 1961; Montgomery 1977; Panshin and de Zeeuw 1970) and ultimately by a one-to-one comparison with specimens in a reference collection of modern specimens.

Identifications were made to the genus level where possible; specific
identifications were made only when 1) only one species of a genus was
native to the area, e.g., Diospyros virginiana; or 2) all other possible
species had been eliminated by a comparison of morphology, e.g., Solanum
americanum.

Results

Plant remains were common but not abundant throughout the fills. A
total of 420 l of fill from the 13 features was examined, resulting in
the recovery of 16.2 g of charred botanical material. The overall
average 10 l sample of feature fill contained material weighing 0.4 g
and consisting of 17 nutshell fragments, 11 wood fragments, and 39
seeds. Use of both wild and cultivated indigenous plants was evidenced,
as well as use of two exotic domesticates, squash and tobacco. The data
are presented in Table 38.

Nut

Nutshell was the most abundant class of plant remains recovered from
the Fish Lake site; all but one of the features analyzed yielded
nutshell. The composition and distribution of nutshell are indicated in
Table 39. Thick-shelled hickory nutshell was by far the most common
type. A few fragments of pecan and hazelnut were also recovered. Acorn
shell was somewhat more common than pecan or hazelnut, occurring in
almost half the analyzed features. The high acorn percentage (39.4%) in
Table 39, however, is almost entirely due to a concentration of acorn
shell in one sample taken from the basin of structure Feature 34.

The abundance and ubiquity of nut remains, dominated by
thick-shelled hickories, are typical of Late Woodland assemblages in the
American Bottom.

Wood

Wood charcoal was less abundant in the Fish Lake feature samples
than is typical for other sites of the same time period in the area.
The average frequency of 11 fragments per 10 l at Fish Lake contrasted
with averages of 199 and 386 fragments per 10 l at the Patrick phase
components at the Range and Dohack sites, respectively.

The composition of the wood charcoal from Fish Lake was also
atypical. At each of 15 other Late Woodland sites analyzed, the
majority of the wood charcoal fragments (from 70% to 98%) were composed
of a combination of oak and hickory. In contrast, oak and hickory at
the Fish Lake site made up only 19% of the wood charcoal fragments; the
three most common wood taxa, in addition to some hickory, were birch,
elm/hackberry, and honey locust. This difference in the wood

Table 38. Flotation-recovered Plant Remains from the Fish Lake Site

						Features								Total	
	9	26	34	36	37	43	49	80	81	82	93	95	104	N of Fragments	Wt(g)
Nut (N of fragments)															
hickory (Carya sp.)	15	28	6	83	22	21	-	29	14	5	74	13	8	318	-
pecan hickory (C. illinoensis)	-	-	-	-	-	-	-	6	1	1	-	-	-	8	-
hazelnut (Corylus americana)	-	-	-	-	-	-	-	-	-	-	1?	-	-	1?	-
hickory and walnut (Juglandaceae)	14	11	4	16	5	3	-	8	12	4	7	6	6	96	-
acorn (Quercus sp.)	-	1	271	3	-	3	-	3	-	-	1	-	-	282	-
unidentifiable	-	2	-	5	-	3*	-	-	-	-	1	-	-	11	-
Total	29	42	281	107	27	30	-	46	27	10	84	19	14	716	8.8
Wood (N of fragments)															
maple (Acer sp.)	-	-	-	-	-	-	-	-	-	-	2	-	-	2	-
birch (Betula sp.)	-	9	2	5?	-	25	-	1	16?	-	-	-	-	37,21?	-
hickory (Carya sp.)	-	-	7	-	8	-	-	9	-	-	4	-	-	28	-
dogwood (Cornus sp.)	-	-	-	-	-	-	-	-	-	-	1	3	6	10	-
persimmon (Diospyros virginiana)	-	-	-	-	-	-	-	1?	-	-	-	-	-	1?	-
honey locust (Gleditsia triacanthos)	10	-	-	-	-	3	-	-	-	-	2	-	-	15	-
cherry (Prunus sp.)	-	-	-	-	-	8	-	-	-	-	-	-	-	8	-
oak (Quercus sp.)	-	-	-	1	-	-	-	-	-	-	1	-	-	2	-
oak, red group	1	1	-	-	-	-	-	-	1	-	-	1	-	4	-
oak, white group	-	1	-	-	-	-	-	-	-	-	-	-	-	1	-
cottonwood/willow (Salicaceae)	-	5	1	-	8	-	-	-	-	-	-	-	-	14	-
elm/hackberry (Ulmaceae)	-	1	8	-	3	-	-	6	-	-	9	-	-	27	-
bark	-	-	-	4	1	4	-	-	-	-	1	4	-	11	-
diffuse porous	-	-	2	12	6	1	-	1	-	4	1	-	4	31	-
ring porous	3	2	6	3	-	2	-	-	-	-	6	-	1	23	-
unidentifiable	9	10	5	6	12	17	-	3	9	3	3	6	6	89	-
Total (Frags. examined)	23	29	31	31	38	57	-	21	26	7	30	14	17	480	7.4
Total (frags. recovered)	47	41	53	33	39	73	-	54	37	7	65	14	17		
Seeds (N of seeds)															
amaranth (Amaranthus sp.)	-	-	-	-	-	5	-	-	-	-	-	-	-	5	-
goosefoot (Chenopodium sp.)	3	7	5	3	-	197	-	3	1	-	5	-	-	224	-
goosefoot/amaranth (Cheno-Am)	-	-	-	2	-	-	-	-	-	-	-	-	-	2	-
grass (Gramineae)	-	-	-	3	-	1	-	3	-	-	-	-	-	7	-
grass (Gramineae Type 6F)	-	-	-	-	-	2	-	-	-	-	-	-	-	2	-
grass (Gramineae Type 6L)	-	2	1	-	1	48	-	2	-	-	3	-	-	56	-
grass (Gramineae Type 20/21)	-	-	-	-	-	3	-	-	-	2	-	-	-	5	-
marsh elder (Iva annua)	-	1	-	-	-	-	-	-	-	-	-	-	-	1	-
prairie clover? (cf. Lespedeza sp.)	-	-	-	-	-	3	-	-	-	-	-	-	-	3	-
maygrass (Phalaris caroliniana)	-	7	5	8	1	107	-	3	9	43	51	-	2	236	-
knotweeds (Polygonum spp.)	16	-	9	2	-	14	-	5	5	7	-	-	-	58	-
purslane (Portulaca oleracea)	-	-	2	-	-	11	-	-	1	-	-	-	-	14	-
poison ivy (Rhus cf. radicans)	1	-	-	-	-	-	-	-	-	-	-	-	-	1	-
elderberry (Sambucus canadensis)	-	-	1	-	-	8	-	-	-	-	-	-	-	9	-
prickly mallow (Sida spinosa)	1	1	-	-	-	-	-	-	-	-	-	-	-	2	-
black nightshade (Solanum americanum)	-	-	-	-	-	-	-	-	-	-	2	-	-	2	-
nightshade/ground cherry (Solanum/Physalis)	-	-	-	-	-	11	-	-	-	-	-	-	-	11	-
wild bean (Strophostyles sp.)	-	-	-	-	-	2	-	1	-	-	-	-	-	3	-
mullein? (cf. Verbascum sp.)	-	-	-	-	-	-	-	-	-	-	1	-	-	1	-
grape (Vitis sp.)	-	-	-	-	-	2	-	3	-	1	3	-	-	9	-
unknown**	-	2	9	-	-	7	-	-	-	8	2	-	-	28	-
unidentifiable**	11	27	18	40	22	484	3	12	45	54	27	10	2	755	-
Total***	32	50	50	59	24	1075	3	34	62	117	108	10	4	1627***	-
Exotic Cultigens (N of fragments)															
tobacco, seeds (Nicotiana sp.)	-	3?	-	1?	-	169,1?	-	2	1?	2	14	-	-	187,6?	-
squash, rind frags. (Cucurbita sp.)	-	2	6	1	-	5	-	8	-	24	-	-	-	46	-
squash, seed (Cucurbita sp.)	-	-	-	-	-	1	-	-	-	-	-	-	-	1	-
Total	-	5?	6	2?	-	175,1?	-	10	1?	26	14	-	-	240	-
Other (N of fragments)															
fungal fructification	-	-	-	-	-	-	-	2	-	-	-	-	-	2	-
stems with buds	-	-	-	-	-	9	-	-	-	-	-	-	-	9	-
unknown fragments	-	-	2	-	-	25	-	16	-	1	8	-	-	52	-
amorphous fragments	-	12	-	13	4	17	3	4	8	22	15	7	4	109	-
Total	-	12	2	13	4	51	3	22	8	23	23	7	4	172	16.2
Total Wt. Charcoal (g)	1.1	1.2	1.7	2.6	0.7	1.9	0.0	1.3	1.1	0.2	3.8	0.3	0.3		
Total Vol. Flot. (l)	20	20	50	30	30	50	10	50	70	20	30	10	30		

Key
   ? identification not secure
   * nut husk
   ** seeds are classified as unidentifiable if in a poor state of
      preservation; as unknown if (although well-preserved) the
      analyst could not identify them
   *** tobacco seeds are included in seed totals

Table 39. Composition and Distribution of Nut and
Wood Types from the Fish Lake Site

Taxon	% of Identified Fragments	% of Features from which Recovered
Nut	N=716	N=13
thick-shelled hickory (Carya sp.)	44.4	92.3
acorn (Quercus sp.)	39.4	46.2
hickory and walnut (Juglandaceae)	13.4	92.3
pecan hickory (Carya illinoensis)	1.1	23.1
hazelnut (Corylus americana)	0.1	7.8
unidentified	1.5	
Wood	N=181	N=13
birch (Betula sp.)	32.0	46.2
hickory (Carya sp.)	15.5	30.8
elm and hackberry (Ulmaceae)	14.9	38.5
honey locust (Gleditsia triacanthos)	8.3	23.1
cottonwood/willow (Salicaceae)	7.7	23.1
dogwood (Cornus sp.)	5.5	23.1
cherry (Prunus sp.)	4.4	7.8
oak (Quercus spp.)	3.9	46.2
maple (Acer sp.)	1.1	7.8
persimmon (Diospyros virginiana)	0.6	7.8
bark	6.1	38.5

composition between Fish Lake and other Late Woodland sites can be attributed to differences in the locations of these sites. The other sites analyzed were located either in the uplands, or on the floodplain near (<0.5 km) the bluffs, whereas the Fish Lake site was about 2.5 km out onto the floodplain. The oak-hickory combination that dominated Late Woodland sites other than Fish Lake is typical of, and presumably reflects, the composition of a climax oak-hickory upland forest. Woods dominating the Fish Lake charcoal, however, are typical of floodplain habitats. The taxon most frequently recovered, birch (probably Betula nigra), is a pioneer species in developing new forests along stream bank alluvium (Steyermark 1963:527); in addition, Hus (1908) reports river birch growing near floodplain lakes and streams of the American Bottom. Hackberry, American elm, and honey locust also commonly grow in floodplain forests. Presumably then, fuel-wood was gathered by the inhabitants of the Fish Lake site from floodplain forests near the site.

Seeds and Exotic Cultigens

A total of 1628 seeds were recovered from the 429 l of feature fill analyzed. A minimum of 20 taxa were represented. Table 40 gives the percentage composition and distribution of the seed spectrum.

Over half of the identifiable seeds (52.7%) consisted of just two taxa: maygrass (Phalaris caroliniana) and goosefoot (Chenopodium sp., probably C. bushianum). These two types were part of a complex of indigenous small starchy seed plants that were thought to have been cultivated (Asch and Asch 1980; Cowan 1978; Wilson 1981). This complex of seed types (which includes a knotweed species, Polygonum erectum) begins to dominate the seed spectrum by Middle Woodland times in Illinois (Asch, Farnsworth, and Asch 1979). Data from American Bottom sites reveal that this complex continues to dominate the seed spectrum through the Mississippian period (Johannessen 1982b). Interestingly, although knotweeds (Polygonum spp.) were the fourth most common seed type recovered from the Fish Lake samples, these knotweeds were all of species other than P. erectum, the species most commonly recovered with other members of the starchy seed complex. No explanation for this unusual replacement of P. erectum by knotweeds of other species suggests itself at this time.

Other indigenous seed taxa in the Fish Lake samples included plants with fleshy fruits such as grape, elderberry, and nightshade or ground cherry. Black nightshade bears a fruit that is edible when ripe, although toxic when green. The seeds of this species are regularly recovered from American Bottom sites, much more frequently than other nightshade species (several of which are native to the area), indicating that this species was commonly selected for use. Wild beans (Figure 62) are also frequently recovered. These small legumes are reportedly palatable and nutritious, containing the same number of calories and percentage of protein as the common domesticated bean, Phaseolus vulgaris (Duke 1981). Another category of plants was represented at the

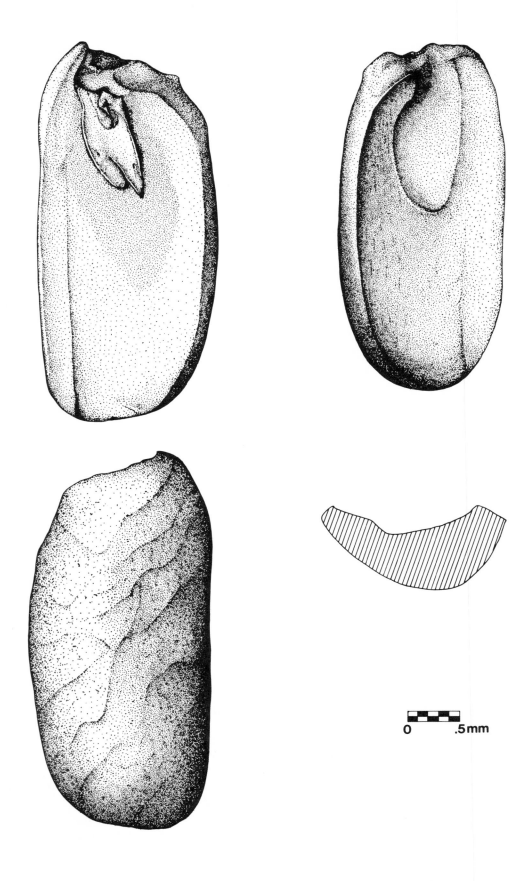

Figure 62. Wild Bean (<u>Strophostyles</u> sp.)

Table 40. Composition and Distribution of Seeds from the Fish Lake Site

Taxon	% of Identified Seeds	% of Features from which Recovered
Seeds	N=873	N=13
maygrass (Phalaris caroliniana)	27.0	76.9
goosefoot (Chenopodium sp.)	25.7	61.5
tobacco (Nicotiana sp.)	22.1	53.8
knotweeds (Polygonum spp.)	6.6	53.8
grass (Gramineae Type 6L)	6.4	46.2
purslane (Portulaca oleracea)	1.6	23.1
nightshade/ground cherry (Solanum/Physalis)	1.3	7.8
elderberry (Sambucus canadensis)	1.0	15.4
grape (Vitis sp.)	1.0	30.8
grass (Gramineae)	0.8	23.1
grass (Gramineae Type 20/21)	0.6	15.4
amaranth (Amaranthus sp.)	0.6	7.8
wild bean (Strophostyles sp.)	0.3	15.4
prairie clover (cf. Lespedeza sp.)	0.3	7.8
prickly mallow (Sida spinosa)	0.2	15.4
goosefoot/amaranth (Cheno/Am)	0.2	7.8
grass (Gramineae Type 6F)	0.2	7.8
black nightshade (Solanum americanum)	0.2	7.8
marsh elder (Iva annua)	0.1	7.8
mullein? (cf. Verbascum sp.)	0.1	7.8
poison ivy (Rhus cf. radicans)	0.1	7.8

Fish Lake site by seeds such as prickly mallow and poison ivy. These plants would have had no obvious economic value, and they may have resulted from natural seed rain at the site and then been burned secondarily.

Remains of nonnative cultigens in the Fish Lake samples were squash rinds and seeds, as well as tobacco seeds, each of which were recovered from about 50% of the features analyzed. Squash rind is relatively common in Late Woodland contexts. Remains from Missouri indicate that squash was being grown in the Midwest at least 3000 years before the occupation of the Fish Lake site (King 1980).

Of special interest were the tobacco seeds (Nicotiana sp.). Seven of the features analyzed yielded these minute seeds (ca. 0.8 mm), and one sample from an ash lens near the bottom of a deep bell-shaped pit (Feature 43) contained 170 specimens. It is difficult to distinguish the various species of Nicotiana through seed morphology, but it is likely that these seeds are of N. rustica, since this species was grown extensively in North America at the time of European contact. N. rustica is a long-cultivated species with a possible origin in the Andes (Purseglove 1968:539). Wilbert (1979) states that N. rustica was used by the Indians of South America almost exclusively in ritual contexts, and that it was one of the most important of a number of plants used for magical and religious purposes. The tobacco seeds from American Bottom sites constitute early evidence for the spread of N. rustica into North America. Tobacco seeds have also been recovered from at least two other Late Woodland occupations in the American Bottom: the Range site Patrick phase occupation, and the Mund site Mund phase occupation (ca. 400 A.C. to 600 A.C.; see Fortier et al. 1982). It is significant that the use of tobacco, presumably with ritual connotations, appears to have preceded the widespread use in the area of the Mesoamerican cultigen maize. No remains of maize were recovered from the Fish Lake site, and only one fragment was recovered from the Mund site (Johannessen 1982a). In contrast, in Dohack phase sites (ca. 800 A.C. to 850 A.C.) maize appears rather abruptly in significant quantities (recovered from about 50% of the features analyzed from the Dohack and Joan Carrie sites).

In summary, the plant remains from the Fish Lake site, along with data from other Late Woodland sites in the American Bottom, indicate the existence of a well-developed gardening complex, including both native and introduced cultigens, at a time preceding the widespread use of maize. Resources such as nuts, fruits, legumes, and grasses were also used, presumably gathered from naturally occurring stands.

Seasonality and Distribution

Table 41 lists the months during which the plant taxa identified from the Fish Lake site normally fruit. The fruits of some taxa would have been available for long periods, e.g., knotweeds, which fruit from June to frost, while some would have been available for only a short

Table 41. Fruiting Season of Plant Taxa from the Fish Lake Site

Taxon	May	June	July	August	September	October	November
maygrass	X	X	X				
goosefoot		X	X	X	X	X	
knotweeds		X	X	X	X	X	
amaranth			X	X	X	X	
purslane			X	X	X	X	
prickly mallow			X	X	X	X	
nightshade/ ground cherry			X	X	X	X	
squash			X	X	X	X	
hazelnut				X	X		
prairie clover				X	X	X	
elderberry				X	X	X	
wild bean				X	X	X	
poison ivy				X	X	X	X
black nightshade				X	X	X	X
marsh elder					X	X	
grape					X	X	
tobacco					X	X	
acorn					X	X	X
hickory					X	X	X

time. Marsh elder, for example, is thought to have an effective harvest season of only about two weeks (Asch and Asch 1978:311). Overall, the season of availability stretches from May, when the first florets of maygrass begin to mature (Cowan 1978:267), to November, when the last of the nut masts may still be on the ground. Therefore, if the plant products identified from the site were cultivated and gathered by the inhabitants of the site while they lived there (rather than being carried in as dried, stored commodities), the site must have been occupied by at least a part of the group from spring, when the ground was prepared for planting, to late fall. Of course, the evidence does not preclude winter occupation; the site may well have been occupied year-round.

The distribution of the plant remains among the features analyzed was quite homogeneous. Except for Feature 49, all features analyzed yielded wood charcoal, nutshell fragments, and small seeds. The amount of material present in the samples from the various features was quite low and relatively even. There were two exceptions to this: one was a sample from the house basin of Feature 34 that contained a concentration of acorn shell, and the second was a small ash lens near the bottom of Feature 43 (a deep, bell-shaped pit) that yielded a large quantity of seeds, as well as other debris.

A puzzling feature of the distribution of the plant remains is that the various features were generally similar both in the quantities of plant remains and in the types of plants represented. Table 38 shows that there was little segregation of the different plant taxa among the features; all features yielded similar floral assemblages. One might expect to see spatial segregation by feature (or at least by zones within a feature) of plants that were processed differently or were gathered at different times of the year. However, this was not the case with the Fish Lake samples. Seasonal segregation was not evident; for example, several samples (from Features 80, 82, and 93) yielded seeds from plants whose fruiting seasons do not even overlap, i.e., maygrass and grape. The most striking example of this mixture of taxa was in the sealed ash lens in Feature 43, which presumably resulted from a single episode of deposition. One sample from this lens, in addition to deer bone, fish bone, and fish scale, yielded hickory nutshell, acorn, maygrass, goosefoot, grasses, knotweeds, tobacco, purslane, ground cherry, grape, elderberry, amaranth, and a squash seed. It is difficult to imagine how such a wide variety of plant and animal materials, representing such different seasons of collection and methods of preparation, could have been deposited at one time. Interestingly, the samples from the upper zones of the same feature (Zones A1, A2, and A3) contained many of the same taxa as the ash lens, although in lesser quantities.

Asch et al. (1972:9) note a similar phenomenon in the samples from the Koster site: "the uniformity of nut percentages from one flotation sample to the next is striking...". They believe that arguments of shifting activity areas or mixing by prehistoric pit digging are insufficient to explain the observed uniformity, and conclude that "the pronounced uniformity of nut percentages from sample to sample suggests that there was short-term stability in man's use of nuts at Koster as well as long-term stability at least during the periods when the site was occupied" (Asch et al. 1972:10). However, it seems unlikely that the pronounced homogeneity, both quantitatively and qualitatively, of the plant remains among the features at the Fish Lake site resulted from a homogeneity of use, if that is what is meant by "short-term stability". The uniformity (and great mixture of taxa) seen in the Fish Lake samples recovered from both structures and pits, as well as from all zones within pits, was more likely a result of the accumulation of debris in features over fairly long periods of time. Refuse from multiple episodes of processing and cooking, some of which occurred outside the pits, others of which occurred within the pits, would presumably have become deposited within single fill zones.

FAUNAL REMAINS

by Lucretia S. Kelly

A moderately large and fairly well-preserved Patrick phase faunal assemblage was recovered from the Fish Lake site. Because of the unmixed cultural affiliation of the assemblage, the data may provide a model for other Patrick phase occupations in the area.

A wide variety of both aquatic and terrestrial habitats were readily accessible to the Fish Lake site prehistoric inhabitants. The variety of fauna recovered reflects this diversity of habitats.

Due to the close proximity of the site (ca. 2 km) to the Mississippi River, the most prevalent fish species recovered are those that prefer large river habitats. The edge environment of the Lunsford-Pulcher terrace and the shallow marshy areas of the Hill Lake meander scar provided ideal habitats for most of the mammals and birds that were recovered from the site.

The entire faunal assemblage was analyzed. Faunal remains totalling 6553 pieces of bone were recovered from 86 features.

Methods

Bones were obtained through two methods. First, animal bone, when exposed during the course of hand excavations, was placed in material bags along with other artifactual debris. These bones were later washed, labeled, and sorted for analysis. Large pieces of bone were usually retrieved by this method. Second, bone was also obtained from flotation samples. A minimum of 10 l of soil was floated from each feature, although some areas were sampled more heavily if large concentrations of bone were noticed. Samples were processed using a modified form of the IDOT flotation system (Wagner 1976). Bone fragments larger than 2 mm were then picked from dried flotation samples. The faunal materials were sorted by major faunal class. Table 42 lists by faunal class the amounts of bone recovered by these two methods, and whether it was burned. The author identified the material to the most specific level possible by using a modern comparative collection.

A minimum number of individuals (MNI) was calculated for the various species identified (Tables 43-46). The most frequently occurring element, after being divided into lefts or rights (when applicable), was used to compute the MNI. Size determinations and relative completeness of the bones were also taken into consideration. The MNI was calculated on a per feature basis within each occupation area, with one exception. For the deer, an MNI was calculated using occupation areas as the units of analysis. This approach to deer seems to be valid since communal sharing of deer meat may have taken place, and bones from one deer may have been deposited into multiple nearby features. If features had been used as the basic analytical units, the number of deer present would have been unrealistically inflated.

Results

Faunal materials were recovered from 26 features in Occupation Area 1, 21 features in Occupation Area 2, 25 features in Occupation Area 3, and 8 features in Occupation Area 4. Six features not associated with these four occupation areas also yielded animal bone.

Mammal

Eleven species of mammals were recovered from the site (Table 43). White-tailed deer (Odocoileus virginianus) remains predominated in all four areas. Most body parts were present in every area, indicating that entire animals were brought back to the site. In Occupation Area 1, nine features yielded deer remains, giving an MNI of three for the area. One individual was relatively young, based on a lack of epiphyseal union of a metatarsal. Another individual was from four to five years old, based on molar wear. A skull fragment (frontal and parietal bones) was recovered that appeared to have had the antlers shed, indicating that this deer was killed during winter.

Seven features in Occupation Area 2 yielded deer bone, giving an MNI of one. Ten features in Occupation Area 3 yielded deer remains, giving an MNI of three. One individual was one year old or less, as indicated by the presence of three deciduous premolars.

Two features in Occupation Area 4 contained one deer bone each. These were the only identifiable mammalian bones recovered from this area.

Table 42. Bone Classes by Occupation Area

	N of Pieces	Floated		Not Floated		Burned		Not Burned		Wt(g)
		N	%	N	%	N	%	N	%	
Occupation 1 (26 Features)										
Mammals	480	174	36.25	306	63.75	99	20.63	381	79.38	599.7
Birds	12	5	41.67	7	58.33	6	50.00	6	50.00	5.6
Fish	265	185	69.81	80	30.19	52	19.62	213	80.38	49.2
Turtles	32	13	40.63	19	59.38	17	53.13	15	46.88	12.4
Unidentifiable	907	425	46.86	482	53.14	463	51.05	444	48.95	56.4
Subtotal	1696	802		894		637		1059		723.3
Occupation 2 (21 Features)										
Mammals	195	20	10.26	175	89.74	22	11.28	173	88.72	253.7
Birds	38	1	2.63	37	97.37	0	0.00	38	100.00	14.5
Fish	194	133	68.56	61	31.44	20	10.31	174	89.69	14.8
Turtles	12	6	50.00	6	50.00	2	16.67	10	83.33	13.5
Unidentifiable	840	529	62.98	311	37.02	334	39.76	506	60.24	39.6
Subtotal	1279	689		590		378		901		336.1
Occupation 3 (25 Features)										
Mammals	279	85	30.47	194	69.53	24	8.60	255	91.40	794.8
Birds	55	19	34.55	36	65.45	14	25.45	41	74.55	15.7
Fish	1377	840	61.00	537	39.00	81	5.88	1296	94.12	479.4
Turtles	55	4	7.27	51	92.73	4	7.27	51	92.73	38.2
Amphibians	3	3	100.00	0	0.00	0	0.00	3	100.0	0.2
Unidentifiable	1637	1091	66.65	546	33.35	504	30.79	1133	69.21	89.4
Subtotal	3406	2042		1364		627		2779		1417.7
Occupation 4 (8 Features)										
Mammals	14	2	14.29	12	85.71	2	14.29	12	85.71	74.8
Birds	4	4	100.00	0	0.00	4	100.00	0	0.00	0.2
Fish	13	7	53.85	6	46.15	8	61.54	5	38.46	0.2
Unidentifiable	112	109	97.32	3	2.68	89	79.46	23	20.54	4.5
Subtotal	143	122		21		103		40		79.7
Miscellaneous (6 Features)										
Mammals	1	1	100.00	0	0.00	1	100.00	0	0.00	0.7
Fish	1	0	0.00	1	100.00	1	100.00	0	0.00	0.2
Unidentifiable	27	25	92.59	2	7.41	21	77.78	6	22.22	0.9
Subtotal	29	26		3		23		6		1.8
Total	6553	3681	56.17	2872	43.83	1768	26.98	4785	73.02	2558.6

Table 43. Mammalian Remains

Occupation Area 1 Features

	3	6	11	27	28	35	37	43	48	81	134	139	164	166	Subtotal****
Scalopus aquaticus (mole)	-	-	-	-	-	-	-	-	-	1 (1)	-	-	-	-	1 (1)
Procyon lotor (raccoon)	-	-	1 (1)	-	-	-	-	-	-	-	-	-	-	-	1 (1)
Canis spp. (dog/coyote)	-	-	-	-	-	-	-	1 (1)	-	-	-	-	-	-	1 (1)
Rodentia (rodent family)	-	-	-	-	-	-	-	-	-	1 (1)	-	-	-	-	1 (1)
Castor canadensis (beaver)	-	-	-	-	-	-	-	1 (3)	-	-	-	-	-	-	1 (3)
Sylvilagus floridanus (cottontail rabbit)	-	-	-	-	-	-	-	1 (3)	-	-	-	-	-	-	1 (3)
Odocoileus virginianus (white-tailed deer)	-	-	1 (2)	1 (5)	1 (2)	1 (1)	1 (2)	1 (6)	-	1 (2)	3 (38)	-	1 (21)	-	11 (79)
Large mammal*	-	-	(5)	(13)	-	-	-	(2)	-	(3)	-	-	-	(25)	(48)
Medium mammal**	-	-	-	-	-	-	-	(1)	-	(2)	-	-	-	-	(3)
Medium-large mammal	(12)	(4)	(104)	-	-	-	-	(11)	-	(27)	(83)	-	-	-	(241)
Indeterminate mammal	-	-	-	-	-	-	-	(1)	(1)	(57)	-	(40)	-	-	(99)
Total	- (12)	- (4)	2 (112)	1 (18)	1 (2)	1 (1)	1 (2)	4 (28)	- (1)	3 (93)	3 (121)	- (40)	1 (21)	- (25)	17 (480)

Occupation Area 2 Features

	9	24	79	80	82	88	89	90	93	98	Subtotal****
Procyon lotor (raccoon)	-	-	-	-	-	-	-	-	-	1 (2)	1 (2)
Rodentia (rodent family)	-	-	1 (7)	-	-	-	-	-	1 (2)	-	2 (9)
Odocoileus virginianus (white-tailed deer)	-	-	-	1 (1)	1 (7)	1 (10)	1 (8)	1 (1)	1 (32)	1 (16)	7 (75)
Large mammal*	(5)	-	-	-	-	-	-	-	-	(3)	(8)
Medium mammal**	(1)	-	-	-	-	-	-	-	-	-	(1)
Medium-large mammal	-	(31)	-	-	(43)	(1)	-	-	(11)	(1)	(87)
Indeterminate mammal	(3)	-	(4)	(4)	-	(2)	-	-	-	-	(13)
Total	- (9)	- (31)	1 (11)	1 (5)	1 (50)	1 (13)	1 (8)	1 (1)	2 (45)	2 (22)	10 (195)

Table 43. Continued

Occupation Area 3 Features

	36	38	40	58	72	73	105	106	123	129	131	146	147	148	149	151	152	Subtotal****
Scalopus aquaticus (mole)	-	-	-	-	-	-	-	-	-	-	-	-	-	1 (1)	-	-	-	1 (1)
Procyon lotor (raccoon)	1 (2)	-	-	-	-	-	-	-	-	-	-	-	-	-	-	-	-	1 (2)
cf. Vulpes fulva (red fox)	-	-	-	-	1 (1)	-	-	-	-	-	-	-	-	-	-	-	-	1 (1)
Canis spp. (dog/coyote)	-	-	-	-	-	-	-	1 (3)	-	-	-	-	-	-	-	-	-	1 (3)
Rodentia (rodent family)	-	1 (6)	-	-	-	-	1 (1)	1 (1)	-	-	-	-	-	-	-	-	-	3 (8)
Sciurus carolinensis (gray squirrel)	1 (3)	-	-	-	-	-	-	-	-	-	-	-	-	-	-	-	-	1 (3)
Sciurus spp. (squirrel)	- (2)	-	-	-	-	-	-	-	-	-	-	-	-	-	1 (1)	-	-	1 (3)
Castor canadensis (beaver)	1 (1)	-	-	-	-	-	-	-	-	-	-	-	-	-	1 (2)	-	-	2 (3)
Ondatra zibethicus (muskrat)	-	-	-	-	-	-	1 (1)	-	-	-	-	-	-	-	-	-	-	1 (1)
Sylvilagus floridanus (cottontail rabbit)	-	-	-	-	-	-	1 (1)	-	1 (1)	-	-	-	-	-	-	-	-	2 (2)
Odocoileus virginianus (white-tailed deer)	1 (9)	3 (12)	-	1 (4)	1 (1)	1 (1)	1 (4)	-	1 (4)	1 (5)	1 (2)	-	-	-	1 (1)	-	-	12 (43)
Large mammal*	-	- (24)	-	-	- (1)	+	-	-	-	-	- (46)	-	-	-	-	-	-	1 (71)
Medium mammal**	(18)	(2)	-	-	(2)	-	-	-	-	-	-	-	-	(2)	-	-	-	(24)
Medium-large mammal	(20)	(6)	-	-	-	-	(1)	-	-	-	-	(6)	(2)	(5)	-	(8)	(1)	(49)
Small mammal***	(2)	-	-	-	-	-	-	-	-	-	-	-	-	-	-	-	-	(2)
Indeterminate mammal	(1)	(16)	(1)	-	(2)	(2)	(5)	(1)	(16)	(5)	-	-	-	(2)	(2)	-	-	(53)
Total	4 (58)	4 (66)	- (1)	1 (4)	2 (7)	2 (13)	4 (13)	2 (5)	2 (21)	1 (10)	1 (48)	- (6)	- (2)	1 (10)	2 (5)	- (9)	- (1)	27 (279)

	Occupation Area 4 Features				Unassociated Feature
	118	119	157	Subtotal	141
Odocoileus virginianus (white-tailed deer)	-	1 (1)	1 (11)	2 (12)	-
Medium-large mammal	(2)	-	-	(2)	(1)
Total	- (2)	1 (1)	1 (11)	2 (14)	- (1)

```
   * deer, beaver, rabbit
  ** raccoon, muskrat, rabbit
 *** mink, large rodents
**** When the MNI of deer were calculated for entire occupation areas, MNI
     figures of 3, 1, and 3 were obtained for Occupation Areas 1, 2, and
     3, respectively.
   + Ten elements of modern cattle, representing one MNI, were
     found in Feature 73.
```

Key
- Minimum number of individuals
(#) - N of elements

Raccoon (Procyon lotor) remains were recovered from Occupation Areas 1, 2, and 3; they represented an MNI of one for each area. Beaver (Castor canadensis), cottontail rabbit (Sylvilagus floridanus), and dog or coyote (Canis sp.) were recovered from Occupation Areas 1 and 3. Muskrat (Ondatra zibethicus), gray squirrel (Scuirus carolinensis), and a possible red fox (cf. Vulpes fulva) were recovered only from Occupation Area 3. Mole (Scalopus aquaticus) [Occupation Areas 1 and 3] and small rodent (Rodentia) remains (Occupation Areas 1, 2, and 3), that may represent post-occupation intrusions were also recovered. Possible cow (Bos) remains were recovered from a historical pit (Feature 73).

The mammals identified could have been taken in various terrestrial and marshy habitats near the site. Beavers and muskrats could have been found in marshy areas around Fish Lake. Raccoons inhabit wooded river bottoms, while gray squirrels prefer wooded stream areas and heavy stands of thickets (Hoffmeister and Mohr 1972). Red foxes, cottontail rabbits, coyotes, and deer all inhabit edge environs.

Birds

Bird remains made up only a small portion of the identifiable bones recovered (3.6%) from the site. Seven species were represented (Table 44). If passerines are excluded, aquatic and nonaquatic birds did not occur together in any pit. Another interesting aspect of the assemblage is that all identifiable bird bones [except for those of turkey (Meleagris gallopavo) and one passerine bone] were wing bones. The turkey remains were leg bones. The terrestrial birds outnumbered the aquatic birds both in total number of elements recovered and in MNI.

Occupation Area 1 yielded four species: Prairie chicken (Tympanuchus cupido), mallard (Anas platyrhynchos), teal (Anas discors or A. carolinensis), and passerine. Occupation Area 2 yielded turkey, passenger pigeon (Ectopistes migratorius), mallard, and teal. Only terrestrial birds were recovered from Occupation Area 3, including passenger pigeon, turkey, prairie chicken, hawk (Buteo sp.), and passerine. Only passerines were recovered from Occupation Area 4.

This represents the first identification of passenger pigeon at an FAI-270 site. This bird once numbered in the millions before its extinction in the early 1900s. Its migration would have brought it into Illinois in February and October, although it occasionally wintered in southern Illinois (Bent 1963:402). Although the birds must have been plentiful, the Indians apparently did not exploit them greatly (Bent 1963:395). The passenger pigeon inhabited forested areas, and its principal foods were nuts, berries, and seeds of weeds and grasses.

Table 44. Avian Remains

	Occupation Area 1 Features					Occupation Area 2 Features						
	43	81	132	134	Subtotal	79	82	89	96	98	104	Subtotal
Anas platyryhnchos (mallard)	-	1 (3)	-	-	1 (3)	1 (1)	-	-	-	-	-	1 (1)
Anas discors/carolinensis (teal)	-	-	-	1 (2)	1 (2)	-	-	-	-	-	1 (1)	1 (1)
Tympanuchus cupido (prairie chicken)	1 (3)	-	-	-	1 (3)	-	-	-	-	-	-	-
Meleagris gallopavo (wild turkey)	-	-	-	-	-	-	-	-	-	1 (6)	-	1 (6)
Ectopistes migratorius (passenger pigeon)	-	-	-	-	-	-	-	-	-	1 (1)	-	1 (1)
Large bird*	-	-	-	-	-	-	1 (1)	-	-	-	-	1 (1)
Medium bird**	(1)	(1)	-	-	(2)	(2)	-	-	-	-	-	(2)
Passerine (perching bird)	-	-	1 (1)	1 (1)	2 (2)	1 (1)	-	-	-	-	-	1 (1)
Unidentifiable bird	-	-	-	-	-	-	-	(1)	(24)	-	-	(25)
Total	1 (4)	1 (4)	1 (1)	2 (3)	5 (12)	2 (4)	1 (1)	- (1)	- (24)	2 (7)	1 (1)	6 (38)

	Occupation Area 3 Features									Occupation Area 4 Features
	36	38	72	105	106	146	148	149	Subtotal	119
Buteo sp. (hawk)	1 (1)	-	-	-	-	-	-	-	1 (1)	-
Tympanuchus cupido (prairie chicken)	-	1 (1)	-	-	-	-	-	-	1 (1)	-
Meleagris gallopavo (wild turkey)	1 (8)	-	-	-	-	-	-	-	1 (8)	-
Ectopistes migratorius (passenger pigeon)	1 (5)	-	-	-	-	-	-	-	1 (5)	-
Large bird*	-	(7)	-	-	-	-	-	-	(7)	-
Medium bird**	-	(5)	-	(2)	(3)	(2)	-	(2)	(14)	-
Small bird***	-	-	-	-	-	-	-	(1)	(1)	-
Medium-small bird	-	-	(3)	-	-	-	-	-	(3)	-
Passerine (perching bird)	-	1 (3)	-	-	-	-	-	-	1 (3)	2 (2)
Unidentifiable bird	(7)	(1)	-	-	-	(3)	-	(1)	(12)	(2)
Total	3 (21)	2 (17)	- (3)	- (2)	- (3)	- (5)	- (1)	- (3)	5 (55)	2 (4)

  * goose/turkey size
  ** duck/prairie chicken size
  *** bobwhite size

Key
- Minimum number of individuals
(#) - N of elements

Table 45. Fish Remains

	Occupation Area 1 Features									
	4	11	27	37	43	81	132	134	137	Subtotal
Lepsisoteus sp. (gar)	-	1 (2)	-	-	1 (5)	1 (3)	-	1 (1)	-	4 (11)
Ictaluridae (catfish family)	-	-	-	-	- (2)	- (3)	1 (1)	-	-	1 (6)
Ictalurus furcatus (blue catfish)	-	-	-	-	1 (1)	-	-	-	-	1 (1)
I. punctatus/furcatus (channel/blue catfish)	-	-	-	-	- (1)	1 (1)	-	-	-	1 (2)
Ictalurus spp. (bullhead)	-	-	-	-	1 (2)	1 (2)	-	1 (1)	-	3 (5)
Catostomidae (sucker family)	(1)	-	-	-	(4)	-	-	-	-	(5)
Ictiobus bubalus (smallmouth buffalo)	-	1 (1)	-	-	-	-	-	-	-	1 (1)
Ictiobus spp. (buffalo)	-	-	-	-	1 (3)	-	-	1 (6)	-	2 (9)
Centrarchidae (sunfish family)	-	1 (1)	-	-	1 (1)	-	-	-	-	2 (2)
Micropterus sp. (bass)	-	-	-	-	-	1 (1)	-	-	-	1 (1)
Aplodinotus grunniens (freshwater drum)	-	1 (1)	-	-	-	-	-	1 (1)	1 (8)	3 (10)
Unidentifiable fish	-	(91)	(1)	(3)	(58)	(41)	-	(17)	(1)	(212)
Total	- (1)	4 (96)	- (1)	- (3)	5 (77)	4 (51)	1 (1)	4 (26)	1 (9)	19 (265)

Table 45. Continued

			Occupation Area 2 Features					
	9	79	80	82	88	93	98	104	Subtotal
Lepsisoteus sp. (gar)	1 (1)	1 (1)	-	-	1 (1)		-	1 (1)	4 (4)
Ictaluridae (catfish family)	1 (1)	- (1)	-	-	- (1)	- (3)	- (8)	-	1 (14)
Ictalurus punctatus (channel catfish)	-	-	-	-	1 (1)	-	-	-	1 (1)
I. punctatus/furcatus (channel/blue catfish)	-	1 (1)	-	-	-	-	-	-	1 (1)
Pylodictis olivaris (flathead catfish)	-	-	-	-	-	1 (1)	-	-	1 (1)
Ictalurus melas (black bullhead)	-	-	-	-	1 (1)	-	-	-	1 (1)
Ictalurus spp. (bullhead)	-	-	-	-	(3)	-	-	-	(3)
Catostomidae (sucker family)	-	-	-	-	(5)	-	-	-	(5)
Ictiobus cyprinellus (largemouth buffalo)	-	-	-	-	1 (2)	-	-	-	1 (2)
Ictiobus spp. (buffalo)	-	1 (1)	-	-	- (4)	-	-	-	1 (5)
Catostomus commersoni (white sucker)	-	-	-	-	1 (1)	-	-	-	1 (1)
Centrarchidae (sunfish family)	-	-	-	-	(4)	-	-	-	(4)
Lepomis spp. (sunfish)	-	-	-	-	1 (1)	-	-	-	1 (1)
Aplodinotus grunniens (freshwater drum)	-	-	1 (8)	1 (1)	1 (1)	-	1 (2)	-	4 (12)
Unidentifiable fish	-	(16)	(1)	-	(68)	(11)	(43)	-	(139)
Total	2 (2)	3 (20)	1 (9)	1 (1)	7 (93)	1 (15)	1 (53)	1 (1)	17 (194)

Table 45. Continued

	21	36	38	40	58	72	76	105	106	121	123	146	147	148	149	151	152	Subtotal
								Occupation Area 3 Features										
Lepsisoteus sp. (gar)	-	1 (6)	1 (2)	-	-	1 (3)	-	1 (2)	-	-	-	-	-	1 (1)	-	-	-	5 (14)
Amia calva (bowfin)	-	1 (7)	1 (3)	-	-	-	-	-	-	-	-	-	-	-	-	-	-	2 (10)
Dorsoma cepedianum (gizzard shad)	-	-	3 (12)	-	-	-	-	-	-	-	-	-	-	-	1 (1)	-	-	4 (13)
Clupeidae (herring family)	-	1 (1)	-	-	-	-	-	-	-	-	-	-	-	-	-	-	-	1 (1)
Cyprinidae (minnow)	-	-	1 (1)	-	-	-	-	-	-	-	-	-	-	-	-	-	-	1 (1)
Ictaluridae (catfish family)	(1)	(6)	(14)	1 (1)	-	(10)	-	(1)	-	-	(1)	-	-	-	(2)	-	-	1 (36)
Ictalurus punctatus (channel catfish)	-	1 (7)	2 (8)	-	-	1 (5)	-	1 (1)	-	-	-	-	-	1 (1)	-	-	-	6 (22)
Ictalurus furcatus (blue catfish)	-	2 (2*)	-	-	-	-	-	-	-	-	-	-	-	1 (1)	-	-	-	3 (3)
I. punctatus/furcatus (channel/blue catfish)	-	-	-	-	-	-	-	-	-	-	-	-	-	-	-	1 (2)	-	1 (2)
Pylodictis olivaris (flathead catfish)	-	3 (7**)	-	-	-	1 (2)	-	-	-	-	-	-	-	1 (1)	-	1 (1)	-	6 (12)
Ictalurus melas (black bullhead)	-	-	2 (7)	-	-	-	-	-	-	-	-	-	-	-	-	-	-	2 (7)
I. melas/nebulosus (black/brown bullhead)	-	1 (1)	1 (2)	-	-	-	-	-	-	-	-	-	-	-	-	-	-	2 (3)
Ictalurus spp. (bullhead)	-	1 (1)	1 (23)	-	-	2 (14)	-	1 (1)	-	-	-	-	-	1 (2)	-	-	-	6 (41)
Catostomidae (sucker family)	-	(8)	(5)	-	-	-	-	-	-	-	(1)	-	-	-	(1)	(10)	-	(25)
Ictiobus cyprinellus (largemouth buffalo)	-	2 (8)	1 (2)	-	-	-	-	-	-	-	-	-	-	-	-	1 (5)	-	4 (15)
Ictiobus bubalus (smallmouth buffalo)	-	1 (2)	1 (24)	-	-	1 (2)	-	-	-	-	-	-	-	-	-	1 (2)	-	4 (30)
Ictiobus spp. (buffalo)	-	(20)	(3)	-	-	(4)	-	-	-	-	1 (1)	-	-	1 (3)	1 (2)	1 (22)	-	4 (55)
Carpiodes spp. (carpsucker)	-	-	-	-	-	-	-	-	-	-	1 (2)	-	-	-	-	-	-	1 (2)
Erimyzon spp. (chubsucker)	-	1 (1)	-	-	-	-	-	-	-	-	-	-	-	-	-	-	-	1 (1)
Cantrarchidae (sunfish family)	-	-	(10)	-	-	(4)	-	1 (1)	-	-	-	-	-	(2)	-	-	-	1 (17)
Micropterus sp. (bass)	-	-	1 (3)	-	-	-	-	-	-	-	-	-	-	1 (1)	-	-	-	2 (4)
Lepomis spp. (sunfish)	-	-	1 (6)	1 (1)	-	1 (2)	-	-	-	-	-	-	-	-	-	-	-	3 (9)
Stizostedion spp. (walleye/sauger)	-	-	-	-	-	1 (1)	-	-	-	-	-	-	-	-	-	-	-	1 (1)
Aplodinotus grunniens (freshwater drum)	-	1 (6)	1 (4)	-	-	1 (1)	-	1 (1)	-	1 (1)	-	-	-	1 (1)	1 (1)	1 (21)	-	8 (36)
Unidentifiable fish	(1)	(297)	(305)	(4)	(6)	(130)	(2)	(10)	(9)	(15)	(10)	(2)	(1)	(16)	(29)	(179)	(1)	(1017)
Total	(2)	16 (381)	17 (434)	2 (6)	(6)	9 (178)	(2)	5 (17)	(9)	1 (16)	1 (11)	1 (6)	(1)	5 (26)	6 (37)	6 (244)	(1)	68 (1378)

Table 45. Continued

	Occupation Area 4 Features			Unassociated Area Features
	118	119	Subtotal	141
Lepsisoteus sp. (gar)	1 (1)	-	1 (1)	-
Catostomidae (sucker family)	1 (1)	-	1 (1)	-
Ictiobus/Carpiodes (buffalo or carpsucker)	-	1 (1)	1 (1)	-
Aplodinotus grunniens (freshwater drum)	1 (5)	-	1 (5)	-
Unidentifiable fish	-	(5)	(5)	(1)
Total	3 (7)	1 (6)	4 (13)	- (1)

* Two skulls were found.
** In addition to these seven elements, one skull was found.

Key
 # - Minimum number of individuals
(#) - N of elements

Fish

Seventeen species of fish were identified in the Fish Lake
assemblage (Table 45). The species that occurred in the greatest
abundance (i.e., channel, blue, and flathead catfish; drum; and buffalo)
reflect the site's proximity to large river and lake environments. It
is significant that the fish in this assemblage were fairly large. Most
fish assemblages from American Bottom sites consisted mainly of small
fish (1/4 lb to 1 lb), with only an occasional large individual. The
Fish Lake assemblage, however, contained many catfish and buffalo that
would have weighed over 5 lbs, with some approaching 30 lbs to 40 lbs.

The number of gar (Lepisosteus sp.) and possibly freshwater drum
(Aplodinotus grunniens) may be overestimated. Gar are almost always
represented solely by scales. The majority of drum remains are
pharyngeal teeth.

Table 45 lists the species of fish, number of elements, and MNI for
each occupation area. As can be seen, Occupation Area 3 contained the
greatest number of species. Feature 36 in Occupation Area 3 yielded
three very large, completely articulated catfish crania, two of which
were blue catfish (Ictalurus furcatus), and the third was a flathead
catfish (Pylodictis olivaris). These remains were representative of
fish of ca. 30 lbs to 40 lbs. While some of the other remains were from
small fish, most of the remains were from fish weighing 5 lbs or more.
Feature 38 from the same area, on the other hand, contained a majority
of small fish (1/4 lb to 1 lb) with only a few individuals of fish in
the 5 lb to 10 lb category. This may reflect differential processing or
preparation of fish based on size or it may reflect differences in the
catches of two different fishing episodes or fishermen.

A fish hook was recovered from Feature 36. It is possible that the
larger fish in this feature were caught by hook and line or possibly
speared, rather than being netted or seined.

Reptile and Amphibian

Turtle remains comprised only a small portion of the assemblage
(3.3%). They were recovered from 16 features in Occupation Areas 1, 2,
and 3 (Table 46). Most of the bones were small pieces of carapace or
plastron and were unidentifiable to any specific level. In Occupation
Area 3, three aquatic species were recognized: softshell (Tionyx spp.),
painted turtle (Chrysemys spp.), and slider (Pseudemys spp.). Several
fragments of carapace and plastron showed evidence of intentional
modification.

Three amphibian remains were recovered from Occupation Area 3. One
was from a toad or frog, and the other two were indeterminate.

Table 46. Turtle Remains

	Occupation Area 1 Features				Occupation Area 2 Features					Occupation Area 3 Features									
	11	27	43	Subtotal	82	88	93	98	Subtotal	36	38	58	72	105	121	130	151	152	Subtotal
Trionyx spp. (softshell)	-	-	-	-	-	-	-	-	-	-	1 (9)	-	-	-	-	-	-	-	1 (9)
Chrysemys spp. (painted)	-	-	-	-	-	-	-	-	-	-	-	-	1 (6)	-	-	-	-	-	1 (6)
Pseudemys spp. (slider)	-	-	-	-	-	-	-	-	-	-	1 (1)	-	-	-	-	-	-	-	1 (1)
Unidentifiable turtle	(10)	(2)	(20)	(32)	(3)	(3)	(3)	(3)	(12)	(1)	(11)	(6)	-	(5)	(1)	(10)	(1)	(4)	(39)
Total	- (10)	- (2)	- (20)	- (32)	- (3)	- (3)	- (3)	- (3)	- (12)	- (1)	2 (21)	- (6)	1 (6)	- (5)	- (1)	- (10)	- (1)	- (4)	3 (55)

Key
- Minimum number of individuals
(#) - N of elements

Shell

All the shell recovered was in poor condition, being flaky and chalky. None of the fragments could be identified. Except for five snail shells, the shell recovered was from naides. One snail shell was recovered from Occupation Area 2, and the others were recovered from Occupation Area 3. Mussel shell fragments were recovered from 14 features in Occupation Areas 1, 2, and 3. Occupation Area 4 contained no shell. One unassociated feature, Feature 143, yielded mussel shell fragments (Table 47). Mussels did not appear to have been heavily exploited at this site. One very small piece of mussel shell showed evidence of decoration.

Summary

Fish made up 61.1% of the identifiable remains at the site. Unlike other American Bottom sites, the fish assemblage from the Fish Lake site included many large river catfish and buffalo. Gar and drum were also relatively well represented. The overall size of the fish in the assemblage was much larger than that at other sites.

Table 47. Features Containing
Shell Fragments

Feature	Shell Type	N of Pieces	Wt(g)
36	mussel	10	60.0
9	snail	1	<0.1
11	mussel	2+	21.6
20	snail	1	<0.1
38	mussel	7+	12.5
	snail	1	0.7
43	mussel	1	0.5
58	mussel	ca. 40	9.5
72	mussel	7+	17.4
88	mussel	10+	10.1
98	mussel	13+	51.7
105	mussel	23+	43.3
	snail	1	<0.1
106	mussel	1	1.8
	snail	1	1.2
79	mussel	8	13.2
143	mussel	6+	16.3
148	mussel	11	1.7
149	mussel	2	3.5
146	mussel	22+	29.1

+ crumbs or flakes found in addition to
countable fragments

Mammal remains comprised 32.0% of the identifiable remains. Deer was by far the most common mammal. Ten other species were present but not in any significant quantity. Most of the mammals were those that inhabit forests or edge environments.

Birds only comprised 3.6% of the identifiable remains. Most of the birds were terrestrial; only two species of waterfowl were present. Hawk and passenger pigeon remains were recovered, neither of which are common at other prehistoric American Bottom sites.

No clear distributional patterns could be observed within or between the occupation areas. Occupation Areas 1, 2, and 3 had relatively wide ranges of fauna. Occupation Area 4 contained the fewest features and those features yielded only insignificant amounts of faunal debris. Although Occupation Areas 1 and 3 had similar numbers of features containing faunal materials, about twice as much bone was recovered from Occupation Area 3 as from Occupation Area 1. An interesting observation that pertains to the entire site is that individual features contained either terrestrial birds or aquatic birds (excluding passerines), never both. This may reflect seasonal procurement factors.

Several deep, multizoned pits were excavated at the Fish Lake site, which appeared to have sterile or slump zones between major fill zones. However, the distinct cultural zones did not contain appreciably different faunal assemblages.

The Fish Lake faunal assemblage differed from the majority of Late Woodland faunal assemblages from American Bottom sites. At other Late Woodland sites, the fish assemblages consisted mainly of small fish, such as bullheads and sunfish that would have frequented backwater sloughs. Further, although white-tailed deer was the most frequently encountered mammal at other sites as well as at Fish Lake, it did not occur at the other sites in quantities as great as those at Fish Lake. Finally, at other Late Woodland sites bird remains, although meager, were primarily representative of waterfowl. These differences may be due to the location of the Fish Lake site, which was far from the uplands and close to the Mississippi River channel. It may also be due to factors such as seasonality of occupation, although this could not be determined from the faunal material alone.

RADIOCARBON DATES

by Andrew C. Fortier

Five samples were submitted to the Illinois State Geological radiocarbon laboratory located at the University of Illinois at Urbana-Champaign. The radiocarbon samples were selected from several different locations within the Late Woodland settlement area, and came from both structure and pit contexts. Features that produced both diagnostic lithics and ceramics were selected over features that contained large amounts of carbonized material but very few diagnostics. Features 126 and 116 from Occupation Area 1, Features 9 and 80 from Occupation Area 2, and Feature 123 from Occupation Area 3 produced the samples used for dating. With the exception of the Feature 9 sample, all consisted solely of wood charcoal. The Feature 9 sample was composed of both wood charcoal and carbonized nutshell. The dates and materials from which the dates were taken are listed in Table 48.

The cultural materials recovered from this site indicated a Patrick phase affiliation. The chronological position of this phase in the American Bottom ranges from 600 A.C. to 800 A.C., a period which comprised the final phase of Late Woodland development. A mean date of 726 A.C. was computed on the basis of 19 radiocarbon dates obtained by the FAI-270 Project for Patrick phase sites, including the five Fish Lake dates. The Fish Lake site dates ranged from 560 A.C. to 920 A.C. (Figure 63).

The archaeological evidence suggested that at least two Late Woodland occupational episodes were represented at the Fish Lake site. However, the overall uniformity of the material assemblage and feature types indicated that only one group of individuals was responsible for

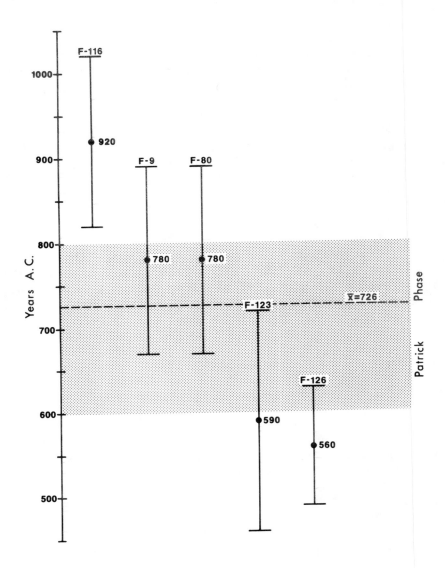

Figure 63. Radiocarbon Dates

Table 48. Radiocarbon Determinations from the Fish Lake Site

Feature	Feature Type	Material Dated	Date (B.P.)	Date (A.C.)	ISGS #
116	keyhole structure	wood charcoal (Betula)	1030 ± 100	920	1046
9	keyhole structure	wood charcoal (Quercus and Ulmaceae) nut shell (Carya)	1170 ± 110	780	1047
80	pit	wood charcoal (Ulmaceae)	1170 ± 110	780	1060
123	pit	wood charcoal (Ulmaceae)	1360 ± 130	590	1062
126	pit	wood charcoal (Quercus)	1390 ± 70	560	1044

these occupations. The chronological interval between settlements,
therefore, was probably not great. The occupation may have even been
continuous. The 200 year gap in the radiocarbon determinations is not
viewed as being realistic. It is difficult to believe that the material
assemblage and the feature types would have remained so uniform over a
100 to 200 year period. It seems more likely that the occupation
identified at this site occurred sometime between 700 A.C. and 750 A.C.,
and probably did not last more than two years. Finally, the radiocarbon
dates confirmed the association of keyhole structures with the Patrick
phase. Such structures appear to be more prevalent during the latter
half of the Patrick phase.

SITE INTERPRETATION

by Andrew C. Fortier

The preceding sections have provided descriptive information
obtained from the 1981 and 1982 excavations at the Fish Lake site.
Analyses focused on the form and configuration of features, the nature
of the recovered artifacts, and the nature of the animal and plant
remains recovered from this Late Woodland community. The following
sections integrate this descriptive data within the context of specific
themes, including site chronology, community organization, nature and
distribution of the material assemblage, and subsistence practices.
These themes served as the primary research objectives of the field and
laboratory investigations. Wide-scale machine removal of plowzone and
excavation of all features at the site were specifically designed to
expose enough of this Late Woodland community to permit a resolution of
these basic research questions.

Chronology and Cultural Affiliation

The archaeological settlement exposed at the Fish Lake site dated to
the Patrick phase of the Late Woodland period in the American Bottom.
The Patrick phase spanned a 200 year period from 600 A.C. to 800 A.C.;
it was the terminal Late Woodland phase in this area. Diagnostic traits
of this phase included grit-tempered and grog-tempered cordmarked jars
and bowls, small flake projectile points, deep processing and cooking
pits (earth ovens), post structures with and without subterranean
basins, and a diversified lithic assemblage characterized by an
exclusive use of local resources. Settlements occurred throughout the
American Bottom floodplain and adjacent uplands, but were most common on
prominent floodplain ridges, on alluvial fans near valley openings, and
on bluff tops overlooking the floodplain. Communities were relatively
small, but often appeared to represent occupations of generational
duration. Although maize had not yet appeared during this phase,
horticultural activities involving other cultigens became an important
part of the subsistence economy. Such activities no doubt provided a
basis for the development of large, long-term settlements during this
period.

The Fish Lake site produced all of the diagnostic traits typically recovered from Patrick Phase communities in this area. In addition, five radiocarbon dates from this site, ranging from 560 A.C. to 920 A.C., with a mean date of 726 A.C., placed the Fish Lake site in the middle portion of the Patrick phase. The association of keyhole structures with the Patrick phase, first noticed at the Range site, was confirmed by the Fish Lake site investigations. These investigations also clearly demonstrated an association between keyhole structures and large single post structures at Patrick phase communities.

Excavations at the Fish Lake site indicated that at least two occupational episodes were represented, although the duration of neither occupation could be established. The initial community probably consisted of the large single post structure, an undetermined number of keyhole structures, and pits, including the pit cluster located directly south of the linear post row in Occupation Area 1. It is suggested that the time interval between the occupational episodes was not great, since the cultural inventories recovered from features from both communities were so uniform. It is conceivable that the community area was even occupied continuously and thus the superpositioning of features represented seasonal shifts in structure use.

The Fish Lake site appears to represent a situation in which an area was utilized for one period of time by a single group of inhabitants. It should be noted that surface collections from the ridge immediately south of the investigated area indicated the existence of yet another Patrick phase community. Multiple ridge localities of the American Bottom floodplain may have been extensively utilized by Patrick phase peoples. Communities may have been moved periodically from ridge to ridge to escape refuse accumulations or to seek new soils for extensive horticultural activities. Such a settlement rotation system may have been seasonal, yearly, or generational in nature and probably occurred over the entire two hundred year period of the Patrick phase.

Community Organization and Duration

The organizing principle of these Late Woodland settlements can only be conjectured due to the lack of complete community plans. Nevertheless, the arrangement of pits and structures in the exposed areas at the Fish Lake site suggested a linearly organized community instead of one organized around a central point or courtyard, as was common during the subsequent Emergent Mississippian period. Keyhole structures appear to have been distributed along a northeast-southwest line, with each structure's ramp directed to the east. This linear arrangement was perpendicular to the axis of the main point bar ridge. Pits, on the other hand, were parallel to the ridge axis, extending for a considerable distance east of the structures. It is obvious that processing, cooking, and refuse disposal activities associated with pits were intentionally conducted away from the structures.

Structure Feature 52 was a large communal structure, situated just east of the keyhole structures in Occupation Area 1. Feature 52 was no doubt an important focal point for one of the occupational episodes at the site. Its relationship with the nearby keyhole structures was less obvious, although its affiliation with the Patrick phase is not in doubt. Several interpretations are possible for this structure.

The authors favor the view that Feature 52 served as the primary habitation unit for the community during the spring and summer months, whereas keyhole structures functioned as nuclear family domiciles during the winter. Perhaps Feature 52 was also used during the winter, but it does not seem likely that the keyhole structures, with their specialized heating adaptations, would have served as summer dwellings. This interpretation suggests that the Late Woodland occupation of this site was continuous and that habitation at this site changed with the seasons.

An alternative interpretation for Feature 52 is that it served as a specialized men's house or ceremonial structure, being utilized for restricted activities during particular times of the year. The chief domiciles would have been the keyhole structures. If, however, the keyhole structures are regarded strictly as winter dwellings and as the sole dwellings at this site, then one must conclude that the occupation was discontinuous, lacking a spring or summer occupation. The occupational episodes at this site would, therefore, have been produced by distinct winter occupations.

Pits were distributed in spatially separate areas that appear to have constituted distinct activity foci. Some important differences in pit type distribution occurred that may indicate functional differences at the site. Occupation Area 3, for example, produced a disproportionately large number of shallow, basin-shaped, limestone-lined pits containing well-preserved faunal remains. Earth ovens were rare in this area. Occupation Area 1, on the other hand, yielded primarily earth ovens and very few shallow, basin-shaped pits. Occupation Area 2 contained a high percentage of straight-sided, flat-bottomed pits, but very few earth ovens or shallow basin-shaped pits. Archaeologically, it is not possible to determine whether these differences in pit type distribution resulted from concurrent activities or from activities carried out at different periods of time. Neither the floral nor faunal remains from the pits provided definite evidence for seasonality.

Within the occupation areas, specific clusters of pits were not apparent. Sometimes pits occurred in short lines or arcs but not usually. No particular pairing of pits by pit type or material contents was observed. This situation contrasted with that of the Late Woodland occupation at the Mund site, where earth ovens and basin-shaped pits formed distinct pairs (Fortier et al. 1982:135-137). Pit-related activities within the occupation areas at the Fish Lake site appear to have been less formally organized than they were at the Mund site.

The Late Woodland occupation at the Fish Lake site may have involved two or more distinct occupational episodes with little, or no, time interval between them. The overall duration of the settlement was probably not long, perhaps as brief as one year. The community appears to have been organized primarily around subsistence-related tasks, and probably arose in this particular location to take advantage of the readily available, abundant, and diverse resources.

The Material Assemblage

The materials recovered from the Fish Lake site were significant because they represented an unmixed Late Woodland Patrick phase assemblage. This assemblage was unique in that it was the first to be recovered from a Patrick phase habitation site located far out in the American Bottom floodplain. Virtually all of the lithic resources recovered from this site would have had to have been recovered from sources located at least 2 km to 3 km distant from the site. Owing to the distances involved in transporting raw materials across the floodplain, the occupants of the Fish Lake site had to make very efficient use of only a small amount of lithic resources. This is reflected archaeologically by 1) the relatively low quantity of materials recovered from features and from the plowzone; 2) the repeated reutilization of limestone in pits; 3) the general scarcity of chert cores and blocks and the correspondingly high frequency of small chert flake tools; 4) the low quantities of nonchert debitage and tools; and 5) the efficient use of raw materials for tools, as exemplified in the high ratio of tools to debitage.

A total of 193,922.6 g of material were recovered from features at this site. Of this total, nearly 21% were ceramics, 7% were chert tools and debitage, and 68% were nonchert tools and debitage. An additional 3% were materials such as burned clay, nonvessel ceramics, and daub. The Late Woodland Mund site material assemblage, in comparison, was approximately seven times greater, by weight, than the Fish Lake assemblage. The Mund site was located at the base of the bluffs in close proximity to many upland lithic resources.

The ceramic assemblage at the Fish Lake site consisted of 151 discrete vessels, various pipes and pipe fragments, effigies and clay effigy fragments, potters' clay, daub, burned clay, and miscellaneous worked clay discs and objects. The vessel assemblage was characterized by cordmarked, subconoidal jars, bowls, and miniature vessels. The vast majority of the vessels (94%) were grog tempered. The predominant use of floodplain-derived pastes probably indicates ceramic manufacture at the Fish Lake site or in its immediate vicinity. Overall the Fish Lake ceramic assemblage was typical of the Patrick phase in this area.

The distributions of vessel types and selected attributes, such as lip impressions, were remarkably uniform across the site. Although an identification of ceramic variation among the various occupation areas was a primary goal of the ceramic analysis, very few differences could, in fact, be identified. This is believed to reflect the single community nature of this settlement. There was a corresponding lack of variation in the distribution of chert types and tools.

An important aspect of this ceramic analysis was the delineation of six categories of lip impressions. Such impressions appeared on 54% of the vessels. Although lip impressions are typical of Patrick phase ceramics in this area, they have rarely been categorized or utilized as a specific variable in intrasite assemblage variation studies. It has been suggested in this volume that the exclusive distributions of several lip impression types may indicate the presence of at least two potters at this site. A similar exclusive distribution pattern of certain lip impression categories was observed at the Late Woodland occupation of the Mund site (Fortier et al. 1982). Although explanations for intra-assemblage variation are still conjectural, the recognition that microvariation indeed existed in Late Woodland ceramic assemblages offers a wide range of possibilities for future studies.

In most respects the material assemblage at the Fish Lake site was typical of the Patrick phase in this area. The chert utilization pattern reflected an exclusive use of local resources, particularly of lower quality cherts from the nearby uplands. This pattern of dependence on local lithic resources has been observed at nearly every Patrick phase site in the American Bottom. The ceramic assemblage was also typical, exhibiting a great deal of internal homogeneity in vessel types and decoration modes. The occurrence of bowls in the vessel assemblage is a characteristic trait of the Patrick phase in this area. Sixteen percent of the Fish Lake ceramic assemblage were bowls.

The Fish Lake site assemblage, however, was atypical in that raw materials were very efficiently utilized. This aspect of the assemblage is probably a function of the distance between the site and its resources. This hypothesis needs to be tested at other Patrick phase sites, although it presently appears that the differences in Patrick phase assemblages may be a direct reflection of a site's location in the American Bottom.

Subsistence and the Local Environment

From an ecological standpoint, the Fish Lake site was situated in a resource-rich environment. It lay along the edge of the Lunsford-Pulcher terrace on a prominent sandy point bar ridge of the Hill Lake meander scar. To the west, at a considerably lower elevation, was the Western Floodplain Proper, consisting of low ridge and swale topography that would have been subjected to periodic inundation from the nearby Mississippi River. At the time of the Late Woodland occupation it is possible that the Mississippi River channel actually incorporated this area, and may have, at some point, abutted against the Lunsford-Pulcher terrace in the Fish Lake locality.

The floodplain zone would have constituted a dynamic, changing environment containing backwater and active sloughs and providing an abundance and diversity of both aquatic animal and plant resources. The higher terrace zone would have offered protection from flooding as well as access to the resources of the lower floodplain zone. The Fish Lake locality emerged as an important settlement and subsistence procurement focus as a direct consequence of its location on the edge of the lower floodplain zone.

The subsistence remains recovered from the Fish Lake site reflect a localized procurement pattern adapted primarily to aquatic animal resources and to wild plant materials readily obtainable in the nearby floodplain environment. Wood charcoal recovered from this site indicated an exclusive use of bottomland woods. The low density of wood charcoal in the feature fills probably also reflects the general scarcity of wood available in the immediate site surroundings. The exceptionally large channel catfish, blue catfish, and buffalo fish found at this site were probably captured from the nearby Mississippi River. Smaller fish, particularly those related to the sunfish family, occur in large numbers at other Patrick phase sites in this area, but they were relatively scarce in the Fish Lake faunal assemblage. This may suggest that hook and line fishing was used exclusively by the Fish Lake site inhabitants, and that seining was not a preferred fish capture technique. The presence of beaver and muskrat at this site also indicated a predominantly floodplain focus in the subsistence pattern. Deer meat comprised a major portion of the diet at this site. Deer were probably captured near the site, although hunting trips into the uplands may also have occurred.

The Fish Lake occupants were also horticulturalists, cultivating both squash and tobacco. Maygrass (_Phalaris_ _caroliniana_) and goosefoot (_Chenopodium_ sp.), which probably represent cultigens, made up nearly 53% of the seeds recovered from the sampled features at this site. The occurrence of horticultural activity suggests minimally a spring to fall occupation of the site. Seeds and certain dried fruits could have been stored through the winter. The occurrence of plant resources such as nuts, fruits, legumes, and grasses, which fructify in the spring and fall months, suggests that the Fish Lake site could have been occupied year-round.

One puzzling aspect of the subsistence inventory was the co-occurrence of spring and fall fruition plants in the same fill episodes of pits. This may suggest that certain pits were left open during the course of an entire year, or that some of the plant remains represent stored remains mixed with subsequently procured plants. Such mixture has effectively masked the specific seasons during which the pits were actually utilized and has precluded determining with certainty the seasons of use for any given occupation area.

SUMMARY

by Andrew C. Fortier

The archaeological investigations at the Fish Lake site revealed a single component Late Woodland Patrick phase settlement consisting of 7 keyhole structures, a large communal post structure, a small irregular post structure, 134 pits, a post row, two fill areas, and 52 nonstructural postmolds. Two or more occupational episodes were indicated, although a single group of people appears to have been responsible for all episodes. The community was probably occupied continuously for at least a year, with the keyhole structures serving as the principle domiciles during the winter months and the large post structure serving as a communal dwelling during the spring and summer months.

The ceramic and lithic assemblages were relatively small, but they were homogeneous and distributed uniformly across the exposed occupation areas. Raw materials were efficiently utilized and were derived exclusively from local resources. The efficient use of raw materials may have been a function of site distance from available upland resources.

The Fish Lake site was situated in an edge environment that had great potential for producing abundant and diverse wildlife and which was relatively secure from the effects of flooding. The existence of the Late Woodland settlement in this locality appears related to the highly productive catchment area of the Fish Lake locality. The site's function was related primarily to subsistence tasks organized around the collection of wild plants and animals in this locality. Horticultural activity also formed an integral part of the subsistence system and may have been a main reason for year-long occupation, in order to accomplish both planting and harvesting.

The Fish Lake site is one of the first Patrick phase communities with keyhole structures to be delineated and analyzed. It provides definite evidence that multidwelling villages were beginning to develop in the American Bottom during the Patrick phase. The linear community configuration at this site contrasts greatly with the circular, courtyard community plans of the Emergent Mississippian period and with the single household and pit cluster plans of the earlier Late Woodland Rosewood and Mund phases. The material assemblage and subsistence remains recovered from this site represent the first published analysis of a complete assemblage associated with keyhole structures in the Midwest. The association of keyhole structures with a Patrick phase lithic and ceramic assemblage is confirmed at this site. Finally, although the initial impetus for the keyhole structures in this area has not been identified, the Fish Lake site keyhole community model should provide a useful comparative standard for future investigations into the origin and function of this unique structure type in the Midwest.

APPENDIX 1. MATERIAL INVENTORY FOR FISH LAKE SITE FEATURES*

Material Inventory from Prehistoric Features

	N	Wt(g)
FEATURE 2		
CERAMICS	2	5.0
FLAKE SCRAPER	1	28.8
FEATURE 3		
LIMESTONE	111	945.1
BURNED CLAY	48	60.0
SANDSTONE	1	51.8
RETOUCHED FLAKES	4	20.6
CHERT	6	19.0
CERAMICS	237	1043.3
CHERT HAMMERSTONE	1	33.9
FEATURE 4		
DAUB	5	14.3
SANDSTONE	1	22.3
RETOUCHED FLAKES	4	16.9
REWORKED CORE	1	16.6
CHERT	17	146.3
CERAMICS	45	65.3
FEATURE 5		
BURNED CLAY	2	1.6
DAUB	1	0.5
WATER WORN PEBBLES	3	0.1
RETOUCHED FLAKES	2	2.6
CERAMICS	10	35.6
FEATURE 6		
LIMESTONE	82	745.3
SANDSTONE	1	10.9
BURNED CLAY	106	137.8
CHERT	19	399.9
RETOUCHED FLAKES	2	12.8
CERAMICS	79	366.7
CELT FRAGMENT	1	10.7
GRINDING STONE	1	746.6
FEATURE 9		
LIMESTONE	131	562.1
SANDSTONE	7	14.6
ROUGH ROCK	3	123.5
SILTSTONE	7	15.2
BURNED CLAY	49	69.8
RETOUCHED FLAKES	7	15.5
CHERT	40	160.4
CERAMICS	223	892.5
BIFACE FRAGMENT	1	42.3
HAMMERSTONE FRAGMENT	1	2.7
FEATURE 11		
LIMESTONE	314	5260.3
SANDSTONE	1	80.0
SILTSTONE	1	10.9
ROUGH ROCK	2	90.4
BURNED CLAY	13	18.4
DAUB	2	4.2
WATER WORN PEBBLES	2	19.4
QUARTZITE	1	10.0
RETOUCHED FLAKES	5	16.3
CHERT	26	299.1
CERAMICS	76	481.0
DENTICULATE	1	3.1
HAMMERSTONE	1	113.8
GRINDING STONE FRAGMENT	1	88.7
FEATURE 13		
LIMESTONE	6	6.3
BURNED CLAY	4	3.0
CHERT	3	9.5
CERAMICS	2	7.0
GRINDING STONE FRAGMENT	1	38.5

	N	Wt(g)
FEATURE 17		
SANDSTONE	1	1.0
FEATURE 18		
LIMESTONE	66	1121.7
SANDSTONE	2	11.1
SILICIFIED SEDIMENT	1	38.3
BURNED CLAY	24	55.9
DAUB	1	4.9
RETOUCHED FLAKES	8	26.1
CHERT	39	217.3
CERAMICS	175	772.2
PERFORATOR	1	10.3
SANDSTONE SLOT ABRADER	1	37.6
SANDSTONE ABRADER	1	22.9
HAMMERSTONE FRAGMENT	1	45.9
CERAMIC PIPE FRAGMENT	1	58.2
FEATURE 19		
LIMESTONE	5	146.6
BURNED CLAY	3	3.0
PERFORATOR/GRAVER	1	8.4
CERAMICS	14	24.4
PIPE FRAGMENT	1	7.2
FEATURE 20		
LIMESTONE	15	205.1
CERAMICS	1	0.1
FEATURE 21		
LIMESTONE	14	419.6
CHERT HAMMERSTONE	1	58.5
RETOUCHED FLAKES	1	11.7
CHERT	10	28.6
CERAMICS	9	20.2
FEATURE 22		
BURNED CLAY	18	17.3
DAUB	2	4.9
CHERT	3	3.5
CERAMICS	12	30.8
FEATURE 23		
LIMESTONE	11	19.9
BURNED CLAY	10	6.6
CHERT	2	2.4
CERAMICS	18	39.9
FEATURE 25		
CERAMICS	1	0.5
FEATURE 26		
LIMESTONE	40	72.4
SANDSTONE	8	145.0
BURNED CLAY	76	139.2
DAUB	20	42.2
WATER WORN PEBBLES	2	1.8
RETOUCHED FLAKES	9	66.5
REWORKED CORE	1	62.9
CHERT	72	236.0
CERAMICS	122	739.1
BIFACE FRAGMENT	1	2.1
FEATURE 27		
LIMESTONE	110	2309.2
BURNED CLAY	45	69.9
DAUB	1	2.1
RETOUCHED FLAKES	6	48.6
CHERT	32	73.1
CERAMICS	197	694.1
SANDSTONE SLOT ABRADER	1	12.3
SANDSTONE ABRADER	1	15.8
GRINDING STONE FRAGMENT	1	96.4

* Features not containing material are not included in table

APPENDIX 1. CONTINUED

FEATURE 28	N	Wt(g)
RETOUCHED FLAKES	1	14.7
BURNED CLAY	1	8.1
QUARTZITE	1	1089.1
CHERT	4	10.2
CERAMICS	30	132.1
HAMMERSTONE	1	126.7

FEATURE 30		
BURNED CLAY	3	1.6
CERAMICS	7	8.3

FEATURE 31		
CERAMICS	1	1.0

FEATURE 32		
LIMESTONE	4	51.9
BURNED CLAY	10	34.6
HEMATITE	2	3.5
RETOUCHED FLAKES	17	121.8
CHERT	70	359.3
CERAMICS	122	576.1
BIFACE FRAGMENT	1	15.3
PERFORATOR	1	14.1

FEATURE 33		
LIMESTONE	4	52.0
BURNED CLAY	8	23.8
ROUGH ROCK	1	9.1
CHERT	4	108.8
CERAMICS	61	69.2

FEATURE 34		
LIMESTONE	3	9.0
SANDSTONE	1	11.4
ROUGH ROCK	1	6.1
BURNED CLAY	29	54.3
DAUB	3	9.9
RETOUCHED FLAKES	5	23.1
CHERT	52	148.3
CERAMICS	203	433.2
PERFORATOR	1	9.2
BIFACE FRAGMENT	1	5.5

FEATURE 35		
RETOUCHED FLAKES	2	9.4
LIMESTONE	155	3140.3
SANDSTONE	1	3.1
BURNED CLAY	14	22.1
DAUB	1	10.3
ROUGH ROCK	2	63.2
CHERT	4	5.5
CERAMICS	10	60.2

FEATURE 36		
LIMESTONE	273	5448.2
SANDSTONE	1	10.8
BURNED CLAY	91	160.6
WATER WORN PEBBLES	1	1.8
RETOUCHED FLAKES	5	16.4
CHERT	29	214.4
CERAMICS	166	1473.5
GROUND STONE TOOL FRAG	1	20.4

FEATURE 37		
LIMESTONE	63	449.2
ROUGH ROCK	3	229.4
BURNED CLAY	28	98.6
WATER WORN PEBBLES	3	4.3
RETOUCHED FLAKES	1	2.4
CHERT	8	446.0
CERAMICS	93	497.5
HAMMERSTONE FRAGMENT	1	30.8

FEATURE 38	N	Wt(g)
LIMESTONE	248	4998.2
SANDSTONE	2	118.3
BURNED CLAY	25	35.3
DAUB	7	24.8
WATER WORN PEBBLES	4	2.7
RETOUCHED FLAKES	16	90.7
CHERT	54	196.6
CERAMICS	320	2217.9
PROJECTILE POINT	1	0.7
PROJECTILE POINT	1	2.8
SANDSTONE SLOT ABRADER	1	45.1
GRINDING STONE FRAGMENT	1	93.4
CERAMIC EFFIGY	1	0.5
CERAMIC DISCOIDAL	1	38.1

FEATURE 39		
LIMESTONE	4	35.0
BURNED CLAY	2	10.2
WATER WORN PEBBLES	1	0.4
CHERT	2	7.8
CERAMICS	9	40.4

FEATURE 40		
LIMESTONE	40	395.1
SANDSTONE	2	3.2
BURNED CLAY	5	5.2
DAUB	3	2.2
RETOUCHED FLAKES	5	11.2
CHERT	4	4.9
CERAMICS	51	298.3
KNIFE BASE	1	8.5
PROJECTILE POINT	1	1.7

FEATURE 41		
LIMESTONE	7	324.8
SANDSTONE	1	10.7
RETOUCHED FLAKES	2	9.7
CHERT	4	67.1
CERAMICS	20	207.0

FEATURE 42		
LIMESTONE	1	12.5
BURNED CLAY	1	10.0
CHERT	1	2.5
CERAMICS	8	27.7

FEATURE 43		
LIMESTONE	135	3123.4
SILTSTONE	1	20.2
BURNED CLAY	187	329.6
DAUB	4	10.1
RETOUCHED FLAKES	9	49.8
CHERT	53	162.7
CERAMICS	130	601.1
BIFACE FRAGMENT	1	14.6
CELT FRAGMENT	1	7.6
KNIFE	1	25.9

FEATURE 44		
LIMESTONE	17	879.6
SANDSTONE	4	41.0
IGNEOUS ROCK	2	227.1
DAUB	1	21.9
RETOUCHED FLAKES	3	21.7
CHERT	12	168.8
CERAMICS	32	181.4

APPENDIX 1. CONTINUED

FEATURE 48	N	Wt(g)
LIMESTONE	14	47.0
IGNEOUS ROCK	2	165.8
MISSOURI RIVER CLINKER	5	43.6
BURNED CLAY	14	14.9
DAUB	4	6.2
CHERT	12	66.5
CERAMICS	37	144.4
GRINDING STONE FRAGMENT	1	40.1

FEATURE 49		
GRINDING STONE FRAGMENT	1	97.1

FEATURE 52		
RETOUCHED FLAKES	1	1.0
SANDSTONE	1	15.8
CERAMICS	3	4.0
HAMMERSTONE	1	21.1

FEATURE 56		
SANDSTONE	1	57.6
LIMESTONE	1	0.8
RETOUCHED FLAKES	1	1.8
CERAMICS	11	32.4

FEATURE 57		
LIMESTONE	2	3.2
SANDSTONE	30	305.4
BURNED CLAY	6	9.3
DAUB	1	2.7
RETOUCHED FLAKES	4	21.1
CHERT	6	67.4
CERAMICS	15	83.3
SANDSTONE ABRADER	1	118.3

FEATURE 58		
LIMESTONE	199	2125.7
SANDSTONE	2	96.0
BURNED CLAY	71	137.8
DAUB	2	2.9
ROUGH ROCK	1	11 0
CHERT	47	175.7
CERAMICS	165	905.7
CERAMIC EFFIGY	1	10.8

FEATURE 60		
LIMESTONE	28	126.7
BURNED CLAY	12	5.9
RETOUCHED FLAKES	7	40.1
CHERT	50	430.5
CERAMICS	256	941.7
SANDSTONE ABRADER	1	35.1
BIFACE FRAGMENT	1	4.5
SANDSTONE ABRADER	1	206.5
SANDSTONE SLOT ABRADER	1	34.5
PROJECTILE POINT	1	1.7
PROJECTILE POINT	1	1.2

FEATURE 61		
CERAMICS	1	3.8

FEATURE 64		
CHERT	1	1.5

FEATURE 65		
BURNED CLAY	1	0.9
CHERT	1	22.0

FEATURE 66		
BURNED CLAY	5	13.2
CINDER	1	4.6
CHERT	4	47.0
CERAMICS	7	25.6

FEATURE 67	N	Wt(g)
BURNED CLAY	41	5.2

FEATURE 68		
CHERT	1	4.8

FEATURE 70		
LIMESTONE	1	2.5
SANDSTONE	2	31.8
BURNED CLAY	16	8.6
RETOUCHED FLAKES	2	6.9
CHERT	14	49.0
CERAMICS	50	241.1
HAMMERSTONE/MAUL	1	256.1
GRINDING STONE	1	494.9

FEATURE 71		
LIMESTONE	2	115.9
SANDSTONE	3	5.2
RETOUCHED FLAKES	1	4.1
CHERT	4	21.4
CERAMICS	4	2.6

FEATURE 72		
LIMESTONE	176	5257.9
SANDSTONE	5	94.9
BURNED CLAY	9	50.4
WATER WORN PEBBLES	1	19.7
RETOUCHED FLAKES	3	26.2
CHERT	14	1020.3
CERAMICS	107	849.7
LIMESTONE SMOOTHER	1	10.0
SANDSTONE ABRADER	1	159.9
LIMESTONE PICK	1	69.7

FEATURE 74		
LIMESTONE	10	97.5
RETOUCHED FLAKES	2	11.5
CHERT	10	33.1
CERAMICS	9	58.8
PROJECTILE POINT	1	2.6

FEATURE 76		
CHERT	1	2.9
CERAMICS	3	16.9

FEATURE 79		
LIMESTONE	90	2012.0
SANDSTONE	8	61.0
BURNED CLAY	19	59.3
DAUB	1	7.6
QUARTZITE	1	13.0
RETOUCHED FLAKES	12	78.1
CHERT	51	328.4
CERAMICS	371	2679.8
SANDSTONE ABRADER	1	14.2
FLAKE SCRAPER	1	10.3
FLAKE SCRAPER	1	7.3

FEATURE 80		
LIMESTONE	63	195.2
BURNED CLAY	55	89.6
IGNEOUS ROCK	1	11.5
WATER WORN PEBBLES	1	25.9
RETOUCHED FLAKES	2	2.1
CHERT	37	115.3
CERAMICS	69	415.7
KNIFE	1	9.6
PROJECTILE POINT	1	1.3
CERAMIC EFFIGY	1	2.3

APPENDIX 1. CONTINUED

FEATURE 81	N	Wt(g)
LIMESTONE	234	1733.8
SANDSTONE	9	182.0
BURNED CLAY	292	263.7
ROUGH ROCK	2	47.7
RETOUCHED FLAKES	18	104.3
CHERT	136	318.7
CERAMICS	520	2204.6
HAMMERSTONE	1	53.4
PERFORATOR	1	7.1
FLAKE SCRAPER	1	6.0
CERAMIC PIPE FRAGMENT	1	5.5

FEATURE 82		
LIMESTONE	177	8505.7
SANDSTONE	4	47.4
BURNED CLAY	2	1.2
WATER WORN PEBBLES	1	3.2
ROUGH ROCK	1	57.3
RETOUCHED FLAKES	4	94.0
CHERT	13	109.2
CERAMICS	135	530.9
CERAMIC PIPE FRAGMENT	1	3.6
GRINDING STONE	1	290.3
CELT FRAGMENT	1	207.3
HAMMERSTONE/MAUL	1	376.3
FLAKE SCRAPER	1	70.5
SANDSTONE SLOT ABRADER	1	58.7

FEATURE 85		
CERAMICS	2	13.5

FEATURE 86		
LIMESTONE	9	52.1
BURNED CLAY	3	16.3
CHERT	2	56.3
CERAMICS	16	87.9

FEATURE 87		
LIMESTONE	10	36.7
BURNED CLAY	14	20.6
WATER WORN PEBBLES	1	0.3
DAUB	1	5.6
CHERT	4	2.2
CERAMICS	11	18.1

FEATURE 88		
LIMESTONE	88	1384.7
SANDSTONE	2	4.4
BURNED CLAY	26	82.5
DAUB	3	1.6
SILTSTONE	1	5.2
RETOUCHED FLAKES	9	75.8
CHERT	28	128.3
CERAMICS	136	852.8
HAMMERSTONE	1	29.4

FEATURE 89		
LIMESTONE	32	259.7
SANDSTONE	5	44.2
SILICIFIED SEDIMENT	1	2.7
BURNED CLAY	9	8.0
RETOUCHED FLAKES	4	39.4
CHERT	18	122.5
CERAMICS	79	195.8
POINT BASE	1	3.2

FEATURE 90		
LIMESTONE	11	55.9
SANDSTONE	1	0.9
SILICIFIED SEDIMENT	1	34.5
BURNED CLAY	20	31.8
RETOUCHED FLAKES	1	1.2
CHERT	3	15.9
CERAMICS	17	60.0

FEATURE 91	N	Wt(g)
LIMESTONE	11	201.7
BURNED CLAY	7	13.4
CHERT	1	21.4
CERAMICS	2	20.8

FEATURE 92		
LIMESTONE	4	4.9
BURNED CLAY	13	16.3
CERAMICS	15	64.8
CERAMIC EFFIGY	1	5.5

FEATURE 93		
LIMESTONE	270	5617.8
SANDSTONE	14	98.0
BURNED CLAY	324	1005.3
RETOUCHED FLAKES	11	52.2
CHERT	138	219.2
CERAMICS	408	1649.3
HAMMERSTONE	1	352.6
FLAKE SCRAPER	1	27.8
PROJECTILE POINT	1	0.7
PROJECTILE POINT	1	1.5
CERAMIC DISC	1	6.8

FEATURE 94		
LIMESTONE	77	538.7
SANDSTONE	1	1.4
BURNED CLAY	1	7.7
RETOUCHED FLAKES	1	9.9
CHERT	8	21.0
CERAMICS	23	186.2
CHERT HAMMERSTONE	1	113.8
PERFORATOR	1	8.4

FEATURE 95		
CERAMICS	48	133.1
LIMESTONE	9	20.6
BURNED CLAY	4	6.4
ROUGH ROCK	2	224.3

FEATURE 96		
LIMESTONE	5	45.4
CHERT	2	5.8
CERAMICS	2	4.9

FEATURE 97		
BURNED CLAY	4	1.5
RETOUCHED FLAKES	1	5.4
CHERT	7	56.0
CERAMICS	38	55.1

FEATURE 98		
LIMESTONE	170	7084.6
SANDSTONE	1	3.1
IGNEOUS ROCK	1	5.1
BURNED CLAY	9	28.9
QUARTZITE	1	16.5
RETOUCHED FLAKES	9	78.5
CHERT	17	217.6
CERAMICS	88	1596.6
SANDSTONE ABRADER	1	253.7
CLEAVER/MAUL	1	210.8
HAMMERSTONE	1	211.8
SANDSTONE ABRADER	1	203.7

FEATURE 99		
CERAMICS	3	1.3

FEATURE 100		
LIMESTONE	11	9.4
BURNED CLAY	14	45.8
CHERT	7	18.4
CERAMICS	27	59.0
GRINDING STONE FRAGMENT	1	109.3

APPENDIX 1. CONTINUED

FEATURE 101	N	Wt(g)
CERAMICS	4	35.8

FEATURE 102	N	Wt(g)
LIMESTONE	4	26.7
QUARTZITE	1	2.4
CERAMICS	1	11.6
SANDSTONE SLOT ABRADER	1	15.4

FEATURE 104	N	Wt(g)
LIMESTONE	179	1080.5
SANDSTONE	4	148.8
IGNEOUS ROCK	1	93.5
BURNED CLAY	7	51.6
RETOUCHED FLAKES	3	42.0
CHERT	23	206.8
CERAMICS	29	78.9
GOUGE/WEDGE	1	57.7
GOUGE/WEDGE	1	98.4
POTTER'S CLAY	1	8.7

FEATURE 105	N	Wt(g)
LIMESTONE	269	10302.9
BURNED CLAY	5	14.3
DAUB	4	8.8
RETOUCHED FLAKES	9	49.3
CHERT	17	30.8
CERAMICS	67	427.2
SANDSTONE ABRADER	1	6.8

FEATURE 106	N	Wt(g)
LIMESTONE	203	4049.7
SANDSTONE	2	18.1
BURNED CLAY	3	84.1
CHERT HAMMERSTONE	1	59.3
CHERT	24	103.7
CERAMICS	104	653.8

FEATURE 116	N	Wt(g)
LIMESTONE	15	29.1
SANDSTONE	22	181.0
CHERT	121	309.4
QUARTZITE	3	56.8
WATER WORN PEBBLES	1	0.6
BURNED CLAY	70	58.0
SANDSTONE ABRADER	1	84.5
SANDSTONE ABRADER	1	8.5
RETOUCHED FLAKES	4	32.9
PROJECTILE POINT	1	1.8
CERAMICS	224	794.3
CERAMIC EFFIGIES	4	8.5

FEATURE 117	N	Wt(g)
BURNED CLAY	45	45.1
LIMESTONE	12	27.0
SANDSTONE	1	47.7
CHERT	37	96.1
SANDSTONE ABRADER	1	19.8
RETOUCHED FLAKES	6	15.5
FLAKE SCRAPER	1	19.5
PROJECTILE POINT	1	1.0
CERAMICS	50	225.7
CERAMIC EFFIGIES	4	5.6

FEATURE 118	N	Wt(g)
LIMESTONE	26	237.6
BURNED CLAY	9	16.7
CHERT	21	286.0
FLAKE SCRAPER	1	17.9
CERAMICS	43	278.3

FEATURE 119	N	Wt(g)
LIMESTONE	93	2183.8
BURNED CLAY	13	16.1
SANDSTONE	2	37.6
CHERT	4	1.7
RETOUCHED FLAKES	1	8.1
WATER WORN PEBBLES	5	0.3
CERAMICS	3	11.3

FEATURE 120	N	Wt(g)
LIMESTONE	29	267.5
SANDSTONE	4	119.2
BURNED CLAY	6	5.5
CHERT	24	98.5
CERAMICS	55	309.3

FEATURE 121	N	Wt(g)
LIMESTONE	34	500.1
BURNED CLAY	28	16.4
CHERT	13	32.2
CERAMICS	5	44.5
CERAMIC PIPE FRAGMENTS	5	6.0

FEATURE 122	N	Wt(g)
LIMESTONE	3	5.7
BURNED CLAY	2	4.8
SANDSTONE	5	110.8
CHERT	2	0.3
CHERT HAMMERSTONE	1	220.8
CERAMICS	4	10.3

FEATURE 123	N	Wt(g)
LIMESTONE	192	4674.8
SANDSTONE	4	199.0
ROUGH ROCK	1	13.1
WATER WORN PEBBLES	2	9.3
QUARTZ	1	1.2
CHERT	36	73.5
BURNED CLAY	24	47.0
RETOUCHED FLAKES	1	1.4
PROJECTILE POINT	1	0.7
CERAMICS	104	443.2

FEATURE 124	N	Wt(g)
LIMESTONE	3	39.5
BURNED CLAY	2	3.7
DAUB	2	23.6
CHERT	13	47.9
CERAMICS	13	120.9

FEATURE 125	N	Wt(g)
CHERT	8	6.7
LIMESTONE	12	1194.6
PROJECTILE POINT	1	0.8
CERAMICS	3	10.2

FEATURE 126	N	Wt(g)
LIMESTONE	5	714.0
SANDSTONE	15	304.4
GROVER GRAVEL	1	79.6
ROUGH ROCK	3	35.6
BURNED CLAY	39	40.5
CHERT	55	92.7
RETOUCHED FLAKES	4	12.6
CERAMICS	52	505.6
CERAMIC OBJECTS	2	8.4

FEATURE 127	N	Wt(g)
CHERT	6	12.9
CERAMICS	7	30.3

APPENDIX 1. CONTINUED

FEATURE 128	N	Wt(g)
BURNED CLAY	22	167.5
IGNEOUS ROCK	2	788.8
SANDSTONE	1	26.5
LIMESTONE	3	19.3
CERAMICS	4	26.8

FEATURE 129		
LIMESTONE	1	3.5
SANDSTONE	1	4.3
BURNED CLAY	1	1.0
CHERT	22	3.9
CERAMICS	3	9.4

FEATURE 130		
LIMESTONE	13	229.2
SANDSTONE	2	7.1
CHERT	12	299.4
RETOUCHED FLAKES	1	9.8
PROJECTILE POINT	1	20.1
CHERT HAMMERSTONE	1	512.7
CERAMICS	28	244.6

FEATURE 131		
LIMESTONE	27	651.2
SANDSTONE	3	110.9
CHERT	4	23.0
RETOUCHED FLAKES	4	31.6
PERFORATOR	1	3.0
CERAMICS	10	63.4

FEATURE 132		
LIMESTONE	12	222.6
SANDSTONE	1	4.0
BURNED CLAY	50	115.2
CHERT	56	25.4
RETOUCHED FLAKES	2	4.9
CERAMICS	190	656.4

FEATURE 134		
LIMESTONE	166	3582.0
BURNED CLAY	142	593.9
SANDSTONE	1	2.9
CHERT	141	279.5
RETOUCHED FLAKES	18	93.6
CHERT HAMMERSTONE	1	48.1
CELT FRAGMENT	1	127.0
BIFACE FRAGMENT	1	6.0
SANDSTONE SLOT ABRADER	1	26.4
PROJECTILE POINT	1	1.2
CERAMICS	203	1130.3

FEATURE 137		
CHERT	38	186.6
BURNED CLAY	32	76.7
SANDSTONE	4	46.9
MISSOURI RIVER CLINKER	1	16.0
LIMESTONE	27	412.6
RETOUCHED FLAKES	2	12.9
BIFACE FRAGMENT	1	11.1
PERFORATOR	1	5.9
CERAMICS	73	503.2
CERAMIC EFFIGY	1	7.5

FEATURE 138		
BURNED CLAY	8	193.1
CHERT	31	46.8
CERAMICS	91	556.1
CERAMIC OBJECT	1	3.4
CERAMIC EFFIGY	1	1.5

FEATURE 139	N	Wt(g)
DAUB	3	17.5
LIMESTONE	24	107.8
SANDSTONE	28	46.7
ROUGH ROCK	3	38.5
BURNED CLAY	75	201.7
CHERT	56	64.9
RETOUCHED FLAKES	2	20.7
WATER WORN PEBBLES	4	5.4
CERAMICS	115	765.5

FEATURE 141		
LIMESTONE	1	2.3
SANDSTONE	4	7.3
BURNED CLAY	4	6.2
CHERT	11	33.2
CERAMICS	52	312.5

FEATURE 142		
LIMESTONE	2	2.5
BURNED CLAY	8	9.4
CHERT	3	4.7
CERAMICS	19	154.8

FEATURE 143		
LIMESTONE	81	1794.6
SANDSTONE	1	30.1
ROUGH ROCK	3	34.2
DAUB	1	5.1
BURNED CLAY	1	0.4
CHERT	19	47.5
RETOUCHED FLAKES	1	6.9
PITTED GRINDING STONE	1	301.1
CERAMICS	74	446.3

FEATURE 144		
LIMESTONE	1	1.1
BURNED CLAY	13	9.7
CHERT	3	1.0
CERAMICS	7	8.4

FEATURE 145		
CHERT	3	2.3

FEATURE 146		
LIMESTONE	83	1527.5
BURNED CLAY	21	45.2
CHERT	27	65.2
CERAMICS	35	197.1

FEATURE 147		
LIMESTONE	38	237.7
BURNED CLAY	11	11 9
SANDSTONE	3	1.7
CHERT	19	6.0
CELT FRAGMENT	1	2.9
CERAMICS	14	35.9

FEATURE 148		
LIMESTONE	112	3757.1
BURNED CLAY	5	9.7
SANDSTONE	4	111.1
CHERT	34	134.8
WATER WORN PEBBLES	1	8.4
RETOUCHED FLAKES	1	5.9
ROUGH ROCK	1	7.5
CERAMICS	31	138.9

APPENDIX 1. CONTINUED

FEATURE 149	N	Wt(g)
SANDSTONE SLOT ABRADER	1	78.4
HEMATITE	1	1.2
WATER WORN PEBBLES	1	15.2
BURNED CLAY	6	14.4
CHERT	70	164.0
PROJECTILE POINT	1	1.5
BIFACE FRAGMENT	1	4.6
RETOUCHED FLAKES	1	14.5
LIMESTONE	91	2642.5
CERAMICS	63	319.7

FEATURE 150		
LIMESTONE	5	25.4

FEATURE 151		
LIMESTONE	46	600.9
BURNED CLAY	6	6.9
SANDSTONE	1	7.8
WATER WORN PEBBLES	1	27.1
CHERT	23	103.6
RETOUCHED FLAKES	3	24.1
CERAMICS	29	260.0

FEATURE 152		
LIMESTONE	64	1486.0
BURNED CLAY	5	24.4
CHERT	20	210.7
RETOUCHED FLAKES	3	13.4
HISTORIC SLAG	1	1.5
CERAMICS	24	85.0

FEATURE 153		
LIMESTONE	12	100.8
BURNED CLAY	26	50.0
CHERT	1	0.8
CERAMICS	9	37.4

FEATURE 154		
LIMESTONE	10	13.5
SANDSTONE	1	0.3
BURNED CLAY	1	0.3
RETOUCHED FLAKES	2	134.4
CERAMICS	2	15.5

FEATURE 155		
BURNED CLAY	21	19.5
LIMESTONE	12	66.0
SANDSTONE	24	313.1
CHERT	15	67.3
CERAMICS	12	57.3

FEATURE 156		
BURNED CLAY	13	48.2
LIMESTONE	3	18.3
ROUGH ROCK	1	46.6
CHERT	24	63.9
CERAMICS	18	102.9
POTTER'S CLAY	1	18.6

FEATURE 157		
LIMESTONE	10	234.0
SANDSTONE	5	404.2
ROUGH ROCK	1	142.1
CHERT	23	71.4
CERAMICS	15	75.3

FEATURE 158		
CHERT	2	3.8

FEATURE 159		
BURNED CLAY	11	12.6
QUARTZITE	1	0.3
CERAMICS	3	7.9

FEATURE 160	N	Wt(g)
LIMESTONE	12	128.7
SANDSTONE	5	242.2
BURNED CLAY	4	3.7
CHERT	54	168.7
CERAMICS	43	334.1
POTTER'S CLAY	11	187.4
CERAMIC PIPE FRAGMENT	1	1.2

FEATURE 161		
LIMESTONE	1	7.5
SANDSTONE	2	101.8
CHERT	27	47.4
CERAMICS	28	152.8
BURNED CLAY	3	0.8

FEATURE 162		
SANDSTONE	2	28.6
CHERT	2	1.0
ROUGH ROCK	2	10.1
CERAMICS	4	17.4

FEATURE 163		
LIMESTONE	2	7.6
BURNED CLAY	2	1.4
CHERT	4	5.8
CERAMICS	7	28.5

FEATURE 164		
BURNED CLAY	9	81.0
SANDSTONE	2	35.8
ROUGH ROCK	2	11.5
WATER WORN PEBBLES	2	5.7
LIMESTONE	103	2345.3
CHERT	40	162.0
PROJECTILE POINT	1	1.6
CERAMICS	56	549.7

FEATURE 165		
LIMESTONE	6	33.5
SANDSTONE	1	2.4
BURNED CLAY	67	212.7
CHERT	120	221.0
RETOUCHED FLAKES	2	11.7
LIMESTONE SMOOTHER	1	4.2
CERAMICS	58	271.2

FEATURE 166		
LIMESTONE	45	482.0
SANDSTONE	5	109.0
BURNED CLAY	120	86.9
IGNEOUS ROCK	3	199.9
CHERT	158	289.1
RETOUCHED FLAKES	3	118.5
CERAMICS	128	780.5
PIPE FRAGMENT	1	4.2

FEATURE 167		
LIMESTONE	9	35.0
SANDSTONE	3	6.6
BURNED CLAY	8	6.3
CHERT	14	11.9
CERAMICS	7	14.8

FEATURE 168		
LIMESTONE	16	142.5
SANDSTONE	5	227.0
BURNED CLAY	14	37.8
CHERT	74	197.3
RETOUCHED FLAKES	6	70.1
LIMESTONE TOOL	1	291.8
PROJECTILE POINT	1	10.1
CERAMICS	54	347.5

FEATURE 169		
LIMESTONE	297	3382.6
BURNED CLAY	97	103.7
WATER WORN PEBBLES	1	9.2
CHERT	39	60.2
CHERT HAMMERSTONE FRAG	1	30.9
RETOUCHED FLAKES	6	35.2
CERAMICS	197	1655.3

APPENDIX 1. CONTINUED

Material Inventory from Historical Features

	N	Wt(g)
FEATURE 73		
CERAMICS	11	160.3
SANDSTONE SLOT ABRADER	1	47.1
KNIFE	1	11.6
CHERT	6	78.9
TILE	1	21.5
PORCELIN	1	0.5
BRICK	9	103.0
IRON	57	375.4
BURNED CLAY	128	35.5
BOTTLE GLASS	1	43.4
LIMESTONE	404	1508649.3
FEATURE 109		
LIMESTONE	1	5.6
COAL	2	0.1
SANDSTONE	1	0.3
BURNED CLAY	1	2.6
FEATURE 110		
LIMONITE	1	0.1
COAL	2	0.8
IGNEOUS ROCK	1	0.9
MUSSEL SHELL	3	0.8
BURNED CLAY	8	6.5
CHERT	2	7.4
FEATURE 111		
LIMESTONE	2	2.0
COAL	1	3.5
CHERT	1	0.6
CERAMICS	1	0.3

APPENDIX 2. FISH LAKE SITE PATRICK PHASE VESSELS

Vessel Number	Vessel Form	Temper	Surface Treatment (ext./int. or ext.)	Vessel Decoration	Rim Form	Lip Form	Lip Thick. (mm)	Ori. Dia. (cm)	Ori. (%)
2-1	jar	grog	cordmarked	int. lip imp.	inslanting	flat. int.	4.5	--	--
3-1	jar	grog	cordmarked	int. lip imp.	vertical	squared vert.	3.0	19	16
3-2	bowl	grog	cordmarked	none	vertical	squared vert.	7.0	--	--
4-1	jar	grog	cordmarked	int. lip imp.	vertical	squared vert.	4.5	--	--
6-1	jar/bowl	grog	cordmarked	int. lip imp.	ind.	ind.	3.5	--	--
9-1	jar	grog	cordmarked	int. lip imp.	vertical	rounded	2.5	12	12
9-2	jar	grog	cordmarked	none	inslanting	flat. int.	3.5	--	--
9-3	jar	grog	cordmarked	none	vertical	squared vert.	5.0	--	--
9-4	bowl	grog	cordmarked	none	outslanting	squared ext.	5.0	--	--
9-5	jar	grog	cordmarked	lip lug	inslanting	flat. int.	5.0	--	--
11-1	jar	grog	cordmarked	int. lip imp.	inslanting	flat. int.	4.0	16	8
11-2	jar	grog	cordmarked	int. lip imp.	vertical	squared vert.	3.0	18	7
11-3	jar	grog	cordmarked	int. lip imp.	vertical	squared vert.	3.0	--	--
18-1	jar	grog	cordmarked	int. lip imp.	inslanting	flat. int.	3.5	32	7
18-2	bowl	grog	cordmarked	none	vertical	squared vert.	7.0	--	--
18-3	bowl	grog	cordmarked	pumpkin effigy	vertical	flat. ext.	4.0	--	--
26-1	jar	grog	cordmarked	none	vertical	squared vert.	5.0	--	--
26-2	jar/bowl	grog	cordmarked	none	ind.	ind.	7.0	--	--
27-1	jar	grog	cordmarked	int. lip imp.	inslanting	flat. int.	4.0	--	--
27-3	bowl	ls.	cordmarked	none	vertical	squared vert.	5.0	--	--
28-1	jar	grog	cordmarked	int. lip imp.	flaring	squared ext.	3.0	--	--
28-2	jar	grog	cordmarked	none	vertical	squared vert.	5.0	--	--
32-1	jar	grog	cordmarked	int. lip imp.	vertical	squared vert.	3.5	--	--
32-3	jar	grog	cordmarked	none	vertical	squared vert.	3.0	--	--
32-4	bowl	grog	cordmarked	none	vertical	squared vert.	5.5	--	--
34-1	jar	grog	cordmarked	int. lip imp.	vertical	squared vert.	4.0	24	14
34-2	jar	grog	cordmarked	int. lip imp.	inslanting	flat. int.	4.5	--	--
34-3	jar	grog	cordmarked	int. lip imp.	inslanting	flat. int.	3.0	--	--
36-1	bowl	grog	cordmarked	none	vertical	squared vert.	5.0	29	7
36-2	jar	grog	cordmarked	int. lip imp.	inslanting	flat. int.	4.0	--	--
37-1	jar	grog	cordmarked	none	inslanting	flat. int.	4.0	--	--
37-2	mini. vessel	grog	plain	lip spout	vertical	rounded	3.0	9	40
38-1	jar	grog	cordmarked	none	vertical	squared vert.	4.0	--	--
38-2	jar	grog	cordmarked	none	inslanting	flat. int.	4.0	--	--
38-3	jar	grog	cordmarked	int. lip imp.	vertical	squared vert.	4.0	21	11
38-4	jar	grog	cordmarked	int. lip imp.	vertical	squared vert.	3.5	--	--
38-5	jar	ls.	cordmarked	int. lip imp.	vertical	squared vert.	6.0	--	--
38-6	jar	grog	cordmarked	lip spout	vertical	rounded	3.0	9	25
38-8	bowl	grog	cordmarked	none	vertical	squared vert.	5.0	32	15
38-9	bowl	grog	cordmarked	none	outslanting	flat. ext.	9.0	40	8
40-1	jar	grog	cordmarked	int. lip imp.	inslanting	flat. int.	3.0	19	18
40-4	jar	grog	cordmarked	int. lip imp.	vertical	squared vert.	4.0	--	--

APPENDIX 2. CONTINUED

Vessel Number	Vessel Form	Temper	Surface Treatment (ext./int. or ext.)	Vessel Decoration	Rim Form	Lip Form	Lip Thick. (mm)	Ori. Dia. (cm)	Ori. (%)
40-5	jar/bowl	grog	cordmarked	int. lip imp.	ind.	ind.	4.0	--	--
43-1	jar	grog	cordmarked	none	vertical	squared vert.	3.5	--	--
43-2	jar	grog	cordmarked	none	vertical	rounded	2.5	8	14
43-3	jar	grog	cordmarked	none	inslanting	flat. int.	4.5	--	--
48-1	jar/bowl	grog	cordmarked	int. lip imp.	ind.	ind.	ind.	--	--
58-1	jar	grog	cordmarked	sup. lip imp.	inslanting	flat. int.	4.0	--	--
58-3	bowl	grog	cordmarked	none	vertical	squared vert.	5.5	--	--
58-4	bowl	grog	cordmarked	none	vertical	squared vert.	4.0	--	--
60-1	bowl	grog	cordmarked	none	vertical	squared vert.	3.0	--	--
60-2	jar	grog	cordmarked	none	vertical	squared vert.	3.0	12	9
60-3	jar	grog	cordmarked	int. lip imp.	vertical	squared vert.	5.0	--	--
60-4	jar	grog	cordmarked	lip lug	vertical	squared vert.	3.0	--	--
60-5	jar	grog	cordmarked	int. lip imp.	vertical	flat. int.	2.5	--	--
70-1	jar	grog	cordmarked	int. lip imp.	inslanting	flat. int.	4.0	--	--
70-2	jar	grog	cordmarked	none	inslanting	rounded	4.0	--	--
72-1	jar	grog	cordmarked	none	inslanting	flat. int.	4.5	--	--
72-2	bowl	grog	cordmarked	none	vertical	squared vert.	4.0	--	--
72-3	jar/bowl	grog	cordmarked	none	ind.	ind.	2.5	--	--
74-1	jar	grog	cordmarked	none	inslanting	flat. int.	3.0	--	--
74-2	mini. vessel	grog	plain	none	vertical	rounded	3.5	--	--
79-1	jar	grog	cordmarked	int. lip imp.	inslanting	flat. int.	2.5	17	13
79-2	jar	grog	cordmarked	sup. lip imp.	vertical	flat. int.	3.5	26	10
79-3	jar	grog	cordmarked	int. lip imp.	inslanting	squared int.	4.0	19	11
79-4	jar	grog	cordmarked	int. lip imp.	inslanting	flat. int.	3.5	11	10
79-5	jar	grog	cordmarked	int. lip imp.	vertical	squared vert.	3.0	12	8
79-6	jar	grog	cordmarked	int. lip imp.	vertical	flat. int.	4.5	--	--
79-8	jar	grog	cordmarked	int. lip imp.	vertical	flat. ext.	4.0	--	--
79-10	bowl	grog	cordmarked	int. lip imp.	vertical	flat. int.	3.0	11	12
80-1	jar/bowl	grog	cordmarked	int. lip imp.	ind.	ind.	5.0	--	--
81-1	jar	grog	cordmarked	int. lip imp.	vertical	squared vert.	3.0	13	34
81-3	jar	grog	cordmarked	int. lip imp.	vertical	squared vert.	3.0	23	14
81-4	jar	grog	cordmarked	int. lip imp.	inslanting	flat. int.	5.5	18	10
81-6	jar	grog	cordmarked	none	inslanting	squared int.	4.0	--	--
81-7	jar	grog	cordmarked	int. lip imp.	vertical	squared vert.	4.0	--	--
81-8	jar	grog	cordmarked	none	inslanting	flat. int.	3.5	--	--
81-10	mini. vessel	grog/ls.	plain	int. lip imp.	vertical	rounded	3.5	--	--
81-11	mini. vessel	ls.	cordmarked	none	vertical	squared vert.	4.0	--	--
82-1	jar	grog	cordmarked	none	vertical	rounded	4.0	28	12
82-2	bowl	grog	cordmarked	int. lip imp./pumpkin effigy	outslanting	flat. ext.	4.0	--	--
82-3	jar	grog	cordmarked	none	vertical	squared vert.	3.5	--	--
82-4	jar	grog	cordmarked	int. lip imp.	vertical	squared vert.	4.0	--	--
87-1	jar	grog	cordmarked	none	vertical	squared vert.	4.5	--	--
88-1	jar	grog	cordmarked	none	inslanting	flat. int.	2.5	16	9
88-2	jar	grog	cordmarked	int. lip imp.	vertical	squared vert.	3.5	--	--

APPENDIX 2. CONTINUED

Vessel Number	Vessel Form	Temper	Surface Treatment (ext./int. or ext.)	Vessel Decoration	Rim Form	Lip Form	Lip Thick. (mm)	Ori. Dia. (cm)	Ori. (%)
89-1	jar	grit/grog	cordmarked	int. lip imp.	vertical	squared vert.	3.5	--	--
93-1	jar	grog	cordmarked	int. lip imp.	vertical	squared vert.	4.0	--	--
93-2	jar/bowl	grog	cordmarked	lip spout	ind.	ind.	4.0	--	--
93-3	bowl	grog	cordmarked	none	outslanting	squared ext.	4.5	20	10
93-6	jar	grog	cordmarked	int. lip imp.	vertical	squared vert.	2.5	--	--
93-8	jar	grog	cordmarked	int. lip imp.	vertical	squared vert.	4.5	--	--
94-1	jar	grog	cordmarked	int. lip imp.	vertical	squared vert.	4.0	--	--
94-2	bowl	grog	cordmarked	none	vertical	squared vert.	4.0	--	--
94-3	jar	grog	cordmarked	none	inslanting	flat. int.	5.0	--	--
98-1	jar	grog	cordmarked	int. lip imp.	vertical	squared vert.	4.0	25	17
98-2	jar	grog	cordmarked	int. lip imp.	vertical	squared vert.	4.0	--	--
98-3	jar	grog	cordmarked	int. lip imp.	vertical	squared vert.	3.0	--	--
101-1	jar	grog	cordmarked	int. lip imp.	vertical	squared vert.	5.0	--	--
105-1	bowl	grog	cordmarked	none	vertical	squared vert.	5.0	38	10
116-1	jar	grog	cordmarked	int. lip imp.	inslanting	flat. int.	3.0	--	--
118-1	jar	grog	cordmarked	int. lip imp.	inslanting	flat. int.	3.0	18	7
118-2	jar	grog/ls.	cordmarked	int. lip imp.	vertical	squared vert.	4.0	--	--
120-1	bowl	grog/ls.	cordmarked	lip spout	vertical	flat. int.	3.0	29	7
120-2	jar	grog	cordmarked	int. lip imp.	vertical	squared vert.	5.0	--	--
123-1	jar	grog	cordmarked	lip effigy	vertical	squared vert.	4.0	--	--
126-1	jar	grog/ls.	cordmarked	int. lip imp.	inslanting	squared vert.	3.5	21	11
126-2	mini. vessel	grog/ls.	plain	int. lip imp.	vertical	rounded	4.5	--	--
126-3	bowl	grog	cordmarked	none	vertical	flat. ext.	3.0	18	13
130-1	jar	grog	cordmarked	int. lip imp.	vertical	squared vert.	2.5	--	--
132-1	jar	grog	cordmarked	int. lip imp./ lip spout	inslanting	squared int.	2.5	10	29
132-3	jar	grog	cordmarked	int. lip imp.	inslanting	flat. int.	4.5	--	--
132-4	bowl	grog/ls.	cordmarked	none	vertical	flat. ext.	3.0	36	4
134-1	jar	grog	cordmarked	int. lip imp.	vertical	squared vert.	4.5	--	--
134-2	jar	grog	cordmarked	none	vertical	squared vert.	3.0	--	--
134-3	jar	grog	cordmarked	int. lip imp.	vertical	squared vert.	4.0	--	--
134-5	jar	grog	cordmarked	none	vertical	squared ext.	4.0	--	--
134-6	bowl	grog	cordmarked	none	outslanting	squared ext.	4.0	--	--
138-1	jar	grog	cordmarked	int. lip imp./ ext. punctates	inslanting	flat. int.	3.0	14	10
138-2	mini. vessel	grog	plain/slip	int./ext. slip	vertical	rounded	7.0	6	27
138-3	jar	grog	cordmarked	int. lip imp.	vertical	rounded	4.5	--	--
138-4	jar	grog	cordmarked	int. lip imp.	vertical	squared vert.	4.5	--	--
139-1	jar	grog	cordmarked	int. lip imp.	inslanting	flat. int.	3.5	--	--
139-2	jar	grog	cordmarked	none	vertical	squared vert.	4.0	--	--
142-1	mini. vessel	grog	plain	none	vertical	rounded	3.5	--	--
143-1	jar	grog	cordmarked	int. lip imp.	vertical	squared vert.	4.0	--	--
143-2	jar/bowl	grog	cordmarked	int. lip imp./ ind.	vertical	ind.	4.0	--	--
143-3	jar	grog	cordmarked	pumpkin effigy sup. lip imp.	inslanting	flat. int.	4.5	--	--

APPENDIX 2. CONTINUED

Vessel Number	Vessel Form	Temper	Surface Treatment (ext./int. or ext.)	Vessel Decoration	Rim Form	Lip Form	Lip Thick. (mm)	Ori. Dia. (cm)	Ori. (%)
146-1	jar	grog	cordmarked	int. lip imp.	inslanting	squared vert.	3.5	--	--
146-3	jar	grog	cordmarked	int. lip imp.	inslanting	flat. int.	4.0	--	--
148-1	jar	grog	cordmarked	int. lip imp.	vertical	squared vert.	5.0	--	--
149-1	jar	grog	cordmarked	int. lip imp.	inslanting	flat. int.	3.0	24	7
152-1	jar	grog	cordmarked	none	vertical	squared vert.	4.0	--	--
152-2	jar	grog	cordmarked	int. lip imp.	inslanting	flat. int.	3.5	--	--
156-1	jar	grog	cordmarked	none	vertical	squared vert.	4.0	--	--
161-1	jar/bowl	grog	cordmarked	none	ind.	ind.	3.5	--	--
164-1	jar	grog	cordmarked	none	vertical	rounded	3.5	20	23
164-4	jar	grog	cordmarked	int. lip imp.	inslanting	flat. int.	4.5	--	--
164-5	jar	grog	cordmarked	lip lug	inslanting	flat. int.	3.0	--	--
165-1	mini. vessel	grog/ls.	cordmarked	none	vertical	squared int.	4.0	--	--
165-2	bowl	grog	cordmarked	none	vertical	squared vert.	4.0	--	--
166-1	jar	grog	cordmarked	int. lip imp.	vertical	squared vert.	5.0	--	--
166-2	jar	grog	cordmarked	int. lip imp.	inslanting	squared int.	3.5	--	--
166-3	bowl	grog	cordmarked	none	vertical	flat. ext.	5.5	--	--
166-4	mini. vessel	grog	plain	lip spout	vertical	rounded	2.5	--	--
167-1	jar	grog	cordmarked	int. lip imp.	inslanting	flat. int.	2.5	--	--
168-1	jar	grog	cordmarked	none	vertical	flat. int.	4.0	--	--
168-2	jar	grog	cordmarked	int. lip imp.	inslanting	squared int.	2.5	--	--
168-3	bowl	grog	cordmarked	none	vertical	squared vert.	4.0	38	6
169-1	jar	grog	cordmarked	none	inslanting	squared int.	5.0	--	--
169-2	jar	grog	cordmarked	int. lip imp.	inslanting	flat. int.	4.0	--	--

Key

ori. - orifice
mini. - miniature
ls. - limestone
int. - interior
ext. - exterior
sup. - superior
imp. - impressions
flat. - flattened
vert. - vertical
ind. - indeterminate

REFERENCES

Asch, David L. and Nancy B. Asch
    1978   The economic potential of <u>Iva</u> <u>annua</u> and its prehistoric importance in the lower Illinois valley. In The nature and status of ethnobotany, edited by Richard I. Ford, pp. 301-341. <u>Museum</u> <u>of</u> <u>Anthropology</u>, <u>University</u> <u>of</u> <u>Michigan</u>, <u>Anthropological</u> <u>Papers</u> 67.

Asch, David L., Kenneth B. Farnsworth, and Nancy B. Asch
    1979   Woodland subsistence and settlement in west central Illinois. In <u>Hopewell</u> <u>archaeology:</u> <u>the</u> <u>Chillicothe</u> <u>Conference</u>, edited by David S. Brose and N´omi Greber, pp. 80-85. Kent State University Press, Kent, Ohio.

Asch, Nancy B. and David L. Asch
    1980   The Dickson Camp and Pond sites: Middle Woodland archaeobotany in Illinois. In Dickson Camp and Pond: two early Havana tradition sites in the central Illinois valley, by Anne-Marie Cantwell, Appendix B, pp. 152-160, <u>Illinois</u> <u>State</u> <u>Museum</u>, <u>Reports</u> <u>of</u> <u>Investigations</u> 36.

Asch, Nancy B., Richard I. Ford, and David L. Asch
    1972   Paleoethnobotany of the Koster site: the Archaic horizons. <u>Illinois</u> <u>State</u> <u>Museum</u>, <u>Reports</u> <u>of</u> <u>Investigations</u> 24.

Bareis, Charles J., James W. Porter, and John E. Kelly
    1977   Report of Investigations and proposed mitigation for the Hill Lake Meander Scar: St. Clair and Monroe Counties, Illinois. <u>Department</u> <u>of</u> <u>Anthropology</u>, <u>University</u> <u>of</u> <u>Illinois</u> <u>at</u> <u>Urbana-Champaign</u>, <u>FAI-270</u> <u>Archaeological</u> <u>Mitigation</u> <u>Project</u>.

Bareis, Charles J. and James W. Porter (editors)
    1981   Archaeology in the American Bottom: progress report of the Illinois FAI-270 Archaeological Mitigation Project. <u>Department</u> <u>of</u> <u>Anthropology</u>, <u>University</u> <u>of</u> <u>Illinois</u> <u>at</u> <u>Urbana-Champaign</u>, <u>Research</u> <u>Report</u> 6.

Beaglehole, Ernest
    1937   Notes on Hopi economic life. <u>Yale</u> <u>University</u> <u>Publications</u> <u>in</u> <u>Anthropology</u> 15.

Bent, Arthur C.
    1963   Life Histories of North American Gallinaceous Birds. Dover Publications, New York.

Binford, Lewis R., Sally R. Binford, Robert C. Whallon, and Margaret A. Hardin
    1970   Archaeology at Hatchery West. Society for American Archaeology, Memoirs 24.

Bullard, William R.
    1962   The Cerro Colorado site and pithouse architecture in the Southwestern United States prior to A.D. 900. Papers of the Peabody Museum of Archaeology and Ethnology, Harvard University XLIV (2).

Cowan, C. Wesley
    1978   The prehistoric use and distribution of maygrass in eastern North America: cultural and phytogeographic implications. In The nature and status of ethnobotany, edited by Richard I. Ford, pp. 263-288. Museum of Anthropology, University of Michigan, Anthropological Papers, 67.

Crabtree, Don E. and B. Robert Butler
    1964   Notes on experiment in flint knapping: 1. heat treatment of silica minerals. Tebiwa 7:1-6.

Culin, Stewart
    1907   Games of the North American Indians. Bureau of American Ethnology Annual Report 24. Washington, D.C.

Dorsey, George A.
    1904   Traditions of the Skidi Pawnee. Houghton, Mifflin, and Company, Boston and New York.

Dragoo, Don W.
    1955   Excavations at the Johnston Site, Indiana County, Pennsylvania. Pennsylvania Archaeologist 25(2):85-141.

Duke, James A.
    1981   Handbook of legumes of world economic importance. Plenum Press, New York.

Finney, Fred A.
    1981   The Carbon Dioxide site: Late Woodland and early Mississippian occupations on the American Bottom. _Department of Anthropology, University of Illinois at Urbana-Champaign, FAI-270 Archaeological Mitigation Project Report_ 33.

Finney, Fred A. and Charles Bentz
    1983   The Columbia Quarry site (11-S-629): a Late Woodland Mund phase occupation in the uplands. In preparation. _Department of Anthropology, University of Illinois at Urbana-Champaign, FAI-270 Archaeological Mitigation Project Report_ 57.

Fortier, Andrew C.
    1981a   Archaeological investigation of the Middle Woodland occupation at the Truck #7 and Go-Kart South sites. _Department of Anthropology, University of Illinois at Urbana-Champaign, FAI-270 Archaeological Mitigation Project Report_ 30.

    1981b   The Carbon Monoxide (11-Mo-593) site: an Early and Middle Woodland occupation in the American Bottom. _Department of Anthropology, University of Illinois at Urbana-Champaign, FAI-270 Archaeological Mitigation Project Report_ 27.

Fortier, Andrew C., Fred A. Finney, and Richard B. Lacampagne
    1982   The Mund site (11-S-435): a stratified, multicomponent occupation in the American Bottom. _Department of Anthropology, University of Illinois at Urbana-Champaign, FAI-270 Archaeological Mitigation Project Report_ 41.

Griffin, James B.
    1952   Some Early and Middle Woodland pottery types in Illinois. In Hopewellian communities in Illinois, edited by Thorne Devel, pp. 93-129. _Illinois State Museum, Scientific Papers_.

Hall, Robert L.
    1980   Ceramics. In Investigations at the Labras Lake site, Volume 1, Archaeology, by James L. Phillips, Robert L. Hall, and Richard W. Yerkes, pp. 366-406. _Department of Anthropology, University of Illinois at Chicago, Reports of Investigations_ 1.

Harn, Alan D.
    1971   An archaeological survey of the American Bottoms in Madison
            and St. Clair counties, Illinois. In Archaeological surveys
            of the American Bottoms and adjacent bluffs, Illinois.
            Illinois State Museum, Reports of Investigations 21:19-39.

Hoffmeister, Donald F. and Carl D. Mohr
    1972   Fieldbook of Illinois Mammals. Dover Publications, New York.

Hus, Henri
    1908   An ecological cross-section of the Mississippi River in the
            region of St. Louis, Missouri. Missouri Botanical Garden,
            Annual Report 19:127-258.

Johannessen, Sissel
    1982a   Plant remains from the Mund site, the Mund phase component.
            In The Mund site (11-S-435): a stratified, multicomponent
            occupation in the American Bottom, by Andrew C. Fortier,
            Fred A. Finney, and Richard B. Lacampagne, pp. 319-339.
            Department of Anthropology, University of Illinois at
            Urbana-Champaign FAI-270 Archaeological Mitigation Project
            Report 41.

    1982b   Paleoethnobotanical Trends in the American Bottom: Late
            Archaic through Mississippian. Paper presented at the 47th
            Annual Meeting of the Society for American Archaeology,
            April 14-17, 1982, Minneapolis, Minnesota.

Kelly, John E.
    1980   Formative developments at Cahokia and the adjacent American
            Bottom: a Merrell Tract perspective. Unpublished
            Ph.D. dissertation, Department of Anthropology, University
            of Wisconsin, Madison.

    1981a   Annual report of investigations at the Range site. In
            Annual report of 1980 investigations, pp. 14-23.
            Department of Anthropology, University of Illinois at
            Urbana-Champaign, FAI-270 Archaeological Mitigation Project
            Annual Report.

    1981b   Variability in Early Bluff culture in the American Bottom
            region. Paper presented at the Midwest Archaeological
            Conference, Madison, Wisconsin.

1981c   Variability in Late Bluff culture in the American Bottom region. Paper presented at the Midwest Archaeological Conference, Madison, Wisconsin.

1982   Annual report of investigations at the Range site. In Annual report of investigations 1981, pp. 7-19. Department of Anthropology, University of Illinois at Urbana-Champaign, FAI-270 Archaeological Mitigation Project Annual Report.

Kelly, John E., Jean R. Linder, and Theresa J. Cartmell
1979   The archaeological intensive survey of the proposed FAI-270 alignment in the American Bottom region of southern Illinois. Illinois Transportation Archaeology Scientific Reports 1.

King, Frances B.
1980   Plant remains from Phillips Spring, a multicomponent site in the western Ozark highland of Missouri. Plains Anthropologist 25:217-227.

Lacampagne, Richard B. and Charles Bentz
1982   The Cramer #2 site: a Late Woodland Patrick phase occupation in St. Clair County, Illinois. Department of Anthropology, University of Illinois at Urbana-Champaign, FAI-270 Archaeological Mitigation Project Report 56.

1983   The Steinberg site (11-S-653): a Late Woodland Rosewood phase occupation. Department of Anthropology, University of Illinois at Urbana-Champaign, FAI-270 Archaeological Mitigation Project Report 62.

Lowie, Robert H.
1983   The Crow Indians. University of Nebraska Press, Lincoln. (originally published 1935, Rinehart, New York).

McElrath, Dale L. and Andrew C. Fortier
1981   The Missouri Pacific #2 site: a Late Archaic occupation in the American Bottom. Department of Anthropology, University of Illinois at Urbana-Champaign, FAI-270 Archaeological Mitigation Project Report 34.

Martin, Alexander C. and William D. Barkley
    1961   Seed identification manual. University of California Press,
            Berkeley.

Milner, George R. with Joyce A. Williams
    1981a   The Julien site (11-S-63): an Early Bluff and Mississippian
            multicomponent site. Department of Anthropology, University
            of Illinois at Urbana-Champaign, FAI-270 Archaeological
            Mitigation Project Report 31.

    1981b   The Turner (11-S-50) and DeMange (11-S-447) sites: an early
            Mississippian occupation of a floodplain locality.
            Department of Anthropology, University of Illinois at
            Urbana-Champaign, FAI-270 Archaeological Mitigation Project
            Report 37.

Montgomery, Frederick H.
    1977   Seeds and fruits of plants of eastern Canada and the
            northeastern United States. University of Toronto Press.

Munson, Patrick J.
    1971   An archaeological survey of the Wood River Terrace and
            adjacent bottoms and bluffs in Madison County, Illinois. In
            Archaeological surveys of the American Bottoms and adjacent
            bluffs, Illinois. Illinois State Museum, Reports of
            Investigations 21:3-17.

Nie, Norman H., C. Hadlai Hull, Jean G. Jenkins, Karin Steinbrenner, and
            Dale H. Bent
    1975   Statistical package for the social sciences (Second
            edition). McGraw Hill, New York.

O'Brien, Patricia J.
    1978   Steed-Kisker: a western Mississippian settlement system. In
            Mississippian settlement patterns, edited by Bruce D. Smith,
            pp. 1-19. Academic Press, New York.

Pace, Robert E. and Gary A. Apfelstadt
    1978   Allison-LaMotte culture of the Daugherty-Monroe site,
            Sullivan County, Indiana. Anthropology Laboratory, Indiana
            State University.

Panshin, A.J. and Carl deZeeuw
    1970   Textbook of wood technology. Volume 1 (Third edition).
            McGraw Hill, New York.

Perino, Gregory H.
    1971a   Guide to the identification of certain American Indian
            projectile points. Oklahoma Anthropological Society,
            Special Bulletin 4.

    1971b   The Mississippian component at the Schild site (No. 4),
            Greene County, Illinois. In Mississippian site archaeology
            in Illinois 1: site reports from the St. Louis and Chicago
            areas. Illinois Archaeological Survey, Bulletin 8:1-148.

Porter, James W.
    1964   Southern Illinois University Museum projects. In Third
            annual report: American Bottoms archaeology, July 1,
            1963-June 30, 1964, edited by Melvin L. Fowler, pp. 16-28.
            Illinois Archaeological Survey, Urbana.

Prentice, Guy
    1983   Cottage Industries: concepts and implications. In
            Midcontinental Journal of Archaeology 8:17-48.

Purseglove, J.W.
    1968   Tropical Crops: dicotyledons. Longman, London.

Shelford, Victor E.
    1963   The ecology of North America. University of Illinois Press,
            Urbana.

Shepard, Anna O.
    1956   Ceramics for the archaeologist. Carnegie Institution of
            Washington, Publication 609.

Smith, Ira F. III
    1974   Keyholes, ping pong paddles, or turtle pits. Eastern States
            Archaeological Federation, Bulletin 13:15-16.

1976   A functional interpretation of keyhole structures in the Northeast. _Pennsylvania Archaeologist_ 46(1-2):1-12.

Steyermark, Julian A.
    1963   _Flora of Missouri_. Iowa State University Press, Ames.

Struever, Stuart
    1968   Flotation techniques for the recovery of small-scale archaeological remains. _American Antiquity_ 33:353-362.

Szuter, Christine R.
    1979   _The Schlemmer site: a Late Woodland-Mississippian site in the American Bottom_. Unpublished M.A. thesis, Department of Anthropology, Loyola University, Chicago.

Titterington, Paul F.
    1935   Certain bluff mounds of western Jersey County, Illinois. _American Antiquity_ 1:6-46.

Wagner, Gail E.
    1976   IDOT Flotation procedure manual. Ms. on file, Illinois Department of Transportation, District 8, Fairview Heights.

White, Anta M.
    1968   The lithic industries of the Illinois valley in the Early and Middle Woodland period. _Museum of Anthropology, University of Michigan, Anthropological Papers_ 35.

White, William P.
    1983   Geomorphic research conducted at the Fish Lake site (11-Mo-608). _Department of Anthropology, University of Illinois at Urbana-Champaign, FAI-270 Archaeological Mitigation Project Geomorphological Report_ 10.

Wilbert, Johannes
    1979   Magico-religious use of tobacco among South American Indians. In _Spirits, shamans, and stars: perspectives from South America_, edited by David L. Browman and Ronald A. Schwartz, pp. 13-39. Mouton Publishers, The Hague.

Wilson, Hugh D.
    1981   Domesticated _Chenopodium_ of the Ozark Bluff Dwellers.
            Economic Botany 35:233-239.

Winters, Howard D.
    1969   The Riverton culture: a second millennium occupation in the
            central Wabash valley. _Illinois Archaeological Survey,
            Monograph_ 1.

Wittry, Warren L.
    1981   An archaeological survey of the proposed Fish Lake
            Interchange (FAI-270) and the adjacent proposed industrial
            park area. Department of Anthropology, University of
            Illinois at Urbana-Champaign.

Wray, Donald E. and Richard S. MacNeish
    1961   The Hopewellian and Weaver occupations of the Weaver site,
            Fulton County, Illinois, edited by Warren L. Wittry.
            Illinois State Museum, Scientific Papers 7(2).